LIFE SONGS

NUMBER TWO

In Him was life; and the life
was the light of men.—John 1:4

A COLLECTION OF SACRED SONGS FOR SUNDAY SCHOOLS, YOUNG PEOPLE'S MEETINGS AND EVANGELISTIC SERVICES

PUBLISHED UNDER THE DIRECTION OF A COMMITTEE APPOINTED BY MENNONITE GENERAL CONFERENCE

S. F. COFFMAN, EDITOR

Issued in
Round and Shaped Notes

MENNONITE PUBLISHING HOUSE

Scottdale, Pa.

PREFACE

The publication of LIFE SONGS NUMBER TWO is a sincere endeavor to maintain the standards established by the Committee which produced *Life Songs* (Number One), issued in 1916. *Life Songs* is still used and much appreciated by many congregations. Hymn literature should be essentially scriptural, instructional, and inspirational in order that its use may effect the highest purposes of worship in the service of the Lord. The music should be pure, strong, and elevating in character. Every Christian song should lift the soul above earthly and sensual sentiments to the realm of spiritual appreciation of realities emanating from God and heaven through the Holy Spirit. It is to this end that the Committee has labored as servants of Christ and the Church, and to this purpose commend the use of this book.

The Committee desires to extend sincere thanks to those individuals and organizations whose help in furnishing material and in giving valued counsel has been of great assistance in the compilation of this work.

May the glory of God be magnified by these humble efforts. The Music Committee of General Conference. C. Z. Yoder, Chairman; Chester K. Lehman, Secretary; S. F. Coffman; J. B. Smith; Paul Erb.

CONTENTS

Praise and Worship 1-41
The Lord's Day and Worship 42-46
Morning and Evening 47-55
Prayer 56-71
Holy Spirit 72-73
God and Christ. 74-97
  Love of— 74-90
  Love to— 91-93
  Loyalty to— 94-97
The Word 98-102
Salvation and Redemption 103-130
Evangelistic 131-176
Christian Experience 177-267
  Holiness 177-183
  Aspiration 184-189
  Assurance 190-206
  Trust and Peace 207-220
  Consolation 221-224
  Guidance 225-240
  Encouragement 241-247
  Consecration 248-267
Hope and Heaven 268-277
Christmas 278-283
Easter 284-289
Service and Missions 290-311
Coming Again of Christ 312-318
Doxologies 319-321
Familiar Hymns 322-343

Printed in U. S. A.

LIFE SONGS

NUMBER TWO

God of Our Strength, Enthroned Above 1

FANNY J. CROSBY W. H. DOANE

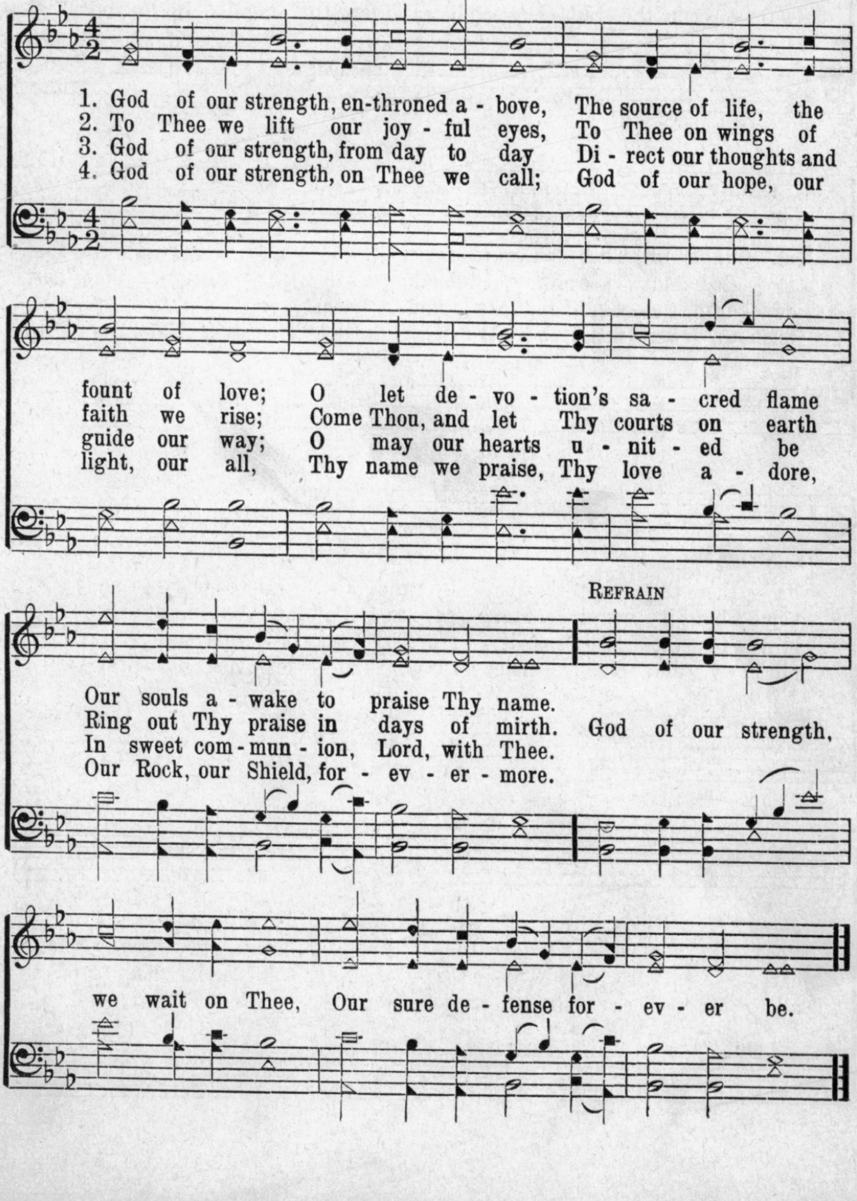
1. God of our strength, en-throned a - bove, The source of life, the
2. To Thee we lift our joy - ful eyes, To Thee on wings of
3. God of our strength, from day to day Di - rect our thoughts and
4. God of our strength, on Thee we call; God of our hope, our
fount of love; O let de - vo - tion's sa - cred flame
faith we rise; Come Thou, and let Thy courts on earth
guide our way; O may our hearts u - nit - ed be
light, our all, Thy name we praise, Thy love a - dore,
Our souls a - wake to praise Thy name.
Ring out Thy praise in days of mirth.
In sweet com - mun - ion, Lord, with Thee.
Our Rock, our Shield, for - ev - er - more.
REFRAIN
God of our strength,
we wait on Thee, Our sure de - fense for - ev - er be.

2 Honor and Glory

AMERICAN HYMN

EDWARD A. DAYMAN — MARTYN KELLER

1. Hon - or and glo - ry, thanks-giv - ing and praise, Mak - er of
2. Thou art the Fa - ther of heav - en and earth; Worlds un - cre-
3. Earth with the moun-tain, the riv - er, the plain, Sky with its
4. O - cean the rest - less, and wa - ters that swell, Light-nings that
all things, to Thee we up - raise: God the Al - might - y, the
a - ted to Thee owe their birth; All the cre - a - tion, Thy
dew - drop, the wind, and the rain, Beast of the for - est, wild
flash o - ver flood, o - ver fell, Own Thee the Mas - ter Al-
Fa - ther, the Lord; God, by the an - gels o - beyed and a-
voice when it heard, Start - ed to life and to light at Thy
bird of the air, All are Thy crea - tures, and all are Thy
might - y, and call Thee the Cre - a - tor, the Fa - ther, of
dored, God, by the an - gels o - beyed and a - dored.
word, Start - ed to life and to light at Thy word.
care, All are Thy crea - tures, and all are Thy care.
all, Thee the Cre - a - tor, the Fa - ther, of all.

Our Great Savior

J. WILBUR CHAPMAN

Arr. by ROBERT HARKNESS

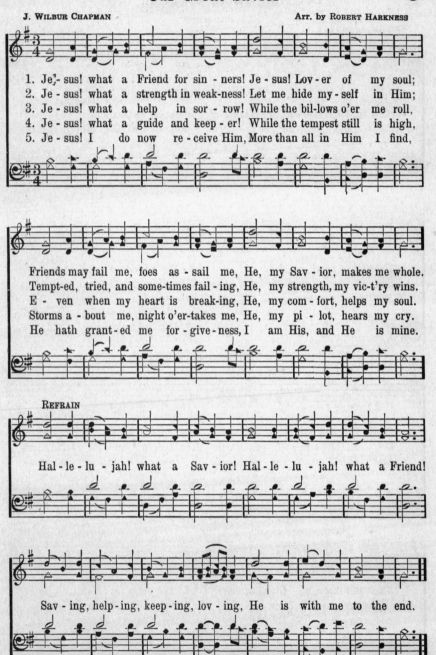

1. Je - sus! what a Friend for sin - ners! Je - sus! Lov - er of my soul;
2. Je - sus! what a strength in weak-ness! Let me hide my - self in Him;
3. Je - sus! what a help in sor - row! While the bil-lows o'er me roll,
4. Je - sus! what a guide and keep - er! While the tempest still is high,
5. Je - sus! I do now re - ceive Him, More than all in Him I find,

Friends may fail me, foes as - sail me, He, my Sav - ior, makes me whole.
Tempt-ed, tried, and some-times fail - ing, He, my strength, my vic-t'ry wins.
E - ven when my heart is break-ing, He, my com - fort, helps my soul.
Storms a - bout me, night o'er-takes me, He, my pi - lot, hears my cry.
He hath grant-ed me for - give - ness, I am His, and He is mine.

REFRAIN

Hal - le - lu - jah! what a Sav - ior! Hal - le - lu - jah! what a Friend!

Sav - ing, help - ing, keep - ing, lov - ing, He is with me to the end.

4 Let the Whole Creation Cry

ROLAND

STOPFORD A. BROOKE — CALEB SIMPER

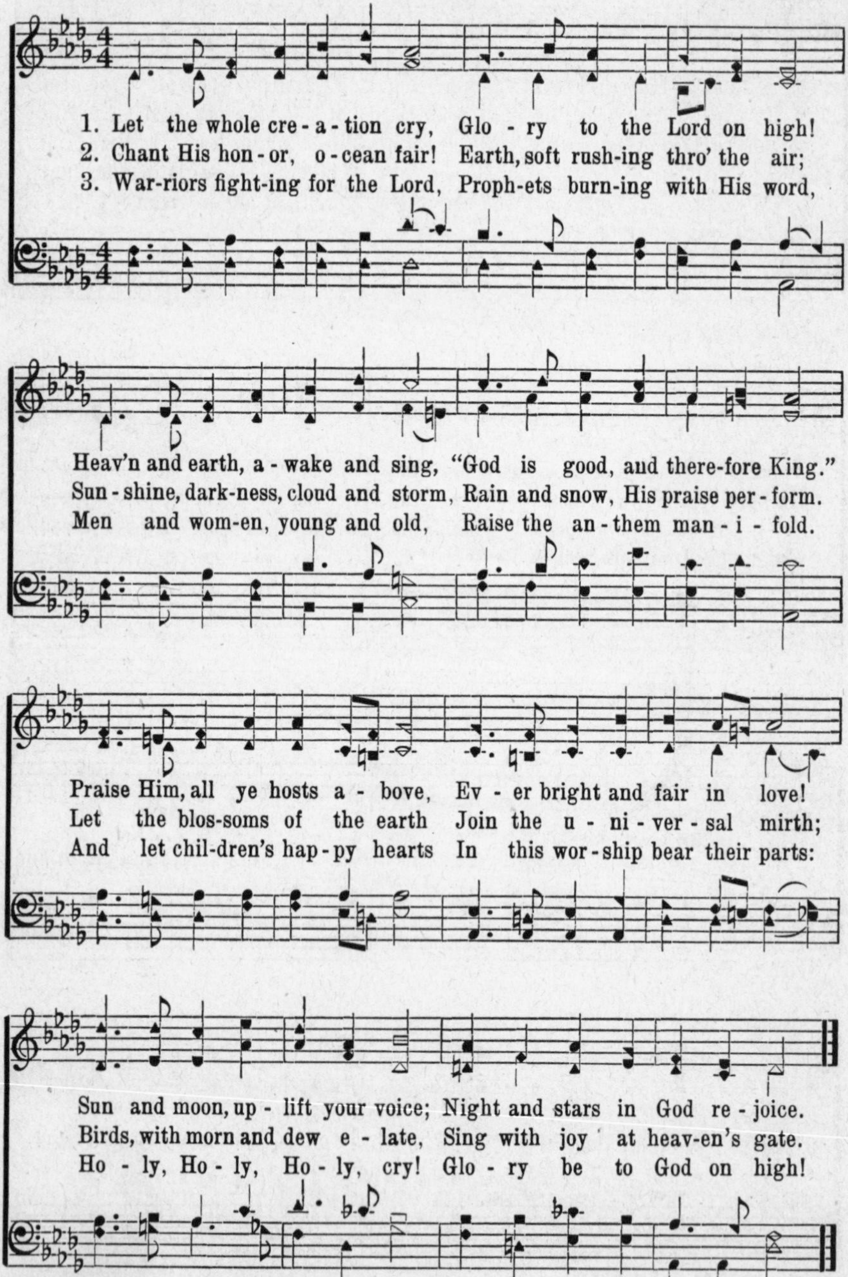
1. Let the whole cre-a-tion cry, Glo-ry to the Lord on high!
2. Chant His hon-or, o-cean fair! Earth, soft rush-ing thro' the air;
3. War-riors fight-ing for the Lord, Proph-ets burn-ing with His word,
Heav'n and earth, a-wake and sing, "God is good, and there-fore King."
Sun-shine, dark-ness, cloud and storm, Rain and snow, His praise per-form.
Men and wom-en, young and old, Raise the an-them man-i-fold.
Praise Him, all ye hosts a-bove, Ev-er bright and fair in love!
Let the blos-soms of the earth Join the u-ni-ver-sal mirth;
And let chil-dren's hap-py hearts In this wor-ship bear their parts:
Sun and moon, up-lift your voice; Night and stars in God re-joice.
Birds, with morn and dew e-late, Sing with joy at heav-en's gate.
Ho-ly, Ho-ly, Ho-ly, cry! Glo-ry be to God on high!

O My Soul, Bless Thou Jehovah

PSALM 103

JAMES MCGRANAHAN

1. O my soul, bless thou Je - ho - vah, All with - in me, bless His name;
2. Who for - gives all thy trans - gres - sions, Thy dis - eas - es all who heals,
3. Far as east from west is dis - tant, He hath put a - way our sin;
4. Bless Je - ho - vah, all His crea - tures Ev - er un - der His con - trol,

Bless Je - ho - vah, and for - get not All His mer - cies to pro - claim:
Who re - deems thee from de - struc - tion, Who with thee so kind - ly deals.
Like the pit - y of a fa - ther Hath the Lord's com - pas - sion been.
All through - out His vast do - min - ion; Bless Je - ho - vah, O my soul.

CHORUS

For as high as is the heav - en, Far a - bove the earth be - low, . . .
the earth be - low,

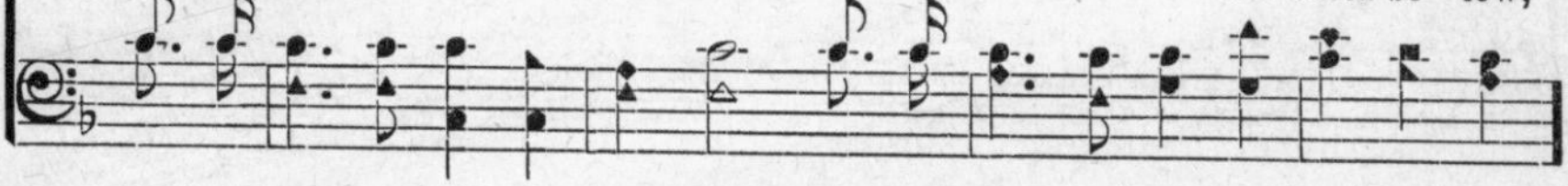

Ev - er great to them that fear Him Is the mer - cy He will show.

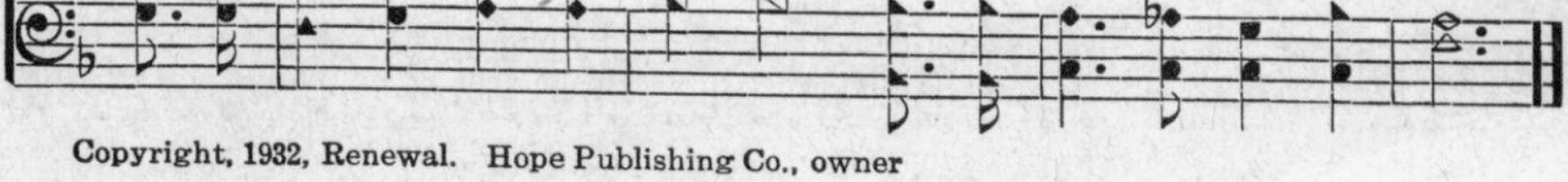

6 Lord, Thy Glory Fills the Heaven

FABEN

RICHARD MANT — JOHN H. WILCOX

1. "Lord, Thy glo - ry fills the heav - en; Earth is with its full-ness stored;
2. Ev - er thus, in God's high prais - es, Breth-ren, let our tongues u - nite,
3. "Lord, Thy glo - ry fills the heav - en; Earth is with its full-ness stored;
Un - to Thee be glo - ry giv - en, Ho - ly, ho - ly, ho - ly Lord!"
While our tho'ts His great-ness rais - es, And our love His gifts ex - cite,—
Un - to Thee be glo - ry giv - en, Ho - ly, ho - ly, ho - ly Lord!"
Heav'n is still with glo - ry ring - ing; Earth takes up the an-gels' cry,
With His ser - aph train be-fore Him, With His ho - ly church be-low,
Thus Thy glo-rious name con-fess - ing, We a - dopt the an-gels' cry,
"Ho - ly, ho - ly, ho - ly," sing-ing, "Lord of hosts, the Lord most high!"
Thus con-spire we to a - dore Him, Bid we thus our an - them flow.
"Ho - ly, ho - ly, ho - ly," bless-ing Thee, the Lord of hosts most high!

Let Us Crown Him

E. PERRONET — JAMES McGRANAHAN

Allegro
1. All hail the pow'r of Je - sus' name! Let an - gels pros - trate fall;
2. Ye cho - sen seed of Is - rael's race, Ye ran - somed from the fall,
3. Let ev - 'ry kin - dred, ev - 'ry tribe, On this ter - res - trial ball,
4. O that with yon - der sa - cred throng We at His feet may fall!
Bring forth the roy - al di - a - dem, And crown Him Lord of all.
Hail Him who saves you by His grace, And crown Him Lord of all.
To Him all maj - es - ty as - cribe, And crown Him Lord of all.
We'll join the ev - er - last - ing song, And crown Him Lord of all.
CHORUS
Let us crown Him, . . . Let us crown Him, . . . Let us
Him Lord of all, Him Lord of all,
crown the great Re - deem - er Lord of all; . . . . Let us crown Him, ...
Him Lord of all,
Let us crown Him, . . . Let us crown Him Lord of all.
Him Lord of all, the great Re - deem - er Lord of all.

8 All Hail the Power

E. PERRONET — CORONATION — OLIVER HOLDEN

1. All hail the pow'r of Je - sus' name! Let an - gels pros - trate fall;
2. Ye cho - sen seed of Is - rael's race, Ye ran - somed from the fall,
3. Let ev - 'ry kin - dred, ev - 'ry tribe, On this ter - res - trial ball,
4. O that with yon - der sa - cred throng We at His feet may fall!
Bring forth the roy - al di - a - dem, And crown Him Lord of all,
Hail Him who saves you by His grace, And crown Him Lord of all,
To Him all maj - es - ty as - cribe, And crown Him Lord of all,
We'll join the ev - er - last - ing song, And crown Him Lord of all,
Bring forth the roy - al di - a - dem, And crown Him Lord of all!
Hail Him who saves you by His grace, And crown Him Lord of all!
To Him all maj - es - ty as - cribe, And crown Him Lord of all!
We'll join the ev - er - last - ing song, And crown Him Lord of all.

[SECOND TUNE] Miles' Lane. C. M. WILLIAM SHRUBSOLE

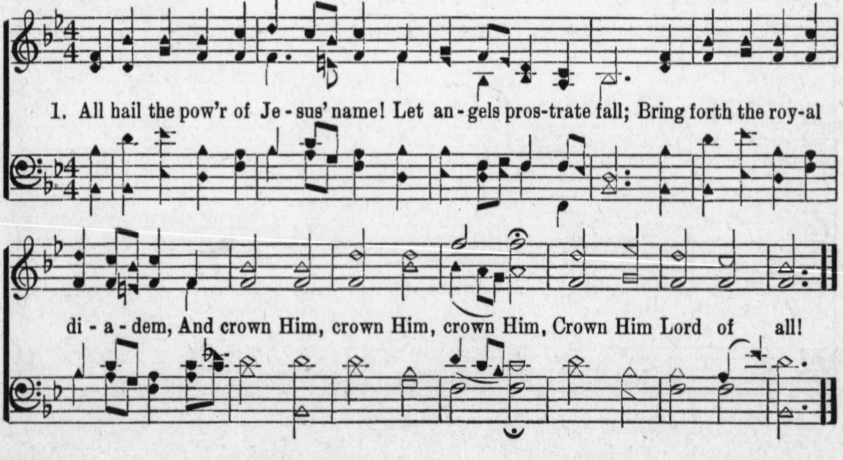
1. All hail the pow'r of Je - sus' name! Let an - gels pros - trate fall; Bring forth the roy - al
di - a - dem, And crown Him, crown Him, crown Him, Crown Him Lord of all!

His Mercy Flows

9

Psalm 136

JAMES McGRANAHAN

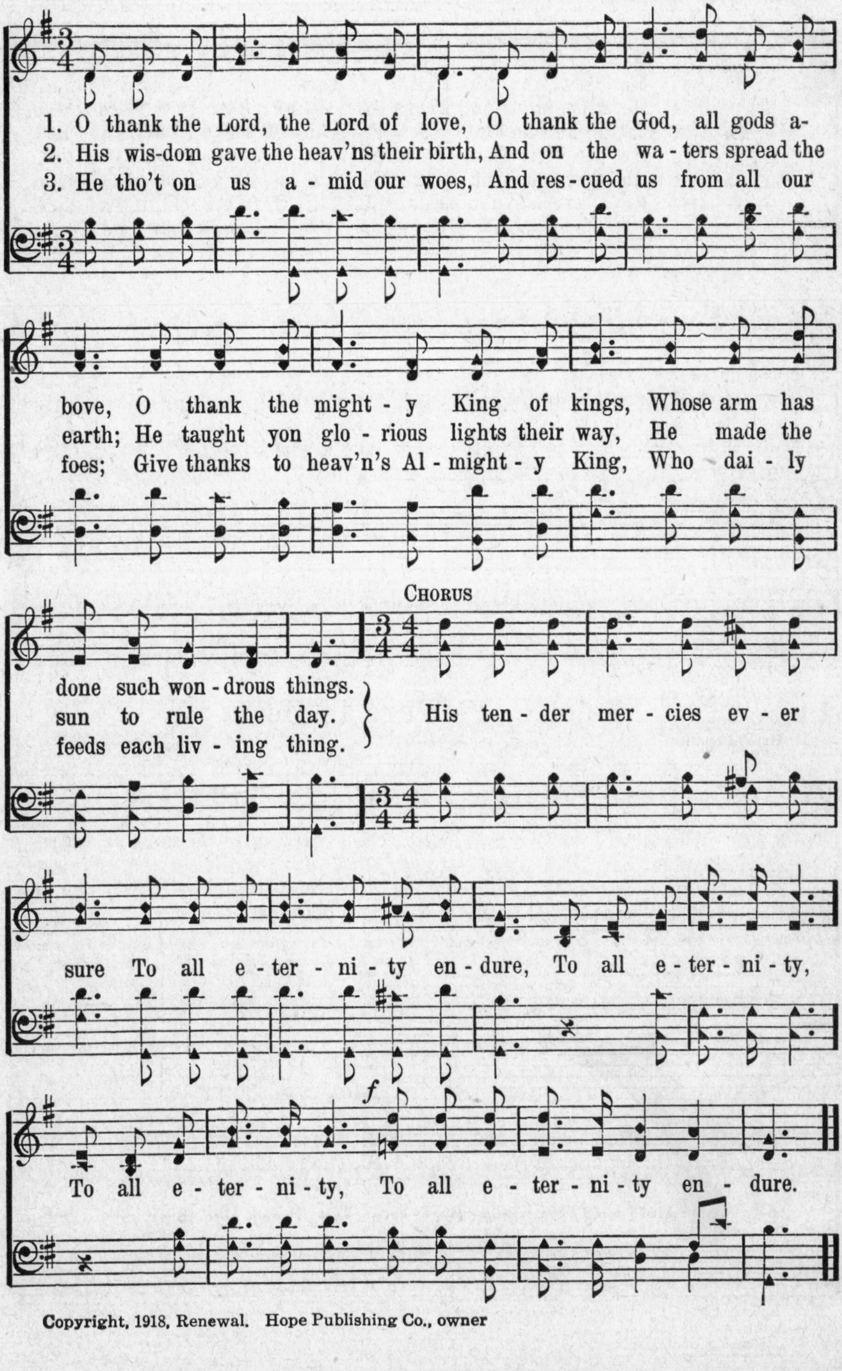
1. O thank the Lord, the Lord of love, O thank the God, all gods a-
2. His wis-dom gave the heav'ns their birth, And on the wa - ters spread the
3. He tho't on us a - mid our woes, And res - cued us from all our
bove, O thank the might - y King of kings, Whose arm has
earth; He taught yon glo - rious lights their way, He made the
foes; Give thanks to heav'n's Al - might - y King, Who dai - ly
done such won - drous things.
sun to rule the day.
feeds each liv - ing thing.
CHORUS
His ten - der mer - cies ev - er
sure To all e - ter - ni - ty en - dure, To all e - ter - ni - ty,
f
To all e - ter - ni - ty, To all e - ter - ni - ty en - dure.

10 Who is He in Yonder Stall?

B. R. H. — BENJAMIN R. HANBY

Only moderately fast

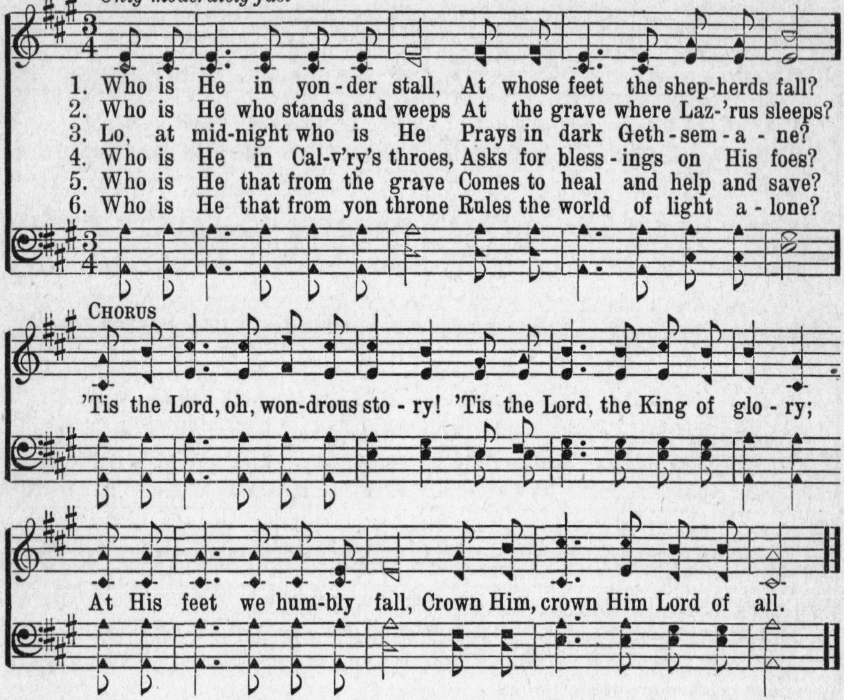

1. Who is He in yon-der stall, At whose feet the shep-herds fall?
2. Who is He who stands and weeps At the grave where Laz-'rus sleeps?
3. Lo, at mid-night who is He Prays in dark Geth-sem-a-ne?
4. Who is He in Cal-v'ry's throes, Asks for bless-ings on His foes?
5. Who is He that from the grave Comes to heal and help and save?
6. Who is He that from yon throne Rules the world of light a-lone?

CHORUS

'Tis the Lord, oh, won-drous sto-ry! 'Tis the Lord, the King of glo-ry;
At His feet we hum-bly fall, Crown Him, crown Him Lord of all.

11 Rejoice, Ye Pure in Heart

E. H. PLUMPTRE — MARION — A. H. MESSITER

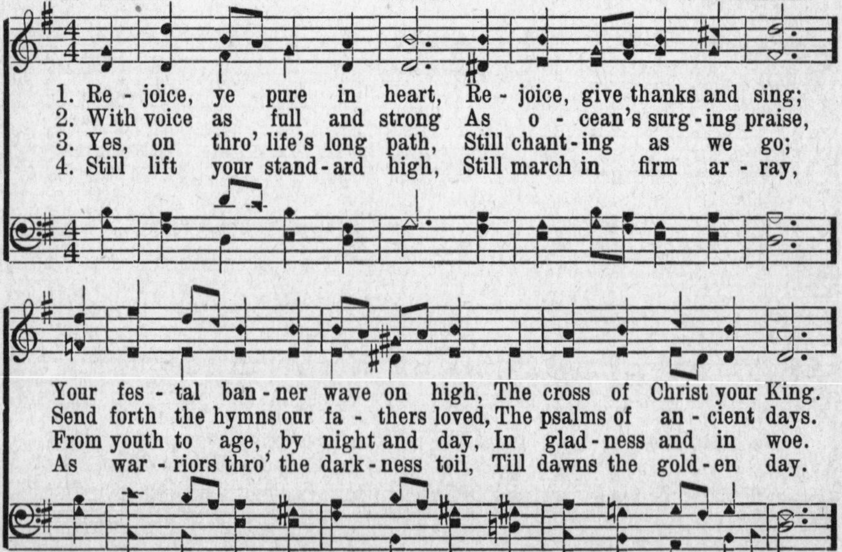

1. Re-joice, ye pure in heart, Re-joice, give thanks and sing; Your fes-tal ban-ner wave on high, The cross of Christ your King.
2. With voice as full and strong As o-cean's surg-ing praise, Send forth the hymns our fa-thers loved, The psalms of an-cient days.
3. Yes, on thro' life's long path, Still chant-ing as we go; From youth to age, by night and day, In glad-ness and in woe.
4. Still lift your stand-ard high, Still march in firm ar-ray, As war-riors thro' the dark-ness toil, Till dawns the gold-en day.

Rejoice, Ye Pure in Heart

Refrain
Re - joice, re - joice, Re - joice, give thanks and sing.
Re - joice, re - joice,

Round the Lord in Glory Seated 12

Richard Mant — MOULTRIE — Gerard F. Cobb

1. Round the Lord in glo - ry seat - ed, Cher - u - bim and ser - a - phim
2. Heav'n is still with glo - ry ring - ing, Earth takes up the an - gels' cry,
3. "Lord, Thy glo - ry fills the heav - en; Earth is with its full-ness stored;
Filled His tem - ple, and re - peat - ed Each to each th' al - ter - nate hymn:
"Ho - ly, ho - ly, ho - ly," sing - ing, "Lord of hosts, the Lord most high!"
Un - to Thee be glo - ry giv - en, Ho - ly, ho - ly, ho - ly Lord!"
"Lord, Thy glo - ry fills the heav - en; Earth is with its full-ness stored;
With His ser - aph train be - fore Him, With His ho - ly church be - low,
Thus Thy glo-rious name con-fess - ing, We a - dopt the an - gels' cry,
Un - to Thee be glo - ry giv - en, Ho - ly, ho - ly, ho - ly, Lord!"
Thus con-spire we to a - dore Him, Bid we thus our an-them flow:
"Ho - ly, ho - ly, ho - ly," bless-ing Thee, the Lord of hosts most high!

13 Glory to God the Father

Maj. D. W. WHITTLE (El Nathan) — JAMES MCGRANAHAN

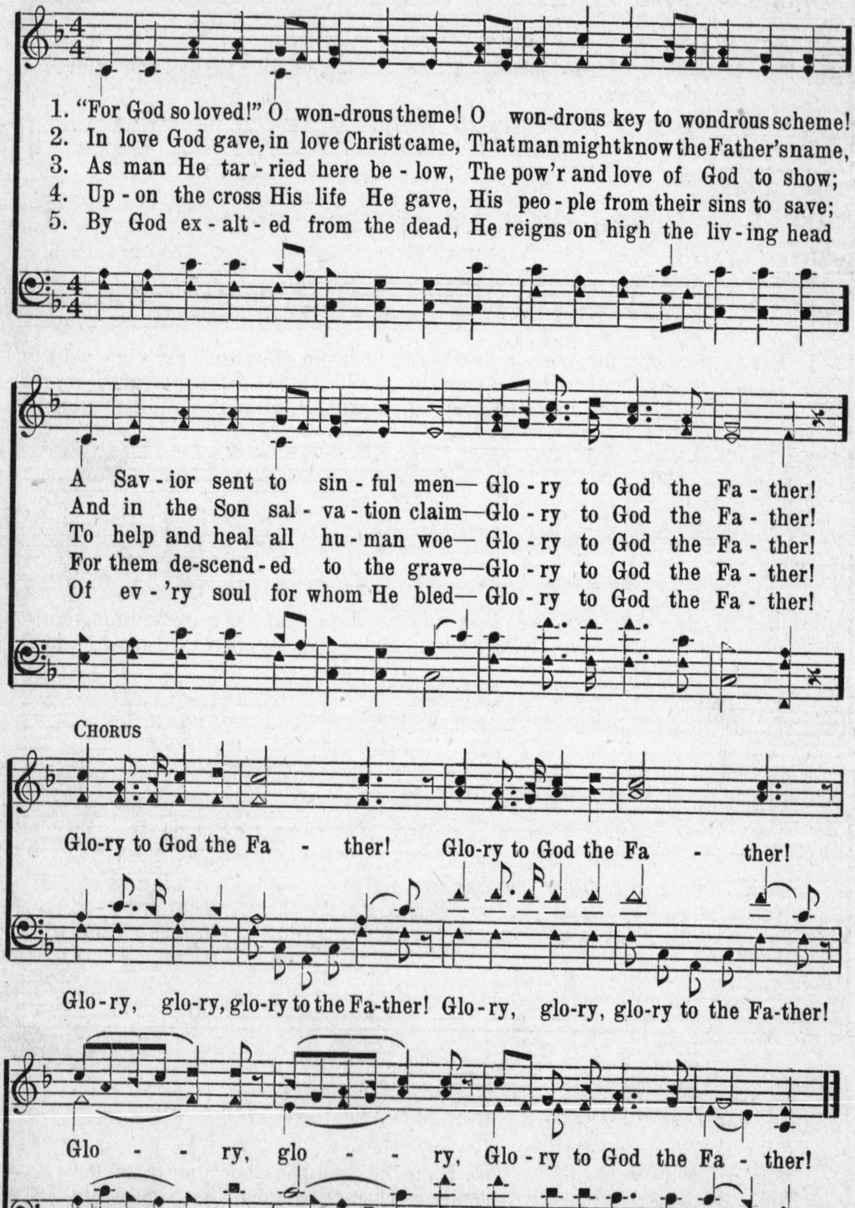
1. "For God so loved!" O won-drous theme! O won-drous key to wondrous scheme!
2. In love God gave, in love Christ came, That man might know the Father's name,
3. As man He tar-ried here be-low, The pow'r and love of God to show;
4. Up-on the cross His life He gave, His peo-ple from their sins to save;
5. By God ex-alt-ed from the dead, He reigns on high the liv-ing head
A Sav-ior sent to sin-ful men— Glo-ry to God the Fa-ther!
And in the Son sal-va-tion claim—Glo-ry to God the Fa-ther!
To help and heal all hu-man woe— Glo-ry to God the Fa-ther!
For them de-scend-ed to the grave—Glo-ry to God the Fa-ther!
Of ev-'ry soul for whom He bled— Glo-ry to God the Fa-ther!
CHORUS
Glo-ry to God the Fa - ther! Glo-ry to God the Fa - ther!
Glo-ry, glo-ry, glo-ry to the Fa-ther! Glo-ry, glo-ry, glo-ry to the Fa-ther!
Glo - - ry, glo - - ry, Glo-ry to God the Fa - ther!

Hosanna, Loud Hosanna

ELLACOMBE. 7. 6. 7. 6. D.

JEANNETTE THRELFALL

Gesangbuch der Herzogl

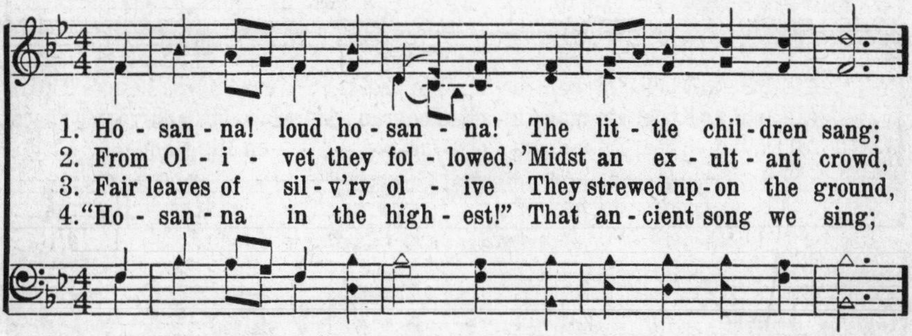
1. Ho - san - na! loud ho - san - na! The lit - tle chil - dren sang;
2. From Ol - i - vet they fol - lowed, 'Midst an ex - ult - ant crowd,
3. Fair leaves of sil - v'ry ol - ive They strewed up - on the ground,
4. "Ho - san - na in the high - est!" That an - cient song we sing;

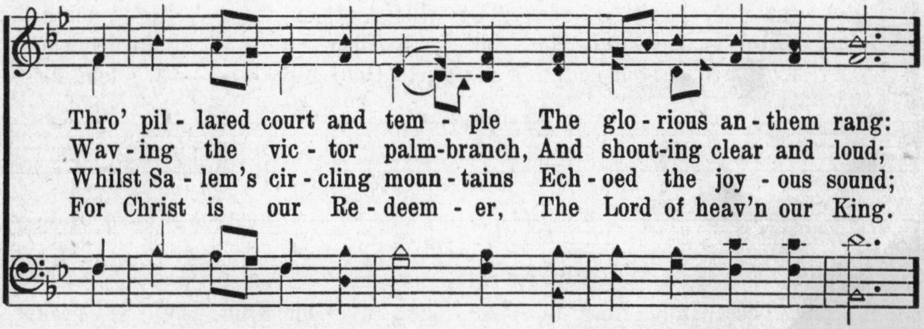
Thro' pil - lared court and tem - ple The glo - rious an - them rang:
Wav - ing the vic - tor palm-branch, And shout-ing clear and loud;
Whilst Sa - lem's cir - cling moun - tains Ech - oed the joy - ous sound;
For Christ is our Re - deem - er, The Lord of heav'n our King.

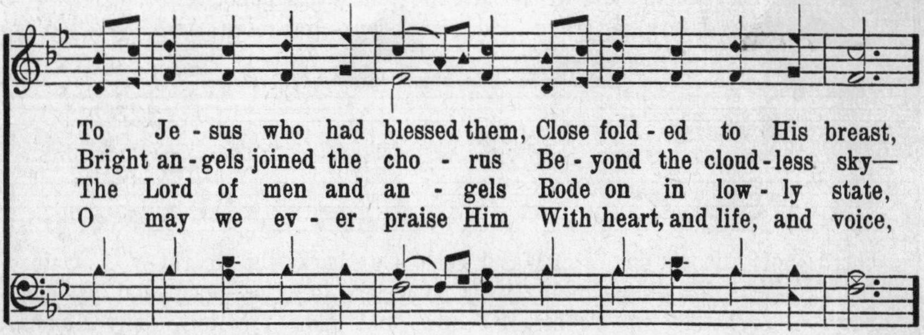
To Je - sus who had blessed them, Close fold - ed to His breast,
Bright an - gels joined the cho - rus Be - yond the cloud - less sky—
The Lord of men and an - gels Rode on in low - ly state,
O may we ev - er praise Him With heart, and life, and voice,

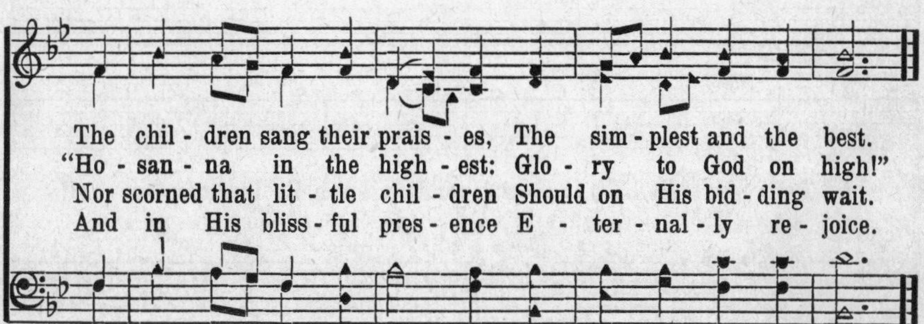
The chil - dren sang their prais - es, The sim - plest and the best.
"Ho - san - na in the high - est: Glo - ry to God on high!"
Nor scorned that lit - tle chil - dren Should on His bid - ding wait.
And in His bliss - ful pres - ence E - ter - nal - ly re - joice.

15 All Hail, Immanuel

D. R. van Sickle — Chas. H. Gabriel

1. All hail to Thee, Im-man-u-el, We cast . . . our crowns be-fore Thee;
2. All hail to Thee, Im-man-u-el, The ran - somed hosts surround Thee;
3. All hail to Thee, Im-man-u-el, Our ris - - en King and Sav-ior!
Let ev-'ry heart o-bey Thy will, And ev - - - 'ry voice a-
And earth-ly mon-archs clam-or forth Their Sov - - 'reign King to
Thy foes are van-quished, and Thou art Om-nip - - - - o - tent for-
dore Thee. In praise to Thee, our Sav-ior King, The vi-brant
crown Thee. While those re-deemed in a-ges gone, As-sem-bled
ev - er. Death, sin and hell no lon-ger reign, And Sa-tan's
chords of Heav-en ring, And ech-o back the might-y strain:
round the great white throne, Break forth in-to im-mor-tal song:
pow'r is burst in twain; E - ter-nal glo-ry to Thy Name:
ff
All hail! all hail! All hail! all hail! Im-man-u-el!
All hail! all hail!

All Hail. Immanuel

16 To God Be the Glory

Fanny J. Crosby | W. H. Doane

1. To God be the glo-ry,—great things He hath done, So loved He the world that He gave us His Son, Who yield-ed His life an a-tone-ment for sin, And o-pened the Life-gate that all may go in.
2. O per - fect re-demp-tion, the purchase of blood, To ev - 'ry be-liev - er the prom-ise of God; The vil - est of-fend-er who tru-ly be-lieves, That moment from Je - sus a par-don receives.
3. Great things He hath taught us, great things He hath done, And great our re-joicing thro' Je - sus the Son; But pu - rer, and higher, and greater will be Our won-der, our transport, when Jesus we see.
Chorus
Praise the Lord, praise the Lord, Let the earth hear His voice! Praise the Lord, praise the Lord, Let the peo-ple re - joice! O come to the Fa-ther, thro' Je-sus the Son, And give Him the glo-ry,—great things He hath done.

The Heavens Declare Thy Glory 17

CHENIES. 7. 6. 7. 6. D.

THOMAS R. BIRKS — TIMOTHY R. MATTHEWS

1. The heavn's de - clare Thy glo - ry, The fir - ma - ment Thy pow'r;
2. The sun with roy - al splen - dor Goes forth to chant Thy praise;
3. How per - fect, just and ho - ly The pre - cepts Thou hast giv'n!
4. All heav'n on high re - joic - es To do its Mak - er's will;
Day un - to day the sto - ry Re - peats from hour to hour;
And moon-beams soft and ten - der Their gen - tler an - them raise;
Still mak - ing wise the low - ly, They lift the tho'ts to heav'n;
The stars with sol - emn voic - es Re - sound Thy prais - es still;
Night un - to night re - ply - ing, Pro - claims in ev - 'ry land,
O'er ev - 'ry tribe and na - tion That mu - sic strange is poured,
Thy Word hath rich - er treas - ure Than dwells with - in the mine,
So let my whole be - hav - ior, Tho'ts, words and ac - tions be,
O Lord, with voice un - dy - ing, The won - ders of Thy hand.
The song of all cre - a - tion, To Thee, cre - a - tion's Lord.
And sweet - ness be - yond meas - ure At - tends Thy voice di - vine.
O Lord, my strength, my Sav - ior, One cease - less song to Thee.

18 Come, Let Us Sing the Song of Songs

JAMES MONTGOMERY — FLORENCE. L. M. — J. BADEN POWELL

1. Come, let us sing the song of songs, The saints in heav'n be-
2. Slain to re - deem us by His blood, To cleanse from ev - 'ry
3. To Him who suf - fered on the tree, Our souls, at His soul's
4. To Him, en - throned by fil - ial right, All pow'r in heav'n and
5. Long as we live, and when we die, And while in heav'n with

gan the strain, The hom - age which to Christ be - longs, "Wor-thy the
sin - ful stain, And make us kings and priests to God: "Wor-thy the
price, to gain, Bless-ing, and praise, and glo - ry be: "Wor-thy the
earth pro-claim, Hon - or and maj - es-ty, and might: "Wor-thy the
Him we reign, This song our song of songs shall be: "Wor-thy the

Lamb, Wor - thy the Lamb, Wor - thy the Lamb, for He was slain!"
Lamb, Wor - thy the Lamb, Wor - thy the Lamb, for He was slain!"
Lamb, Wor - thy the Lamb, Wor - thy the Lamb, for He was slain!"
Lamb, Wor - thy the Lamb, Wor - thy the Lamb, for He was slain!"
Lamb, Wor - thy the Lamb, Wor - thy the Lamb, for He was slain!"

19 Bless the Lord, O My Soul

From PSALM 103: 1 — H. D. WEAVER

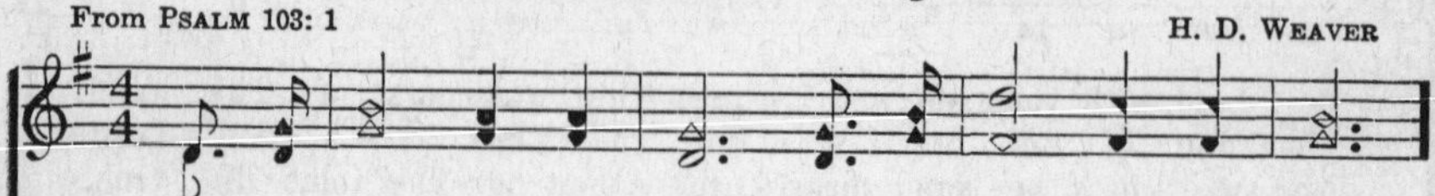

Bless the Lord, O my soul, Bless the Lord, O my soul;

Bless the Lord, O My Soul

ritard.
Bless the Lord, O my soul, Bless His ho - ly name. A - MEN.

Every Day Will I Bless Thee

20

PSALM 145

JAMES McGRANAHAN

Not too slow
1. I will ex - tol Thee, O my God, And praise Thee, O my King;
2. Great is the Lord, our might - y God, And great - ly to be praised;
3. Up - on Thy glo - rious maj - es - ty And hon - or I will dwell,
4. The Lord, our God, is good to all, From Him all bless - ing flows;
Yea, ev - 'ry day and ev - er - more Thy prais - es I will sing.
His great - ness is un - search - a - ble, A - bove all glo - ry raised.
And all Thy grand and glo - rious works And all Thy great - ness tell.
On all His works His ten - der love And mer - cy He be - stows.
CHORUS
Ev - 'ry day will I bless Thee; Ev - 'ry day will I bless Thee;
And I will praise, will praise Thy name For - ev - er and ev - er.

21 Ye Watchers and Ye Holy Ones

LASST UNS ERFREUEN. 8. 8. 4. 4. 8. 8. With Alleluias

ATHELSTAN RILEY — German Melody

1. Ye watch-ers and ye ho - ly ones, Bright seraphs, cher-u-bim and thrones,
2. O high - er than the cher - u - bim, More glorious than the ser - a - phim,
3. O friends, in glad-ness let us sing, Su - per-nal anthems ech-o - ing,

Raise the glad strain, Al-le-lu - ia! Cry out, dominions, princedoms, pow'rs,
Lead their prais-es, Al-le-lu - ia! Thou bear-er of th' e-ter-nal Word,
Al - le-lu - ia, Al-le-lu - ia! To God the Fa-ther, God the Son,

Vir-tues, arch-an-gels, an-gels' choirs, Al-le-lu - ia, Al-le-lu - ia,
Most gracious, mag-ni-fy the Lord, Al-le-lu - ia, Al-le-lu - ia,
And God the Spir-it, Three in One. Al-le-lu - ia, Al-le-lu - ia,

Al-le-lu - ia, Al-le-lu - ia, Al-le-lu - ia!
Al-le-lu - ia, Al-le-lu - ia, Al-le-lu - ia!
Al-le-lu - ia, Al-le-lu - ia, Al-le-lu - ia! A - MEN.

Jesus, Rose of Sharon

IDA A. GUIREY

CHAS. H. GABRIEL

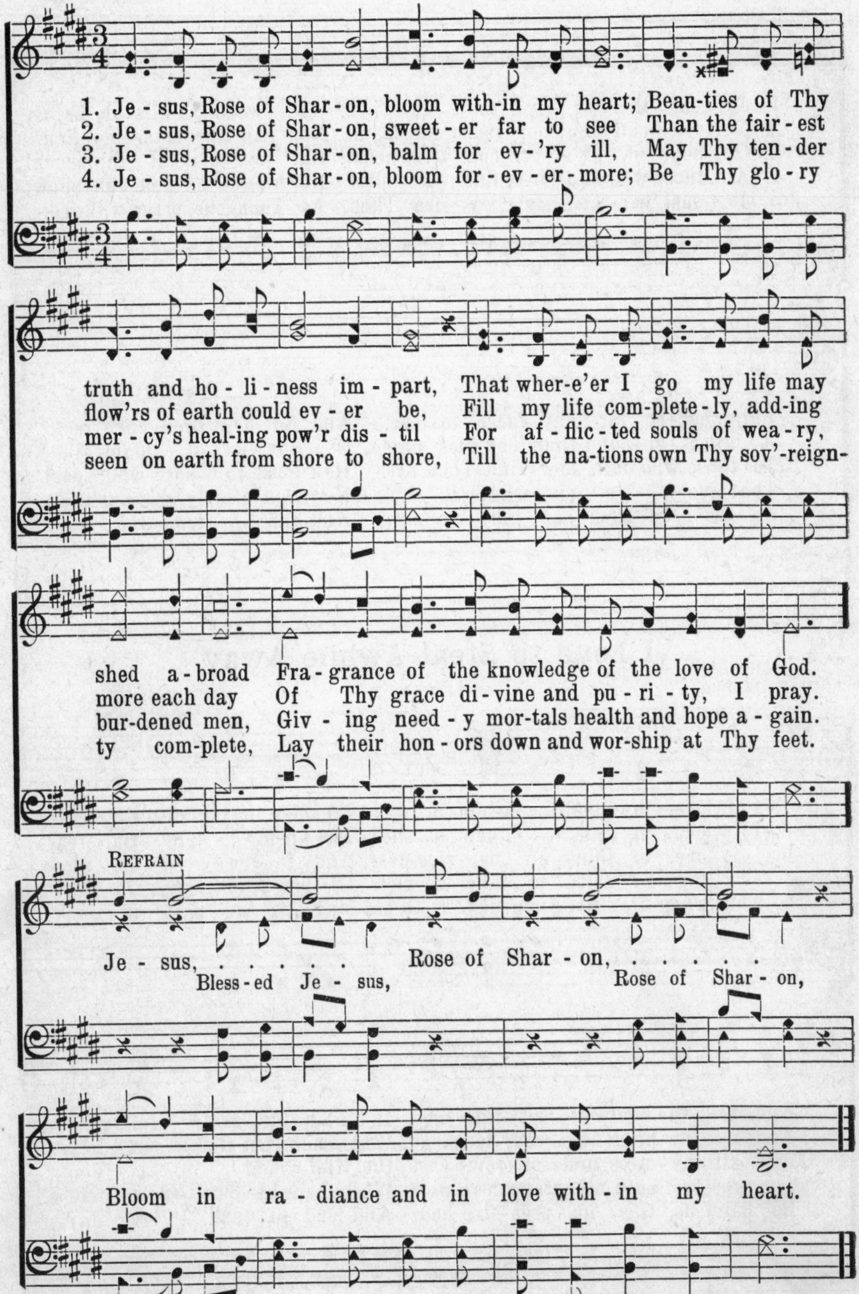
1. Je - sus, Rose of Shar - on, bloom with - in my heart; Beau - ties of Thy
2. Je - sus, Rose of Shar - on, sweet - er far to see Than the fair - est
3. Je - sus, Rose of Shar - on, balm for ev - 'ry ill, May Thy ten - der
4. Je - sus, Rose of Shar - on, bloom for - ev - er - more; Be Thy glo - ry
truth and ho - li - ness im - part, That wher - e'er I go my life may
flow'rs of earth could ev - er be, Fill my life com - plete - ly, add - ing
mer - cy's heal - ing pow'r dis - til For af - flic - ted souls of wea - ry,
seen on earth from shore to shore, Till the na - tions own Thy sov' - reign -
shed a - broad Fra - grance of the knowledge of the love of God.
more each day Of Thy grace di - vine and pu - ri - ty, I pray.
bur - dened men, Giv - ing need - y mor - tals health and hope a - gain.
ty com - plete, Lay their hon - ors down and wor - ship at Thy feet.
REFRAIN
Je - sus, ... Rose of Shar - on, ...
Bless - ed Je - sus, Rose of Shar - on,
Bloom in ra - diance and in love with - in my heart.

23 Jesus, the Very Thought of Thee

E. CASWALL, tr. ST. AGNES. C. M. JOHN B. DYKES

1. Je - sus, the ver - y tho't of Thee, With sweetness fills my breast;
2. Nor voice can sing, nor heart can frame, Nor can the mem - 'ry find
3. Oh, hope of ev - 'ry con - trite heart! Oh, joy of all the meek!
4. And those who find Thee, find a bliss Nor tongue nor pen can show;
5. Je - sus! our on - ly joy be Thou, As Thou our prize wilt be;

But sweet - er far Thy face to see, And in Thy pres - ence rest.
A sweet - er sound than Thy blest name, O Sav - ior of man - kind!
To those who fall, how kind Thou art! How good to those who seek!
The love of Je - sus, what it is None but His loved ones know.
Je - sus! be Thou our glo - ry now, And thro' e - ter - ni - ty.

24 I Love to Steal Awhile Away

P. H. BROWN LELLA. C. M. CHAS. EDW. POLLOCK

Softly with expression

1. I love to steal a - while a - way From ev - 'ry cum - b'ring care,
2. I love in sol - i - tude to shed The pen - i - ten - tial tear,
3. I love to think on mer - cies past, And fu - ture good im - plore,
4. I love by faith to take a view Of bright - er scenes in heav'n,
5. Thus, when life's toil - some day is o'er, May its de - part - ing ray

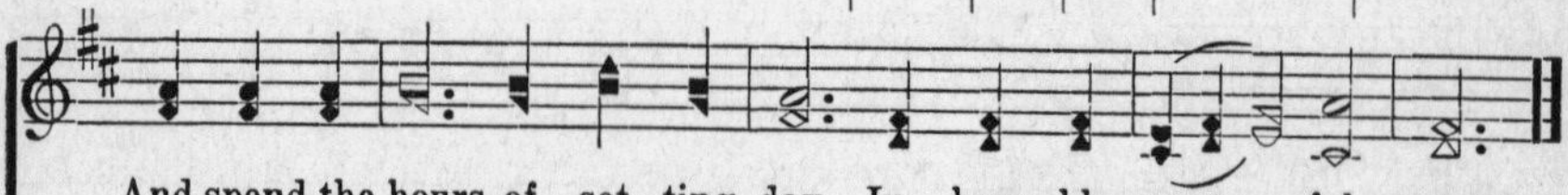

And spend the hours of set - ting day In hum - ble, grate - ful prayer.
And all His prom - is - es to plead, Where none but God can hear.
And all my cares and sor - rows cast On Him whom I a - dore.
The pros - pect doth my strength re - new, While here by tem - pests driv'n.
Be calm as this im - pres - sive hour, And lead to end - less day.

We May Not Climb the Heavenly Steeps

J. G. WHITTIER — SERENITY. C. M. — Arr. from W. V. WALLACE

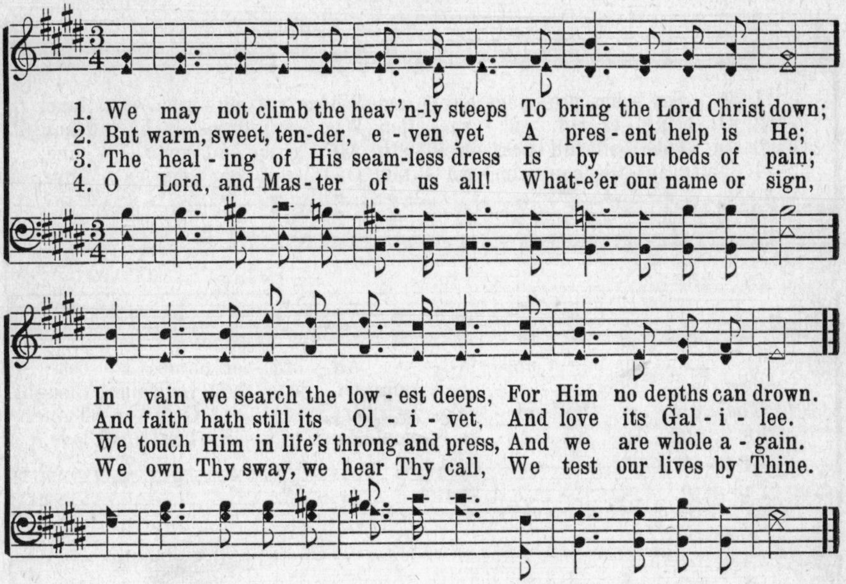
1. We may not climb the heav'n-ly steeps To bring the Lord Christ down;
2. But warm, sweet, ten-der, e - ven yet A pres - ent help is He;
3. The heal - ing of His seam-less dress Is by our beds of pain;
4. O Lord, and Mas-ter of us all! What-e'er our name or sign,
In vain we search the low - est deeps, For Him no depths can drown.
And faith hath still its Ol - i - vet, And love its Gal - i - lee.
We touch Him in life's throng and press, And we are whole a - gain.
We own Thy sway, we hear Thy call, We test our lives by Thine.

How Beauteous Were the Marks Divine

A. CLEVELAND COXE — CANONBURY. L. M. — ROBERT SCHUMANN

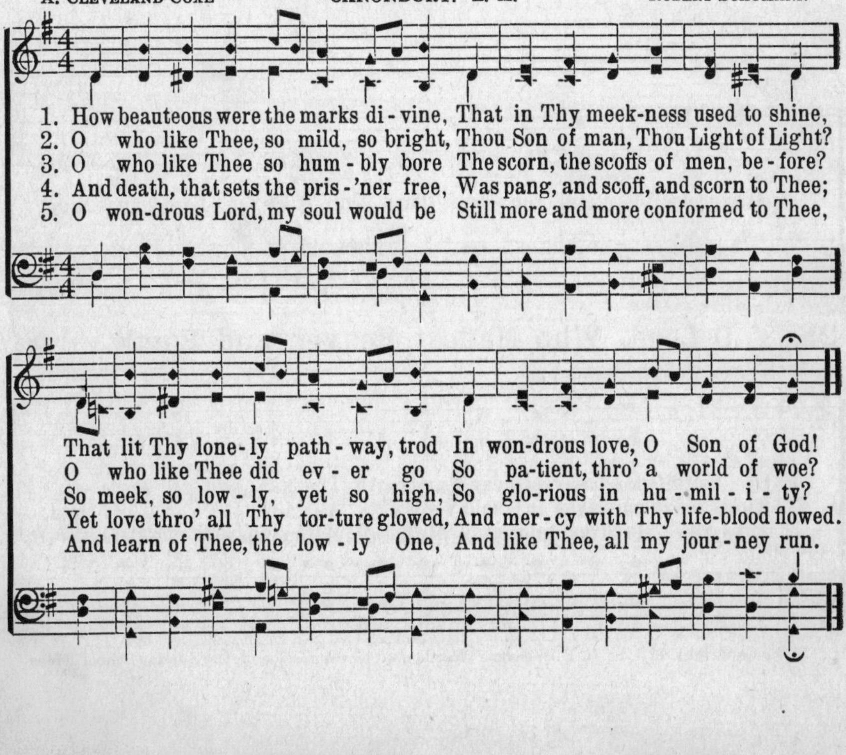
1. How beauteous were the marks di - vine, That in Thy meek-ness used to shine,
2. O who like Thee, so mild, so bright, Thou Son of man, Thou Light of Light?
3. O who like Thee so hum - bly bore The scorn, the scoffs of men, be - fore?
4. And death, that sets the pris - 'ner free, Was pang, and scoff, and scorn to Thee;
5. O won-drous Lord, my soul would be Still more and more conformed to Thee,
That lit Thy lone-ly path - way, trod In won-drous love, O Son of God!
O who like Thee did ev - er go So pa-tient, thro' a world of woe?
So meek, so low - ly, yet so high, So glo-rious in hu - mil - i - ty?
Yet love thro' all Thy tor-ture glowed, And mer - cy with Thy life-blood flowed.
And learn of Thee, the low - ly One, And like Thee, all my jour - ney run.

27 O Savior, Precious Savior

FRANCES R. HAVERGAL — J. H. BURKE

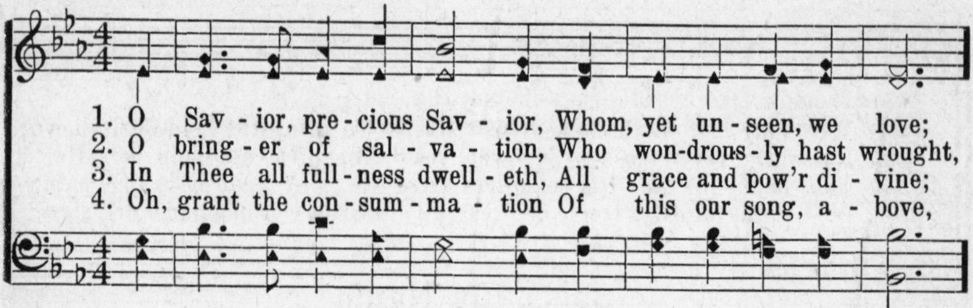

1. O Savior, precious Savior, Whom, yet unseen, we love;
2. O bringer of salvation, Who wondrously hast wrought,
3. In Thee all fullness dwelleth, All grace and pow'r divine;
4. Oh, grant the consummation Of this our song, above,

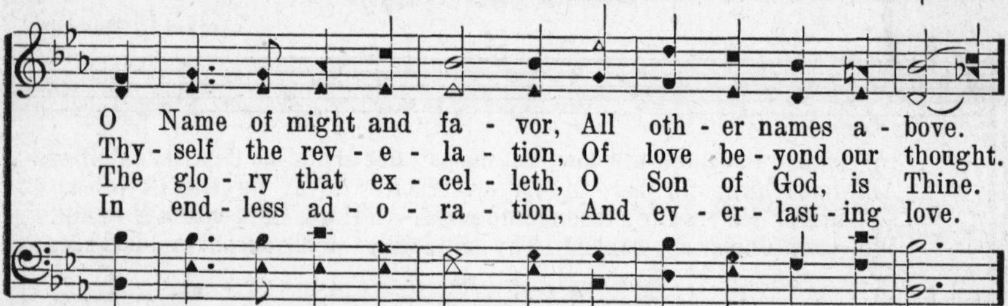

O Name of might and favor, All other names above.
Thyself the revelation, Of love beyond our thought.
The glory that excelleth, O Son of God, is Thine.
In endless adoration, And everlasting love.

CHORUS

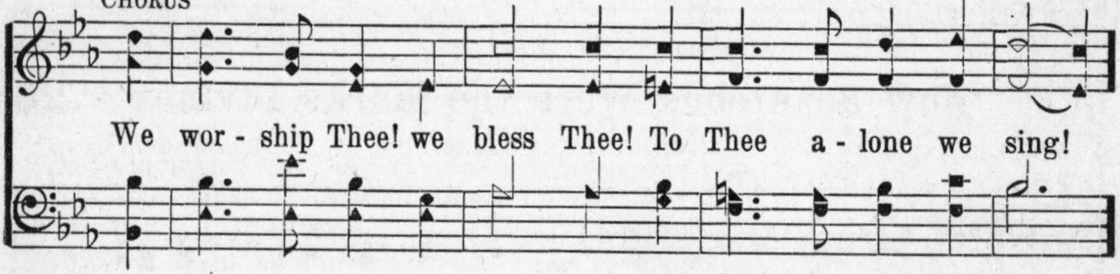

We worship Thee! we bless Thee! To Thee alone we sing!

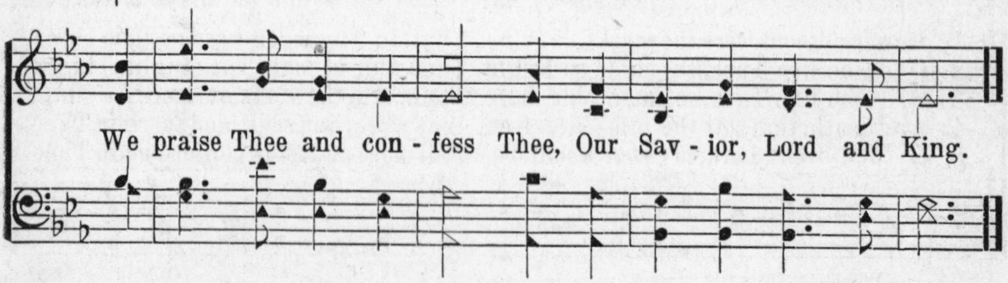

We praise Thee and confess Thee, Our Savior, Lord and King.

28 O Lord, Who Madest Heaven and Earth

ELLA BROADUS ROBERTSON — H. D. WEAVER

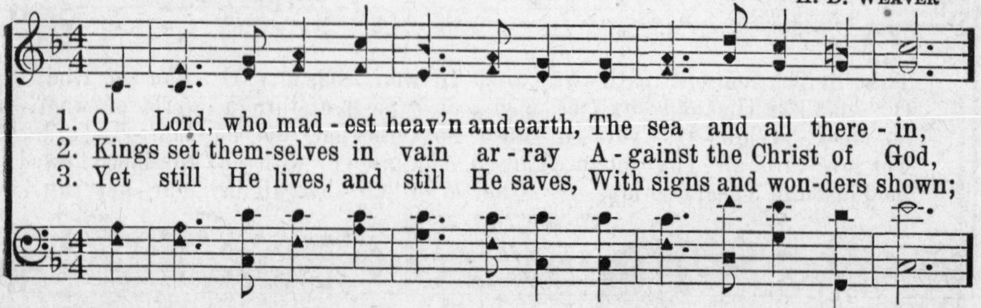

1. O Lord, who madest heav'n and earth, The sea and all therein,
2. Kings set themselves in vain array Against the Christ of God,
3. Yet still He lives, and still He saves, With signs and wonders shown;

O Lord, Who Madest Heaven and Earth

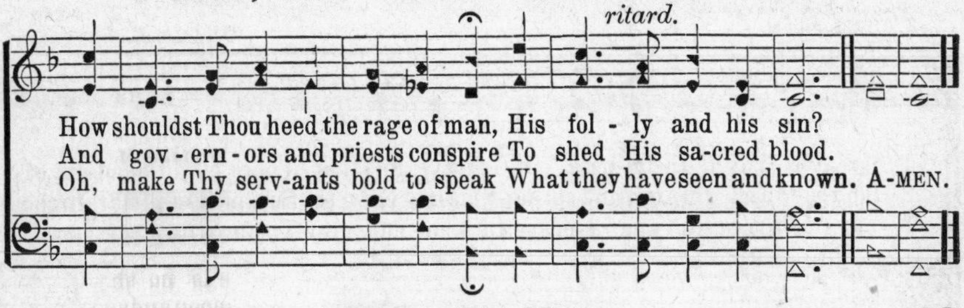
ritard.
How shouldst Thou heed the rage of man, His fol - ly and his sin?
And gov - ern - ors and priests conspire To shed His sa-cred blood.
Oh, make Thy serv-ants bold to speak What they have seen and known. A-MEN.

Bless His Name

29

LAURENE HIGHFIELD — SAMUEL W. BEAZLEY

1. Bless the Lord, let all with - in me Praise and bless His ho - ly name;
2. Bless the Lord for He is gra-cious, Slow to an - ger, swift to aid;
3. Bless the Lord so true and righteous, I His judg-ments will re - ceive;
4. Bless the Lord who can de - liv - er From the bonds of sin and death;
All His ben - e - fits and mer-cies Glad - ly let my tongue pro-claim.
Serv - ing Him in truth and spir - it, Nev - er need I be a - fraid.
Know-ing all things work to-geth - er, Bring-ing good if I be - lieve.
I will praise His name for - ev - er, Laud Him while He gives me breath.
CHORUS
Bless His ho - ly name, His mer - cies tell;
Bless His ho - ly name, ... mer-cies tell;
Bless His ho - ly name, He do - eth all things well.
Bless His ho - ly name, ...

30 Great is Thy Faithfulness

T. O. CHISHOLM

WILLIAM M. RUNYAN

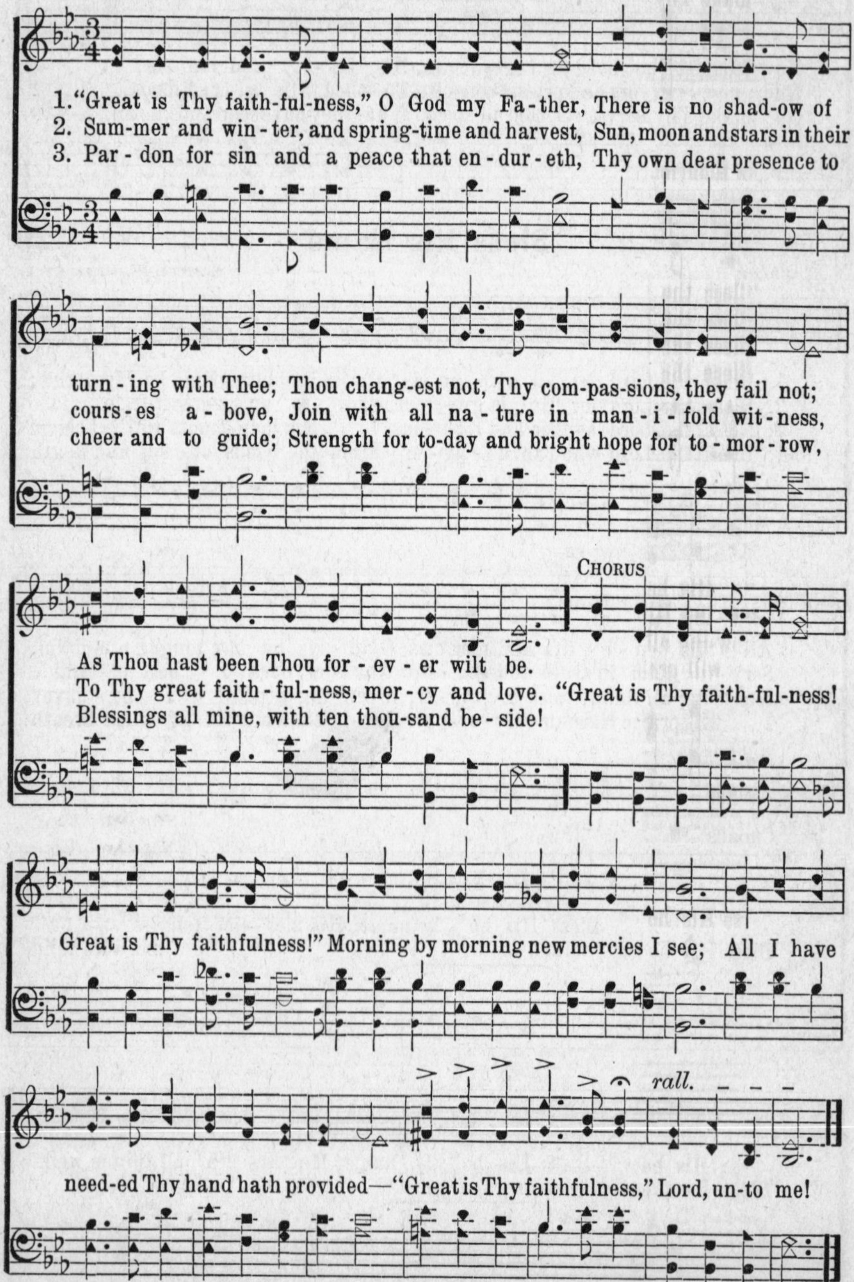
1. "Great is Thy faith-ful-ness," O God my Fa-ther, There is no shad-ow of
2. Sum-mer and win-ter, and spring-time and harvest, Sun, moon and stars in their
3. Par-don for sin and a peace that en-dur-eth, Thy own dear presence to
turn-ing with Thee; Thou chang-est not, Thy com-pas-sions, they fail not;
cours-es a-bove, Join with all na-ture in man-i-fold wit-ness,
cheer and to guide; Strength for to-day and bright hope for to-mor-row,
As Thou hast been Thou for-ev-er wilt be.
To Thy great faith-ful-ness, mer-cy and love.
Blessings all mine, with ten thou-sand be-side!
CHORUS
"Great is Thy faith-ful-ness!
Great is Thy faithfulness!" Morning by morning new mercies I see; All I have
rall.
need-ed Thy hand hath provided—"Great is Thy faithfulness," Lord, un-to me!

Praise to the Lord, the Almighty

LOBE DEN HERREN. 14. 14. 4. 7. 8.

Joachim Neander
Tr. by Catherine Winkworth

From Praxis Pietatis Melica

1. Praise to the Lord, the Al - might - y, the King of cre - a - tion! O my soul, praise Him, for He is thy health and sal - va - tion! All ye who hear, Now to His tem - ple draw near; Join me in glad ad - o - ra - tion!
2. Praise to the Lord, who o'er all things so won - drous - ly reign - eth, Shield-eth thee un - der His wings, yea, so gen - tly sus - tain - eth! Hast thou not seen How thy de - sires e'er have been Grant-ed in what He or - dain - eth?
3. Praise to the Lord, who doth pros - per thy work and de - fend thee; Sure - ly His good - ness and mer - cy here dai - ly at - tend thee. Pon - der a - new What the Al - might - y can do, If with His love He be - friend thee.

32 O Thou, in Whose Presence

JOSEPH SWAIN FREEMAN LEWIS

1. O Thou in whose pres - ence my soul takes de - light, On
2. Where dost Thou, dear Shep - herd, re - sort with Thy sheep, To
3. O why should I wan - der an a - lien from Thee, Or
4. Ye daugh-ters of Zi - on, de - clare, have you seen The
whom in af - flic - tion I call, My com - fort by day, and my
feed them in pas - tures of love? Say, why in the val - ley of
cry in the des - ert for bread? Thy foes will re - joice when my
star that on Is - ra - el shone? Say, if in your tents my Be-
song in the night, My hope, my sal - va - tion, my all!
death should I weep, Or a - lone in this wil - der - ness rove?
sor - rows they see, And smile at the tears I have shed.
lov - ed has been, And where with His flocks He is gone.

33 God Moves in a Mysterious Way

DAYTON. C. M.

WM. COWPER A. J. SHOWALTER

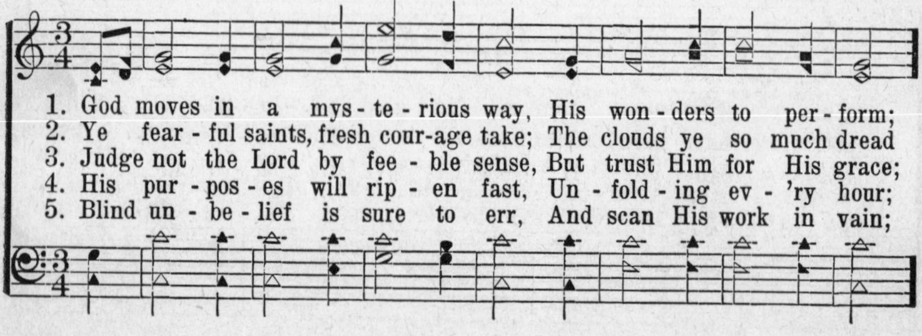
1. God moves in a mys - te - rious way, His won - ders to per - form;
2. Ye fear - ful saints, fresh cour - age take; The clouds ye so much dread
3. Judge not the Lord by fee - ble sense, But trust Him for His grace;
4. His pur - pos - es will rip - en fast, Un - fold - ing ev - 'ry hour;
5. Blind un - be - lief is sure to err, And scan His work in vain;

God Moves In a Mysterious Way

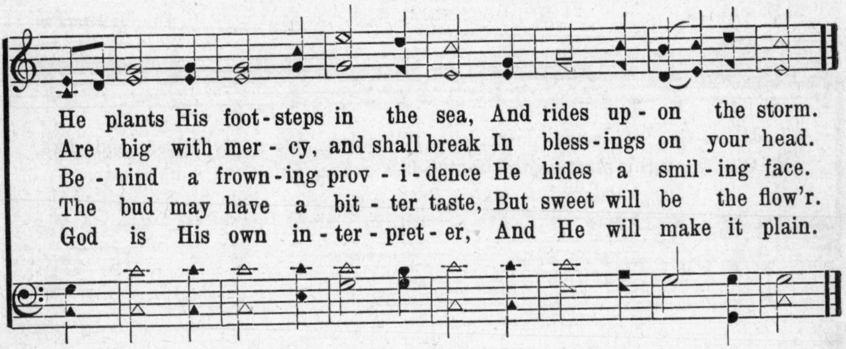
He plants His foot-steps in the sea, And rides up-on the storm.
Are big with mer-cy, and shall break In bless-ings on your head.
Be-hind a frown-ing prov-i-dence He hides a smil-ing face.
The bud may have a bit-ter taste, But sweet will be the flow'r.
God is His own in-ter-pret-er, And He will make it plain.

Summer Suns Are Glowing

WILLIAM WALSHAM HOW — RUTH. 6s. 5s. D. — SAMUEL SMITH

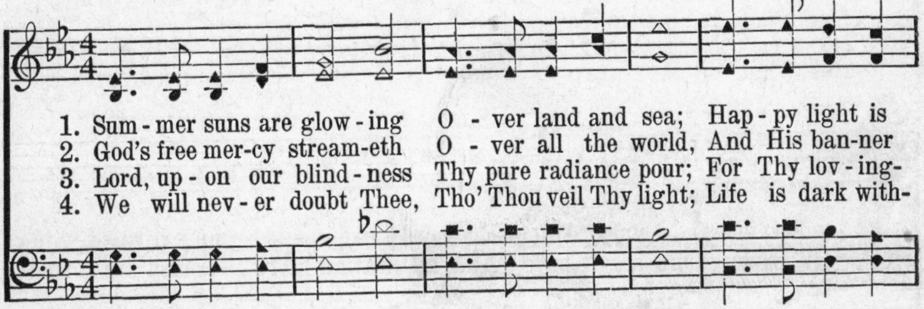
1. Sum-mer suns are glow-ing O-ver land and sea; Hap-py light is
2. God's free mer-cy stream-eth O-ver all the world, And His ban-ner
3. Lord, up-on our blind-ness Thy pure radiance pour; For Thy lov-ing-
4. We will nev-er doubt Thee, Tho' Thou veil Thy light; Life is dark with-

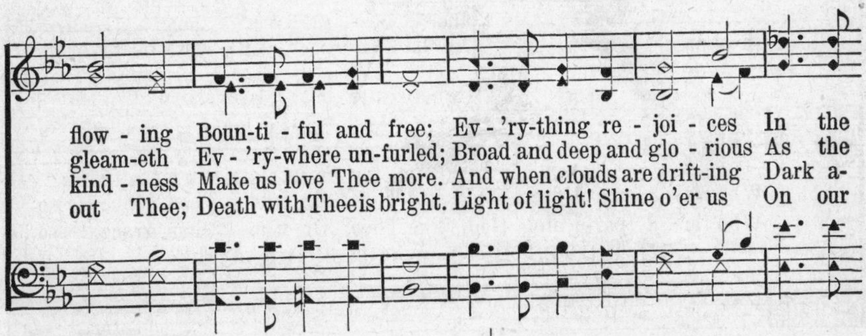
flow-ing Boun-ti-ful and free; Ev-'ry-thing re-joi-ces In the
gleam-eth Ev-'ry-where un-furled; Broad and deep and glo-rious As the
kind-ness Make us love Thee more. And when clouds are drift-ing Dark a-
out Thee; Death with Thee is bright. Light of light! Shine o'er us On our

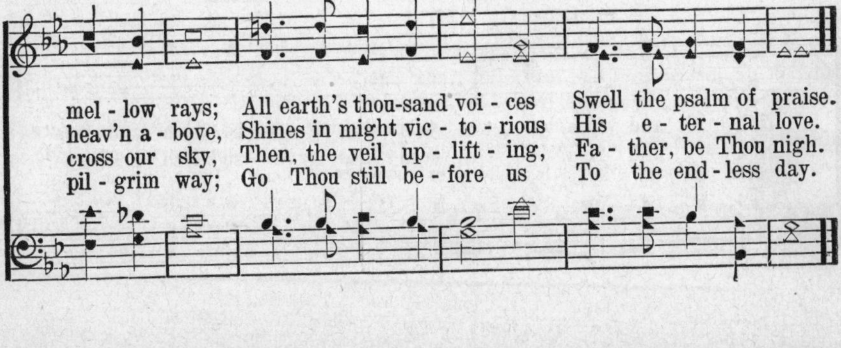
mel-low rays; All earth's thou-sand voi-ces Swell the psalm of praise.
heav'n a-bove, Shines in might vic-to-rious His e-ter-nal love.
cross our sky, Then, the veil up-lift-ing, Fa-ther, be Thou nigh.
pil-grim way; Go Thou still be-fore us To the end-less day.

35 Great God of Wonders

S. DAVIES — HUDDERSFIELD. 8. 8. 8. 8. D. — J. NEWTON

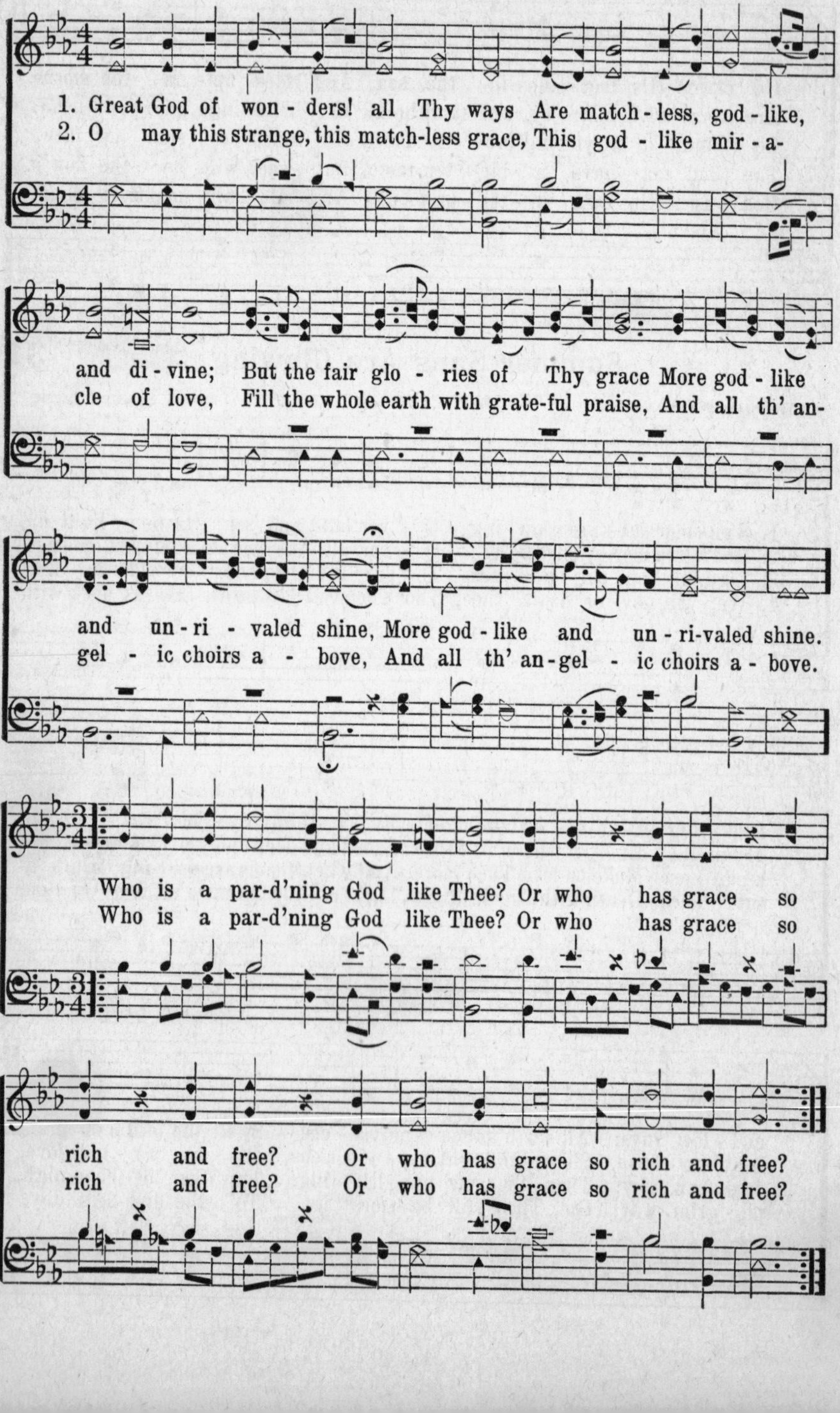
1. Great God of won - ders! all Thy ways Are match - less, god - like,
2. O may this strange, this match-less grace, This god - like mir - a-
and di - vine; But the fair glo - ries of Thy grace More god - like
cle of love, Fill the whole earth with grate-ful praise, And all th' an-
and un - ri - valed shine, More god - like and un - ri-valed shine.
gel - ic choirs a - bove, And all th' an-gel - ic choirs a - bove.
Who is a par-d'ning God like Thee? Or who has grace so
Who is a par-d'ning God like Thee? Or who has grace so
rich and free? Or who has grace so rich and free?
rich and free? Or who has grace so rich and free?

O Worship the Lord 36

R. L. ROBERT LOWRY

Earnestly
O wor-ship the Lord in the beau-ty of ho-li-ness, in the
beau-ty of ho-li-ness, in the beau-ty of ho-li-ness.
Sopranos & Altos
1. Glo-ry to the Fa-ther, a-bound-ing in mer-cy! Be
2. Glo-ry be to Je-sus, our gra-cious Re-deem-er! We
3. Glo-ry to the Spir-it, the Ho-ly Re-veal-er! We
joy-ful, all ye peo-ple, and mag-ni-fy Je-ho-vah.
praise Him, for He loved us, and bro't a great sal-va-tion.
praise Him with the Fa-ther and with the Son, our Sav-ior.
CHORUS
O glo-ry, hal-le-lu-jah, Hal-le-lu-jah, Hal-le-lu-jah!
O come be-fore His pres-ence and glo-ri-fy His name.

37 **Arise, My Soul, Arise**

CHARLES WESLEY

Har. by D. B. TOWNER

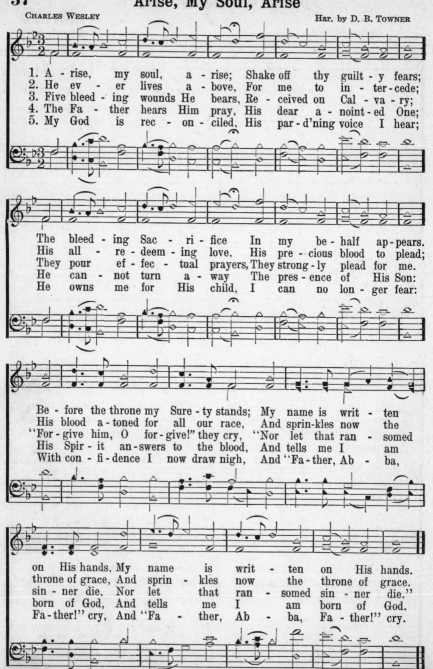

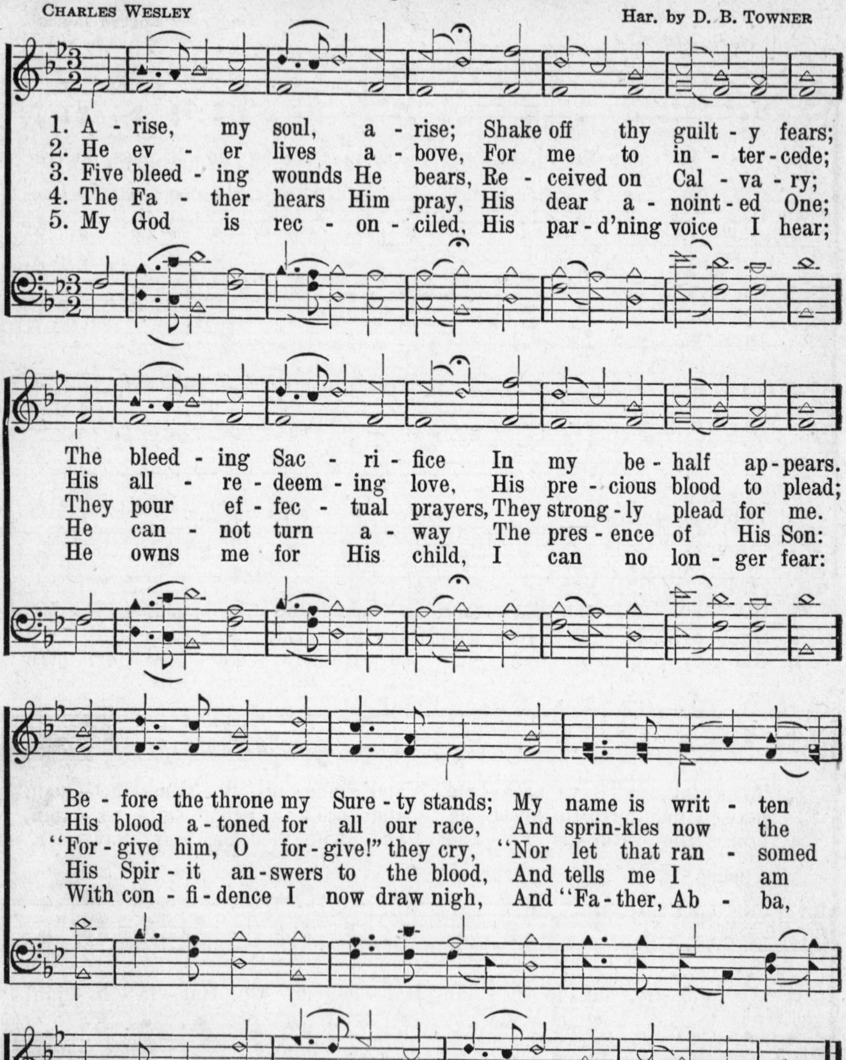
1. A - rise, my soul, a - rise; Shake off thy guilt - y fears;
2. He ev - er lives a - bove, For me to in - ter - cede;
3. Five bleed - ing wounds He bears, Re - ceived on Cal - va - ry;
4. The Fa - ther hears Him pray, His dear a - noint - ed One;
5. My God is rec - on - ciled, His par - d'ning voice I hear;
The bleed - ing Sac - ri - fice In my be - half ap - pears.
His all - re - deem - ing love, His pre - cious blood to plead;
They pour ef - fec - tual prayers, They strong - ly plead for me.
He can - not turn a - way The pres - ence of His Son:
He owns me for His child, I can no lon - ger fear:
Be - fore the throne my Sure - ty stands; My name is writ - ten
His blood a - toned for all our race, And sprin-kles now the
"For - give him, O for - give!" they cry, "Nor let that ran - somed
His Spir - it an - swers to the blood, And tells me I am
With con - fi - dence I now draw nigh, And "Fa - ther, Ab - ba,
on His hands, My name is writ - ten on His hands.
throne of grace, And sprin - kles now the throne of grace.
sin - ner die, Nor let that ran - somed sin - ner die."
born of God, And tells me I am born of God.
Fa - ther!" cry, And "Fa - ther, Ab - ba, Fa - ther!" cry.

This is My Father's World

MALTBIE D. BABCOCK

Traditional English Melody
Arranged by S. F. L.

1. This is my Fa - ther's world, And to my lis - t'ning ears, All
2. This is my Fa - ther's world, The birds their car - ols raise, The
3. This is my Fa - ther's world, O let me ne'er for - get That
na - ture sings, and round me rings The mu - sic of the spheres.
morn-ing light, the lil - y white, De - clare their Ma - ker's praise.
though the wrong seems oft so strong, God is the Rul - er yet.
This is my Fa - ther's world, I rest me in the thought Of
This is my Fa - ther's world, He shines in all that's fair; In the
This is my Fa - ther's world, The bat - tle is not done, Je- -
rocks and trees, of . . skies and seas—His hand the won - ders wrought.
rus - tling grass I . . hear Him pass, He speaks to me ev - 'ry-where.
sus who died shall be sat - is - fied, And earth and heav'n be one.

39 God of the Earth, the Sky, the Sea

PATER OMNIUM. L. M. With Refrain

SAMUEL LONGFELLOW — HENRY J. E. HOLMES

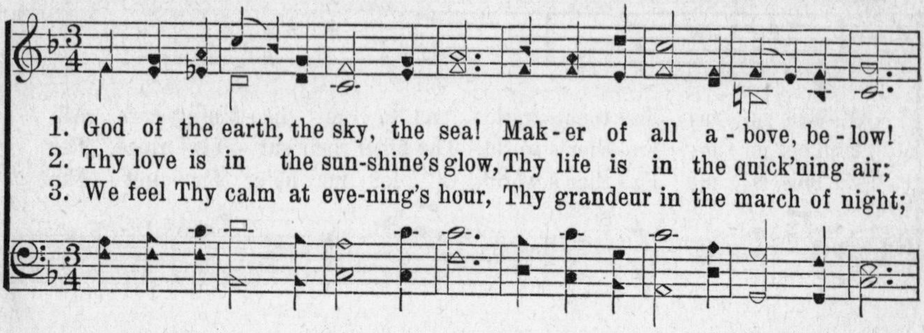
1. God of the earth, the sky, the sea! Mak-er of all a-bove, be-low!
2. Thy love is in the sun-shine's glow, Thy life is in the quick'ning air;
3. We feel Thy calm at eve-ning's hour, Thy grandeur in the march of night;

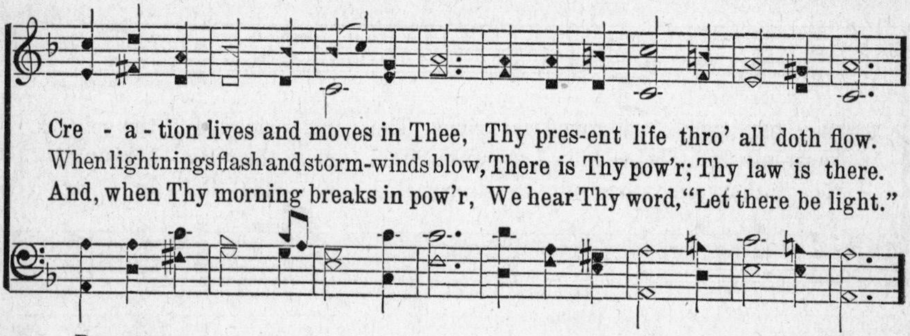
Cre - a-tion lives and moves in Thee, Thy pres-ent life thro' all doth flow.
When lightnings flash and storm-winds blow, There is Thy pow'r; Thy law is there.
And, when Thy morning breaks in pow'r, We hear Thy word, "Let there be light."

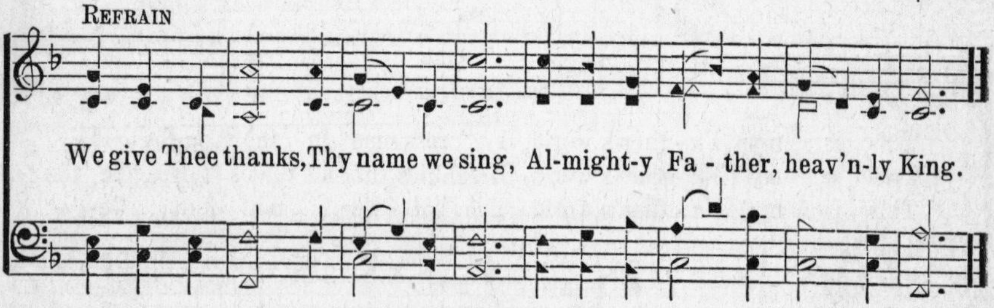
REFRAIN
We give Thee thanks, Thy name we sing, Al-might-y Fa - ther, heav'n-ly King.

40 Jesus Shall Reign

ISAAC WATTS — DUKE STREET. L. M. — JOHN HATTON

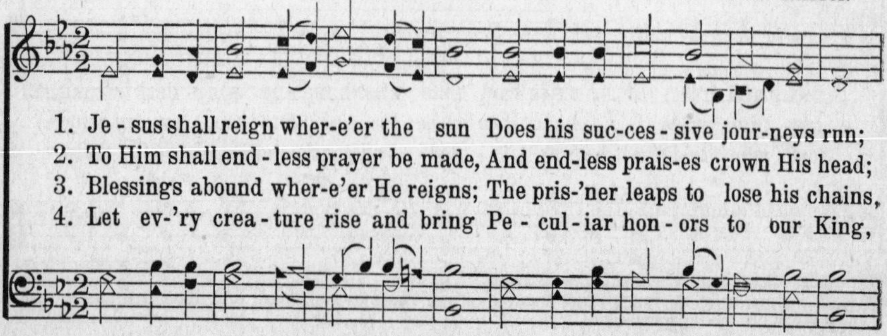
1. Je - sus shall reign wher-e'er the sun Does his suc-ces - sive jour-neys run;
2. To Him shall end - less prayer be made, And end-less prais-es crown His head;
3. Blessings abound wher-e'er He reigns; The pris-'ner leaps to lose his chains,
4. Let ev-'ry crea - ture rise and bring Pe - cul - iar hon - ors to our King,

Jesus Shall Reign

His kingdom stretch from shore to shore, Till moons shall wax and wane no more.
His name, like sweet per-fume, shall rise With ev-'ry morn-ing sac - ri - fice;
The wea-ry find e - ter - nal rest, And all the sons of want are blest.
An - gels de-scend with songs a - gain, And earth re-peat the loud A - men.

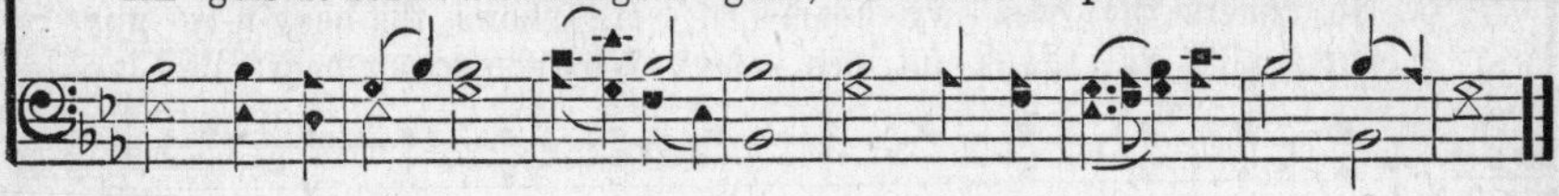

Fairest Lord Jesus 41

CRUSADERS' HYMN. 5. 6. 5. 8.

German, 17th Century — Arr. by RICHARD S. WILLIS

1. Fair - est Lord Je - sus! Rul - er of all na - ture!
2. Fair are the mead - ows, Fair - er still the wood - lands,
3. Fair is the sun - shine, Fair - er still the moon - light,

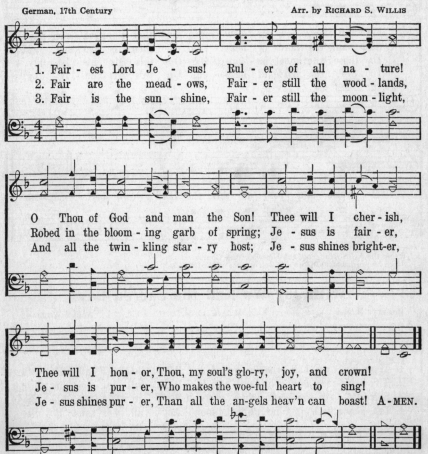

O Thou of God and man the Son! Thee will I cher - ish,
Robed in the bloom - ing garb of spring; Je - sus is fair - er,
And all the twin - kling star - ry host; Je - sus shines bright-er,

Thee will I hon - or, Thou, my soul's glo-ry, joy, and crown!
Je - sus is pur - er, Who makes the woe-ful heart to sing!
Je - sus shines pur - er, Than all the an-gels heav'n can boast! A - MEN.

42 The Earth Is Hushed in Silence

LORD'S DAY. 7. 6. 7. 6. With Refrain

Anonymous — FELIX MENDELSSOHN

1. The earth is hushed in si - lence, Its cares now flee a - way;
2. O call of love and du - ty! Who would not praise and pray,
3. He cheers the wea - ry - heart - ed, He shows the heav'n-ly way
4. Come, all ye thank - ful peo - ple! Why should our hearts de - lay

Let all things bow in rev - 'rence On this the Lord's own day.
And thank the Lord of heav - en On this His cho - sen day?
To those who kneel be - fore Him On this His ho - ly day.
To greet the Lord of heav - en On this His ho - ly day?

REFRAIN

O praise and pray on this, the Lord's own day! A - MEN.

From the *Fifth Reader*, of the New Ed. Mus. Course
Used by permission of Ginn and Co., owners of the Copyright

43 With Joy We Hail the Sacred Day

HARRIET AUBER — MEAR. C. M. — AARON WILLIAMS

1. With joy we hail the sa - cred day Which God hath called His own;
2. Thy cho - sen tem - ple, Lord, how fair! Where will - ing vo-taries throng
3. Spir - it of grace! O deign to dwell With - in Thy Church be - low;
4. Let peace with - in her walls be found; Let all her sons u - nite

With Joy We Hail the Sacred Day

With joy the sum-mons we o - bey To wor - ship at His throne.
To breathe the hum - ble, fer - vent prayer, And pour the chor - al song.
Make her in ho - li - ness ex - cel, With pure de - vo - tion glow.
To spread with grate-ful zeal a - round Her clear and shin - ing light.

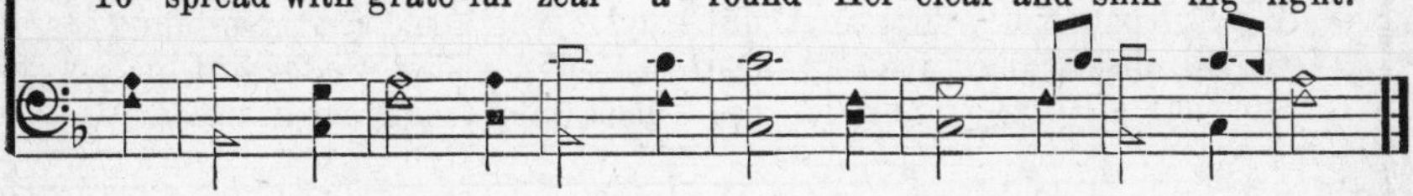

Open Now Thy Gates of Beauty

BENJAMIN SCHMOLCK JOACHIM NEANDER

1. O - pen now thy gates of beau - ty, Zi - on, let me en - ter there,
2. Yes, my God, I come be - fore Thee, Come Thou al - so down to me;
3. Here Thy praise is glad - ly chant - ed, Here Thy seed is du - ly sown;
4. Speak, O God, and I will hear Thee, Let Thy will be done in - deed;

Where my soul in joy - ful du - ty Waits for Him who an-swers prayer:
Where we find Thee and a - dore Thee, There a heav'n on earth must be.
Let my soul, where it is plant - ed, Bring forth pre-cious sheaves a - lone,
May I un - dis-turbed draw near Thee Whilst Thou dost Thy peo - ple feed:

O how bless - ed is this place, Filled with sol - ace, light, and grace.
To my heart, O en - ter Thou, Let it be Thy tem - ple now.
So that all I hear may be Fruit - ful un - to life in me.
Here of life the foun - tain flows, Here is balm for all our woes.

45 Savior, Hear Us, We Pray

LUCY. 6s. With Refrain

W. W. ELLSWORTH

JOHANNES BRAHMS
Arranged by A. CORTADA

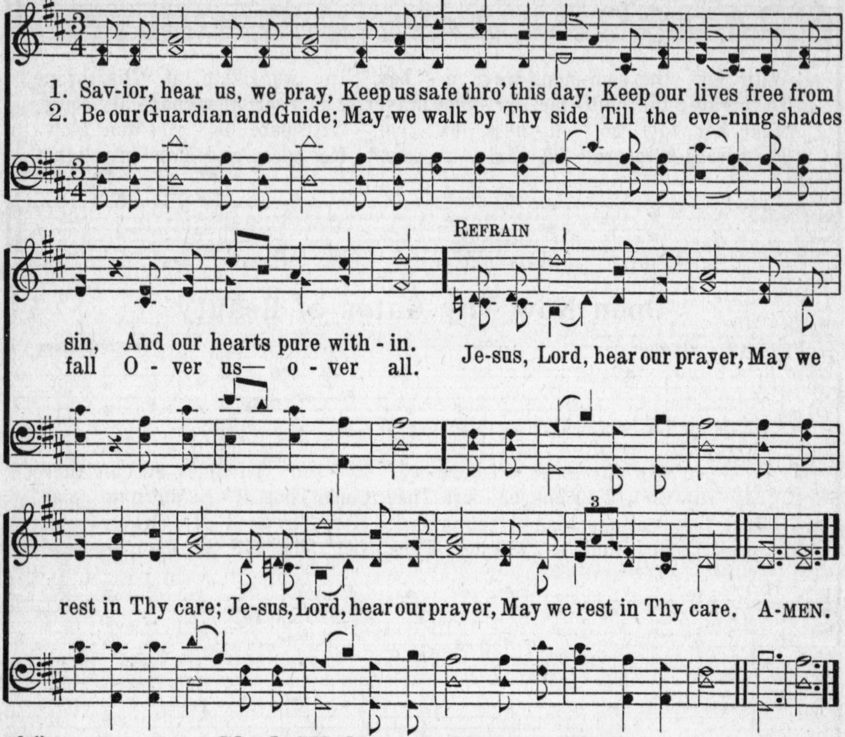
1. Sav-ior, hear us, we pray, Keep us safe thro' this day; Keep our lives free from
2. Be our Guardian and Guide; May we walk by Thy side Till the eve-ning shades
sin, And our hearts pure with - in.
fall O - ver us— o - ver all.
REFRAIN
Je-sus, Lord, hear our prayer, May we
rest in Thy care; Je-sus, Lord, hear our prayer, May we rest in Thy care. A-MEN.
3

46 Glad Welcome Happy Morn

HAYWARD

LISCHER

LOWELL MASON

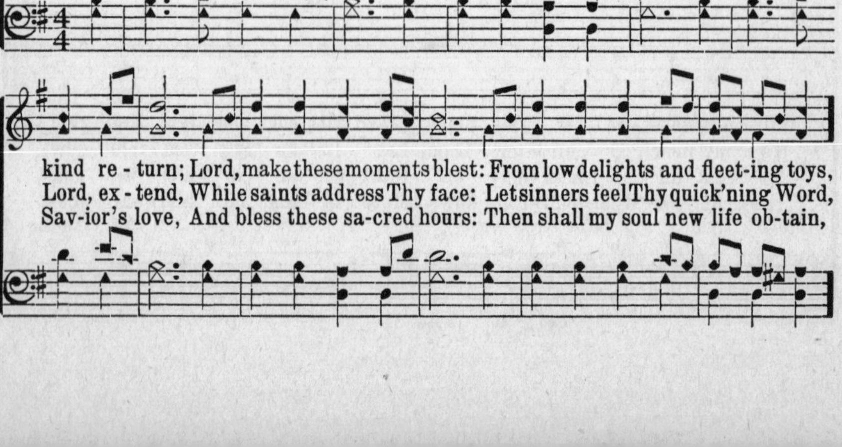
1. Glad wel-come, hap-py morn, Thou day of sa - cred rest! I hail thy
2. Now may the King de - scend, And fill His throne of grace; Thy scep-ter,
3. De - scend, ce - les - tial Dove, With all Thy quick'ning pow'rs, Dis-close a
kind re - turn; Lord, make these moments blest: From low delights and fleet-ing toys,
Lord, ex - tend, While saints address Thy face: Let sinners feel Thy quick'ning Word,
Sav-ior's love, And bless these sa-cred hours: Then shall my soul new life ob-tain,

Glad Welcome, Happy Morn

I soar to reach im-mor-tal joys, I soar to reach im-mor-tal joys.
And learn to know and fear the Lord, And learn to know and fear the Lord.
Nor Lord's Days be enjoyed in vain, Nor Lord's Days be en-joyed in vain.

Light of the World, We Hail Thee

JOHN S. B. MONSELL — SALVE DOMINE. 7. 6. 7. 6. D. — LAWRENCE W. WATSON

1. Light of the world, we hail Thee, Flush-ing the east-ern skies;
2. Light of the world, Thy beau - ty Steals in - to ev - 'ry heart,
3. Light of the world, be - fore Thee Our spir-its pros-trate fall;

Nev-er shall dark-ness veil Thee A - gain from hu-man eyes;
And glo-ri-fies with du - ty Life's poor-est, hum-blest part;
We wor-ship, we a - dore Thee, Thou Light, the Life of all;

Too long, a-las, with-hold - en, Now spread from shore to shore;
Thou rob - est in Thy splen - dor The sim - ple ways of men
With Thee is no for - get - ting Of all Thine hand hath made;

Thy light, so glad and gold - en, Shall set on earth no more.
And help - est them to ren - der Light back to Thee a - gain.
Thy ris - ing hath no set - ting, Thy sun-shine hath no shade.

On Our Way Rejoicing

ST. ALBAN. 6. 5. 6. 5. D. With Refrain

JOHN S. B. MONSELL

FRANZ JOSEPH HAYDN
Arranged by JOHN B. DYKES

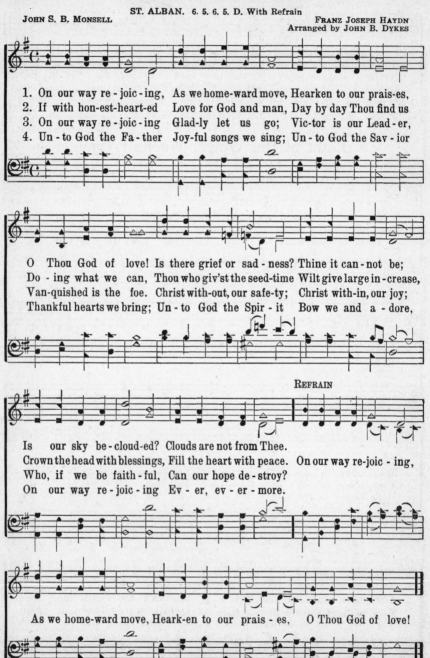

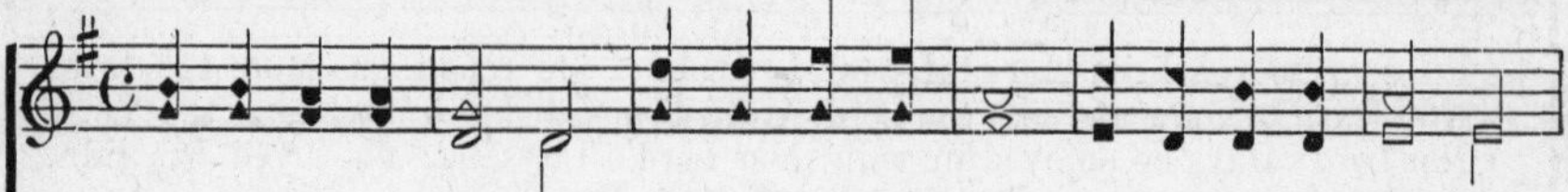

1. On our way re - joic - ing, As we home-ward move, Hearken to our prais-es,
2. If with hon-est-heart-ed Love for God and man, Day by day Thou find us
3. On our way re - joic - ing Glad-ly let us go; Vic-tor is our Lead - er,
4. Un - to God the Fa - ther Joy-ful songs we sing; Un - to God the Sav - ior

O Thou God of love! Is there grief or sad - ness? Thine it can - not be;
Do - ing what we can, Thou who giv'st the seed-time Wilt give large in - crease,
Van-quished is the foe. Christ with-out, our safe-ty; Christ with-in, our joy;
Thankful hearts we bring; Un - to God the Spir - it Bow we and a - dore,

REFRAIN

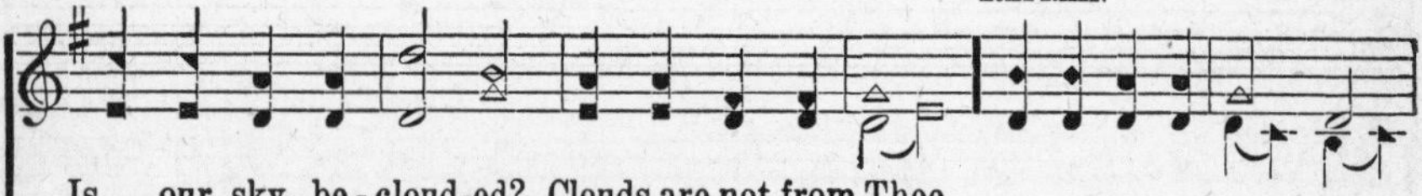

Is our sky be - cloud-ed? Clouds are not from Thee.
Crown the head with blessings, Fill the heart with peace. On our way re-joic - ing,
Who, if we be faith - ful, Can our hope de - stroy?
On our way re - joic - ing Ev - er, ev - er - more.

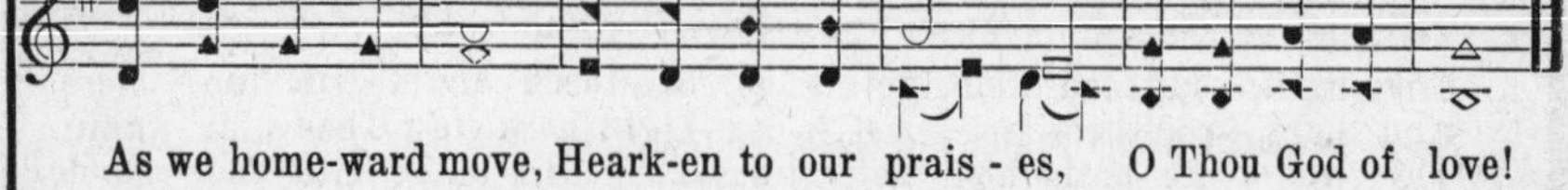

As we home-ward move, Heark-en to our prais - es, O Thou God of love!

Now, On Land and Sea Descend

VESPER HYMN. 8. 7. 8. 7. 8. 6. 8. 7.

SAMUEL LONGFELLOW | DIMITRI S. BORTNIANSKY

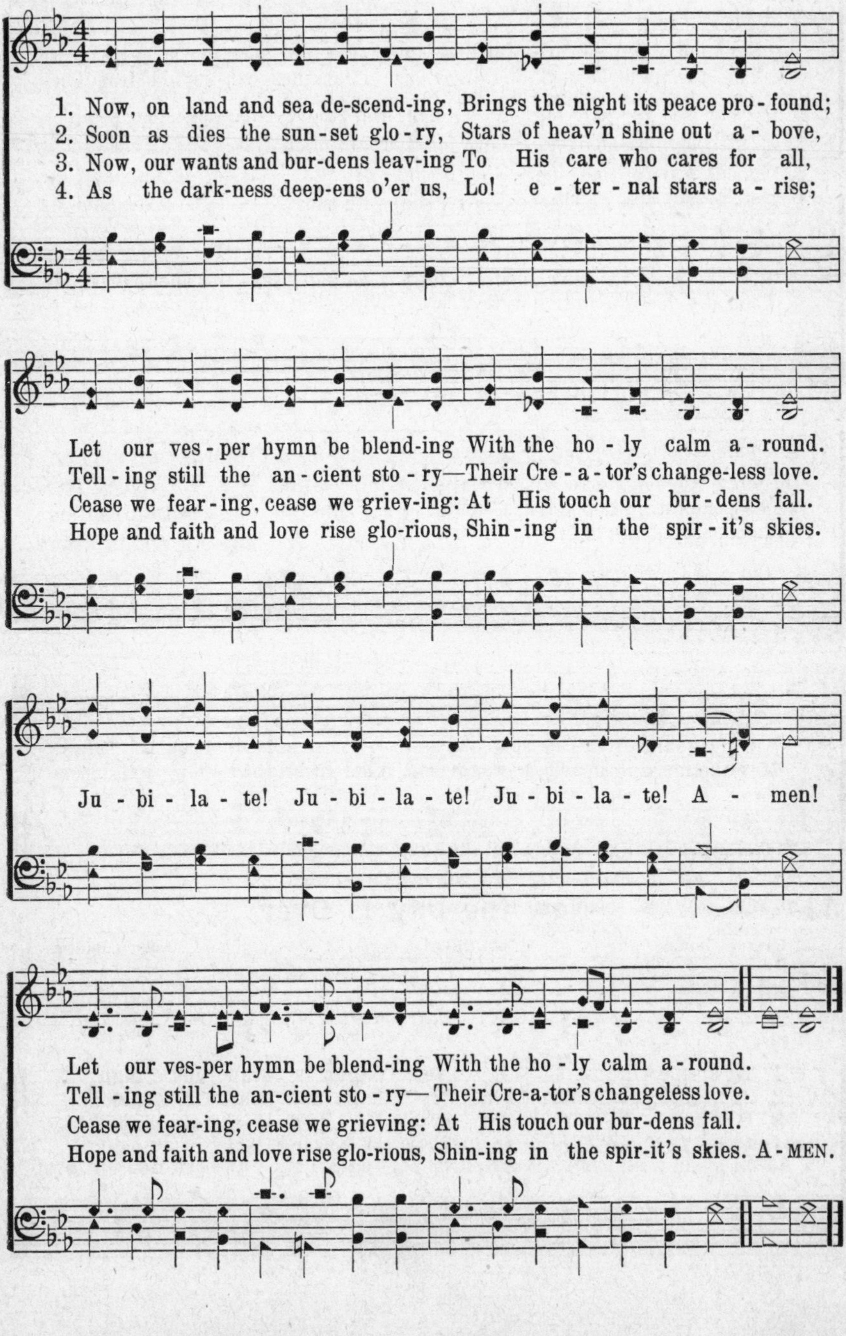
1. Now, on land and sea de-scend-ing, Brings the night its peace pro-found;
2. Soon as dies the sun-set glo-ry, Stars of heav'n shine out a-bove,
3. Now, our wants and bur-dens leav-ing To His care who cares for all,
4. As the dark-ness deep-ens o'er us, Lo! e-ter-nal stars a-rise;
Let our ves-per hymn be blend-ing With the ho-ly calm a-round.
Tell-ing still the an-cient sto-ry—Their Cre-a-tor's change-less love.
Cease we fear-ing, cease we griev-ing: At His touch our bur-dens fall.
Hope and faith and love rise glo-rious, Shin-ing in the spir-it's skies.
Ju-bi-la-te! Ju-bi-la-te! Ju-bi-la-te! A-men!
Let our ves-per hymn be blend-ing With the ho-ly calm a-round.
Tell-ing still the an-cient sto-ry— Their Cre-a-tor's changeless love.
Cease we fear-ing, cease we grieving: At His touch our bur-dens fall.
Hope and faith and love rise glo-rious, Shin-ing in the spir-it's skies. A-MEN.

50 Savior, Breathe an Evening Blessing

EVENING SONG. 8s. 7s. J. H. Hall

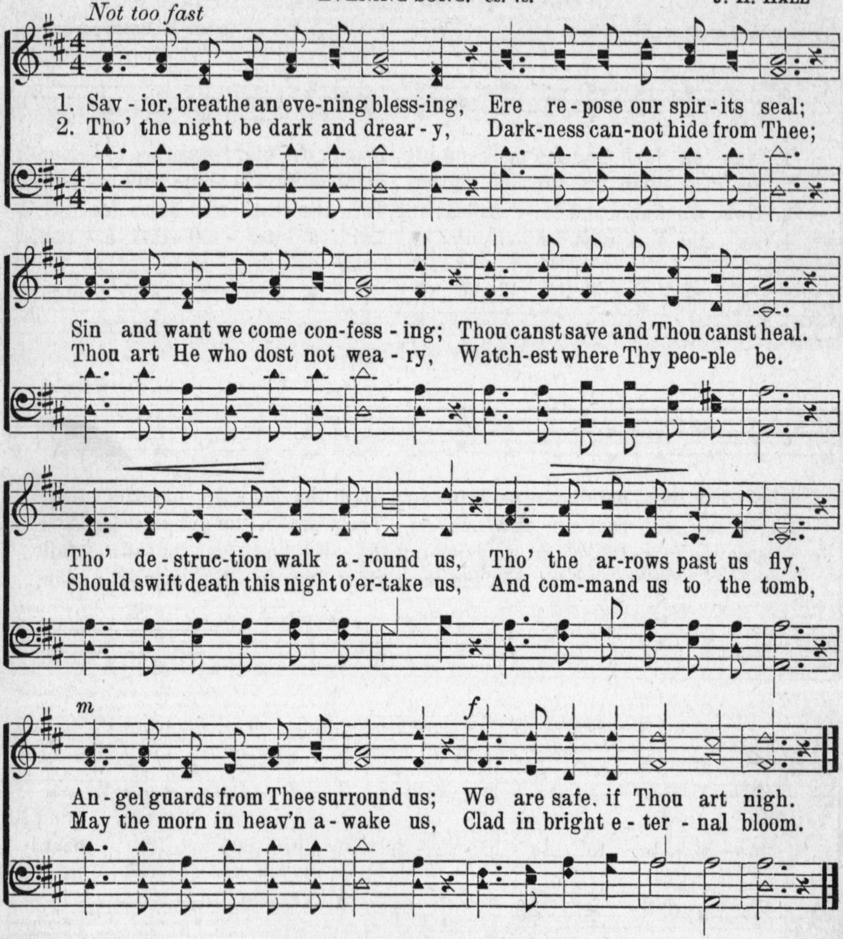
Not too fast
1. Sav - ior, breathe an eve-ning bless-ing, Ere re - pose our spir - its seal;
2. Tho' the night be dark and drear - y, Dark-ness can-not hide from Thee;
Sin and want we come con-fess - ing; Thou canst save and Thou canst heal.
Thou art He who dost not wea - ry, Watch-est where Thy peo-ple be.
Tho' de-struc-tion walk a-round us, Tho' the ar-rows past us fly,
Should swift death this night o'er-take us, And com-mand us to the tomb,
m
f
An - gel guards from Thee surround us; We are safe, if Thou art nigh.
May the morn in heav'n a - wake us, Clad in bright e - ter - nal bloom.

51 Now the Day Is Over

S. Baring-Gould MERRIAL. 6s. 5s. Joseph Barnby

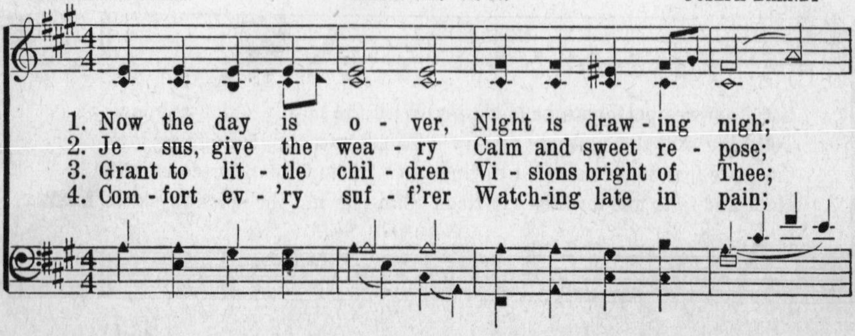
1. Now the day is o - ver, Night is draw - ing nigh;
2. Je - sus, give the wea - ry Calm and sweet re - pose;
3. Grant to lit - tle chil - dren Vi - sions bright of Thee;
4. Com - fort ev - 'ry suf - f'rer Watch-ing late in pain;

Now the Day is Over

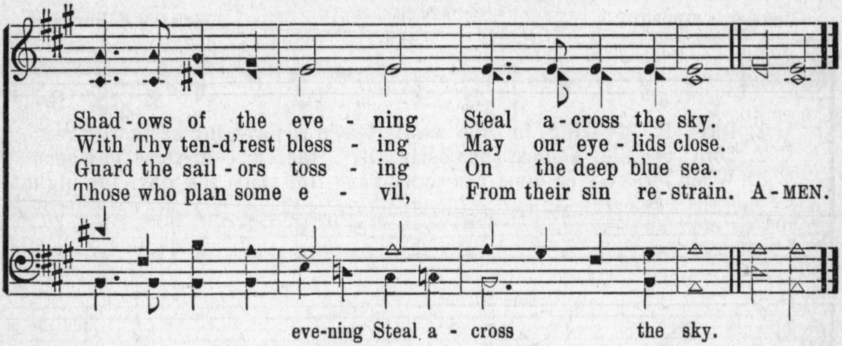
Shad - ows of the eve - ning Steal a - cross the sky.
With Thy ten-d'rest bless - ing May our eye - lids close.
Guard the sail - ors toss - ing On the deep blue sea.
Those who plan some e - vil, From their sin re - strain. A - MEN.
eve-ning Steal a - cross the sky.

Evening Prayer 52

JAMES EDMESTON GEO. C. STEBBINS

1. Sav - ior, breathe an eve - ning bless - ing, Ere re- pose our spir - its seal: . . . Sin and want we come con - fess - ing, Thou canst save and Thou canst heal.
2. Though de - struc - tion walk a - round us, Though the ar - rows past us fly; . . . . An - gel - guards from Thee sur - round us, We are safe if Thou art nigh.
3. Though the night be dark and drear - y, Dark - ness can - not hide from Thee; . . . Thou are He who, nev - er wea - ry, Watch - est where Thy peo - ple be.
4. Should swift death this night o'er - take us, And our couch be - come our tomb, . . . May the morn in heav'n a - wake us, Clad in bright and death - less bloom.
rit.

53 Day Is Dying in the West

MARY A. LATHBURY — WILLIAM F. SHERWIN

1. Day is dy-ing in the west; Heav'n is touch-ing earth with rest;
2. Lord of life, be-neath the dome Of the u-ni-verse, Thy home,
3. When for-ev-er from our sight Pass the stars, the day, the night,
Wait and wor-ship while the night Sets her eve-ning lamps a-light Thro'
Gath-er us, who seek Thy face, To the fold of Thy em-brace, For
Lord of an-gels, on our eyes Let e-ter-nal morn-ing rise, And
all the sky.
Thou art nigh.
shad-ows end.
REFRAIN pp
Ho-ly, ho-ly, ho-ly, Lord God of hosts! Heav'n and
f
earth are full of Thee; Heav'n and earth are praising Thee, O Lord Most High!
ff

54 The Day Is Past and Gone

JOHN LELAND — VESPERS. S. M. — J. D. BRUNK

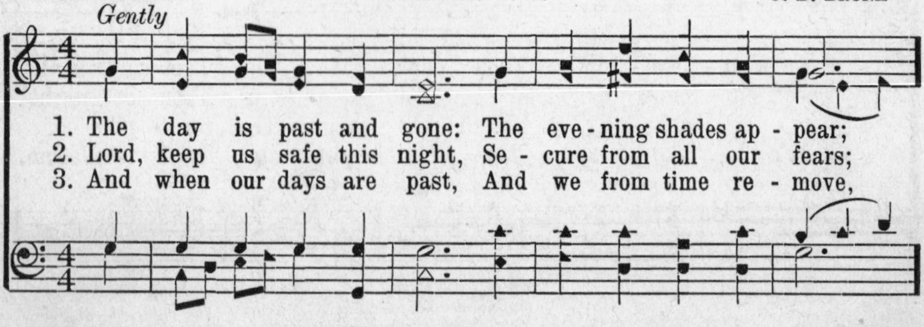
Gently
1. The day is past and gone: The eve-ning shades ap-pear;
2. Lord, keep us safe this night, Se-cure from all our fears;
3. And when our days are past, And we from time re-move,

The Day Is Past and Gone

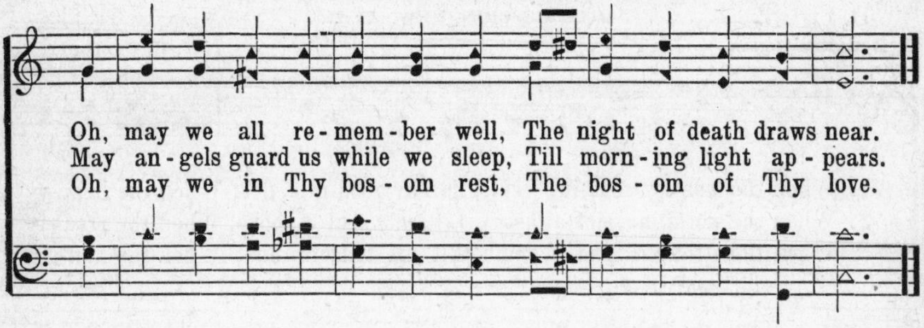

Oh, may we all re-mem-ber well, The night of death draws near.
May an-gels guard us while we sleep, Till morn-ing light ap-pears.
Oh, may we in Thy bos-om rest, The bos-om of Thy love.

God, That Madest Earth and Heaven 55

AR HYD Y NOS. 8s. 4s.

REGINALD HEBER — Welsh Traditional Melody

1. God, that mad-est earth and heav-en, Dark-ness and light;
Who the day for toil hast giv-en, For rest the night;
2. And when morn a-gain shall call us To run life's way,
May we still, what-e'er be-fall us, Thy will o-bey.
3. Guard us wak-ing, guard us sleep-ing; And, when we die,
May we in Thy might-y keep-ing All peace-ful lie.

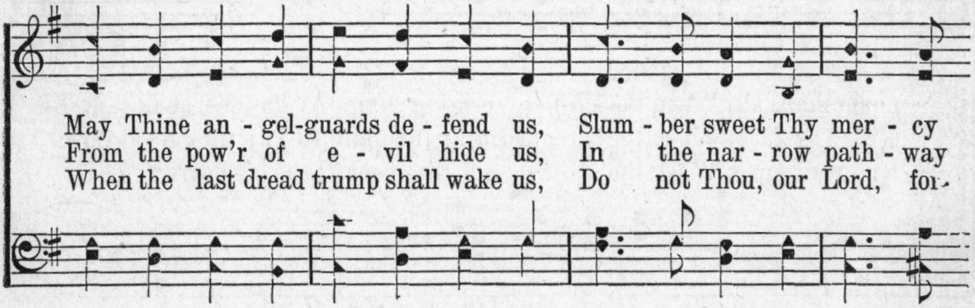

May Thine an-gel-guards de-fend us, Slum-ber sweet Thy mer-cy
From the pow'r of e-vil hide us, In the nar-row path-way
When the last dread trump shall wake us, Do not Thou, our Lord, for-

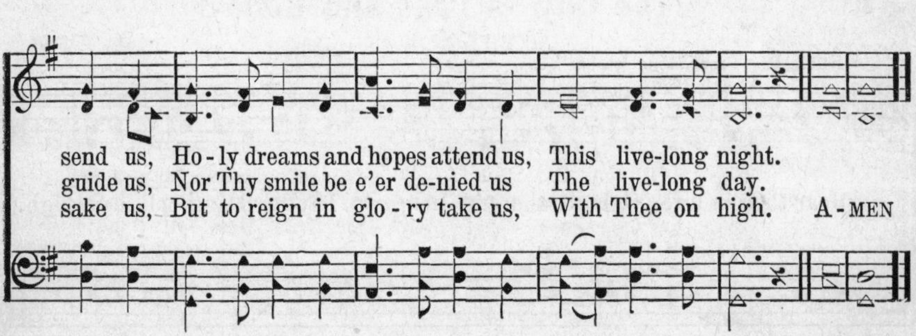

send us, Ho-ly dreams and hopes attend us, This live-long night.
guide us, Nor Thy smile be e'er de-nied us The live-long day.
sake us, But to reign in glo-ry take us, With Thee on high. A-MEN

When the Weary, Seeking Rest

INTERCESSION. NEW. 7s. 5s.

HORATIUS BONAR W. H. CALLCOTT

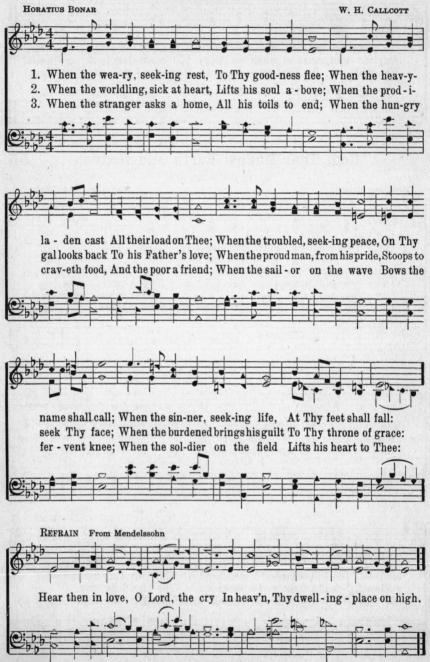

1. When the wea-ry, seek-ing rest, To Thy good-ness flee; When the heav-y-
2. When the worldling, sick at heart, Lifts his soul a-bove; When the prod-i-
3. When the stranger asks a home, All his toils to end; When the hun-gry

la-den cast All their load on Thee; When the troubled, seek-ing peace, On Thy
gal looks back To his Father's love; When the proud man, from his pride, Stoops to
crav-eth food, And the poor a friend; When the sail-or on the wave Bows the

name shall call; When the sin-ner, seek-ing life, At Thy feet shall fall:
seek Thy face; When the burdened brings his guilt To Thy throne of grace:
fer-vent knee; When the sol-dier on the field Lifts his heart to Thee:

REFRAIN From Mendelssohn

Hear then in love, O Lord, the cry In heav'n, Thy dwell-ing-place on high.

Oh, I Love to Talk with Jesus

Words arr. W. G. FISCHER

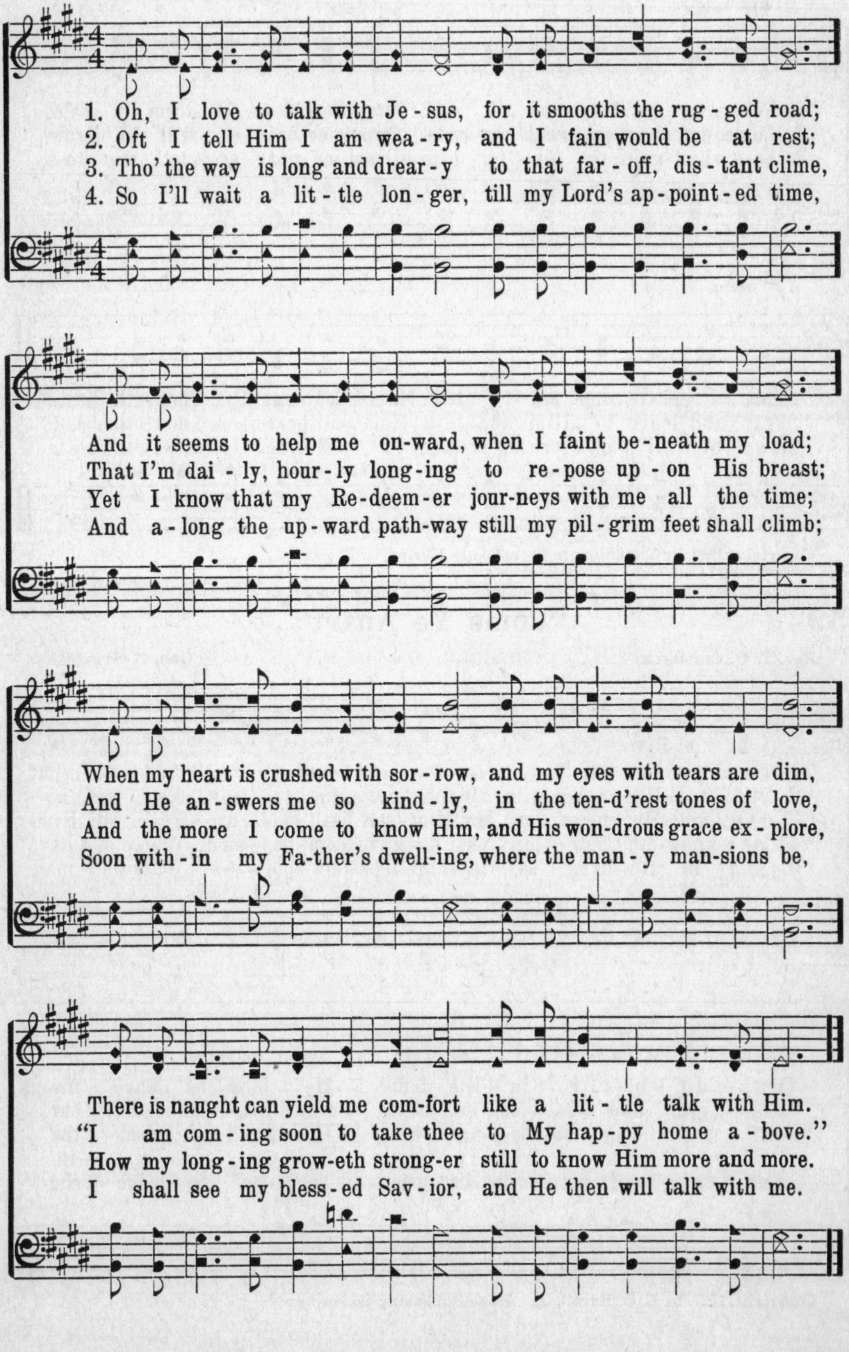
1. Oh, I love to talk with Je - sus, for it smooths the rug - ged road;
2. Oft I tell Him I am wea - ry, and I fain would be at rest;
3. Tho' the way is long and drear - y to that far - off, dis - tant clime,
4. So I'll wait a lit - tle lon - ger, till my Lord's ap - point - ed time,
And it seems to help me on - ward, when I faint be - neath my load;
That I'm dai - ly, hour - ly long - ing to re - pose up - on His breast;
Yet I know that my Re - deem - er jour - neys with me all the time;
And a - long the up - ward path - way still my pil - grim feet shall climb;
When my heart is crushed with sor - row, and my eyes with tears are dim,
And He an - swers me so kind - ly, in the ten - d'rest tones of love,
And the more I come to know Him, and His won - drous grace ex - plore,
Soon with - in my Fa - ther's dwell - ing, where the man - y man - sions be,
There is naught can yield me com - fort like a lit - tle talk with Him.
"I am com - ing soon to take thee to My hap - py home a - bove."
How my long - ing grow - eth strong - er still to know Him more and more.
I shall see my bless - ed Sav - ior, and He then will talk with me.

58 When On Quiet Seas I Sail

Eleanor Allen Schroll — J. H. Fillmore

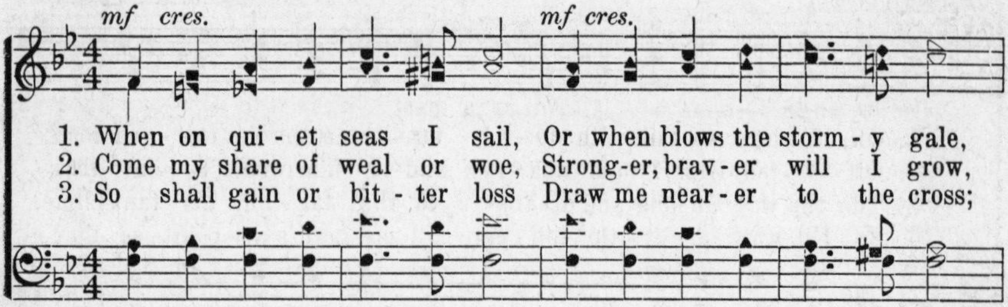
mf cres.
mf cres.
1. When on qui - et seas I sail, Or when blows the storm - y gale,
2. Come my share of weal or woe, Strong-er, brav - er will I grow,
3. So shall gain or bit - ter loss Draw me near - er to the cross;

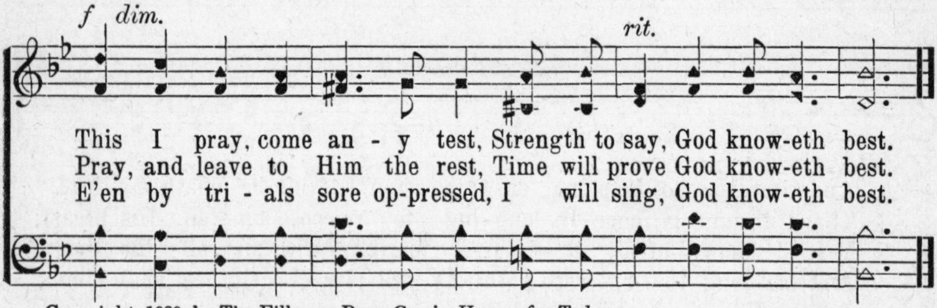
f dim.
rit.
This I pray, come an - y test, Strength to say, God know-eth best.
Pray, and leave to Him the rest, Time will prove God know-eth best.
E'en by tri - als sore op-pressed, I will sing, God know-eth best.

59 "Come Ye Apart"

Rev. T. O. Chisholm — CHISHOLM. 11. 10. 11. 10. — Geo. C. Stebbins

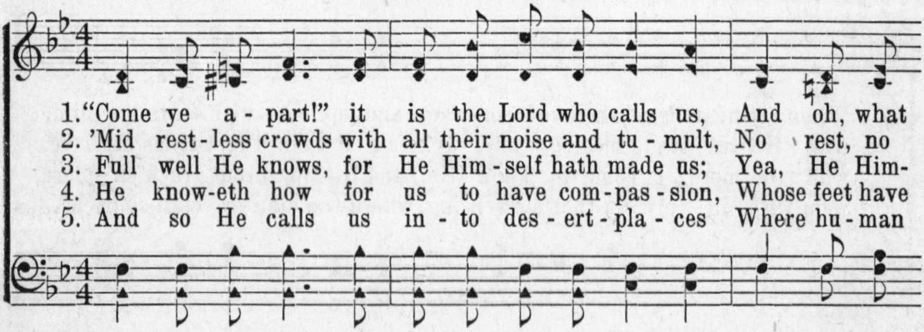
1. "Come ye a - part!" it is the Lord who calls us, And oh, what
2. 'Mid rest-less crowds with all their noise and tu - mult, No rest, no
3. Full well He knows, for He Him - self hath made us; Yea, He Him-
4. He know-eth how for us to have com - pas - sion, Whose feet have
5. And so He calls us in - to des - ert - pla - ces Where hu - man

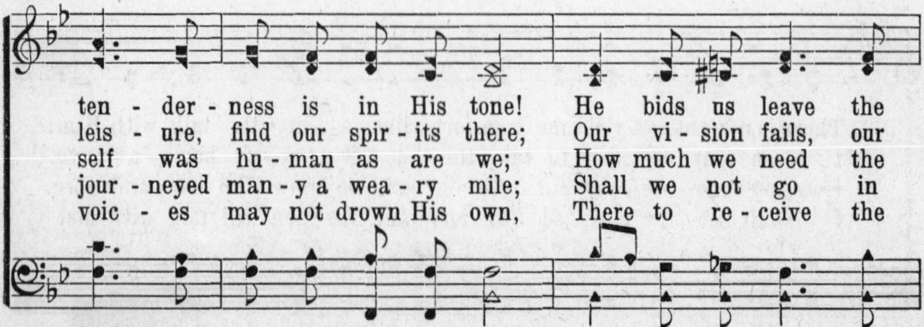
ten - der - ness is in His tone! He bids us leave the
leis - ure, find our spir - its there; Our vi - sion fails, our
self was hu - man as are we; How much we need the
jour - neyed man - y a wea - ry mile; Shall we not go in
voic - es may not drown His own, There to re - ceive the

"Come Ye Apart"

rit.

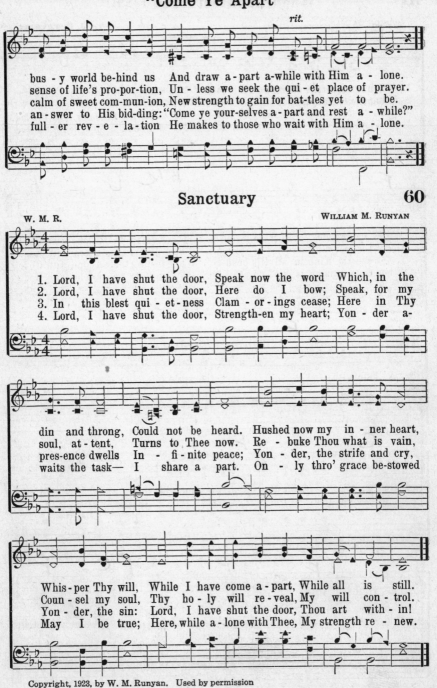

bus - y world be-hind us And draw a-part a-while with Him a - lone.
sense of life's pro-por-tion, Un - less we seek the qui - et place of prayer.
calm of sweet com-mun-ion, New strength to gain for bat-tles yet to be.
an-swer to His bid-ding: "Come ye your-selves a-part and rest a - while?"
full - er rev - e - la - tion He makes to those who wait with Him a - lone.

Sanctuary

60

W. M. R. WILLIAM M. RUNYAN

1. Lord, I have shut the door, Speak now the word Which, in the
2. Lord, I have shut the door, Here do I bow; Speak, for my
3. In this blest qui - et-ness Clam - or-ings cease; Here in Thy
4. Lord, I have shut the door, Strength-en my heart; Yon - der a-

din and throng, Could not be heard. Hushed now my in - ner heart,
soul, at-tent, Turns to Thee now. Re - buke Thou what is vain,
pres-ence dwells In - fi - nite peace; Yon - der, the strife and cry,
waits the task— I share a part. On - ly thro' grace be-stowed

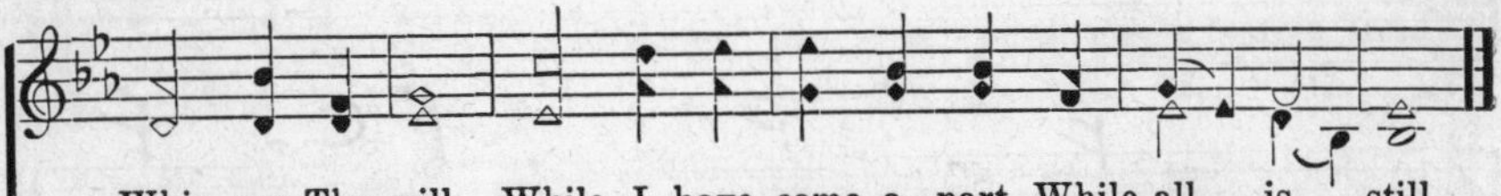

Whis-per Thy will, While I have come a - part, While all is still.
Coun - sel my soul, Thy ho - ly will re - veal, My will con - trol.
Yon - der, the sin: Lord, I have shut the door, Thou art with - in!
May I be true; Here, while a - lone with Thee, My strength re - new.

61 Alone with God

JOHNSON OATMAN, JR. WM. J. KIRKPATRICK

1. When storms of life are round me beat-ing, When rough the path that I have trod,
2. What tho' the clouds have gathered o'er me? What tho' I've passed beneath the rod?
3. 'Tis there I find new strength for du-ty, As o'er the sands of time I plod,
4. And when I see the mo-ment near-ing When I shall sleep beneath the sod,
With-in my clos-et door re-treat-ing, I love to be a-lone with God.
God's per-fect will there lies be-fore me, When I am thus a-lone with God.
I see the King in all His beau-ty, While resting there a-lone with God.
When time with me is dis-ap-pear-ing, I want to be a-lone with God.
CHORUS
A-lone with God, ... the world for-bid-den, A-lone with
A-lone with God,
God, ... O blest re-treat! A-lone with God, ... and in Him
A-lone with God,
A-lone with God,
ritard.
hid-den, To hold with Him . . . . . . com-mun-ion sweet.
To hold with Him

The Beautiful Garden of Prayer

Eleanor Allen Schroll — J. H. Fillmore

1. There's a gar-den where Je-sus is wait-ing, There's a place that is
2. There's a gar-den where Je-sus is wait-ing, And I go with my
3. There's a gar-den where Je-sus is wait-ing, And He bids you to
won-drous-ly fair; For it glows with the light of His pres-ence, 'Tis the
bur-den and care, Just to learn from His lips words of com-fort In the
come meet Him there; Just to bow, and re-ceive a new bless-ing, In the
Refrain
beau-ti-ful gar-den of prayer. O the beau-ti-ful gar-den, the
gar-den of prayer, O the beau-ti-ful gar-den of prayer; There my Sav-ior a-
waits, and He o-pens the gates To the beau-ti-ful gar-den of prayer.

63

Hear Us, O Savior

Charles Bruce | Ira D. Sankey

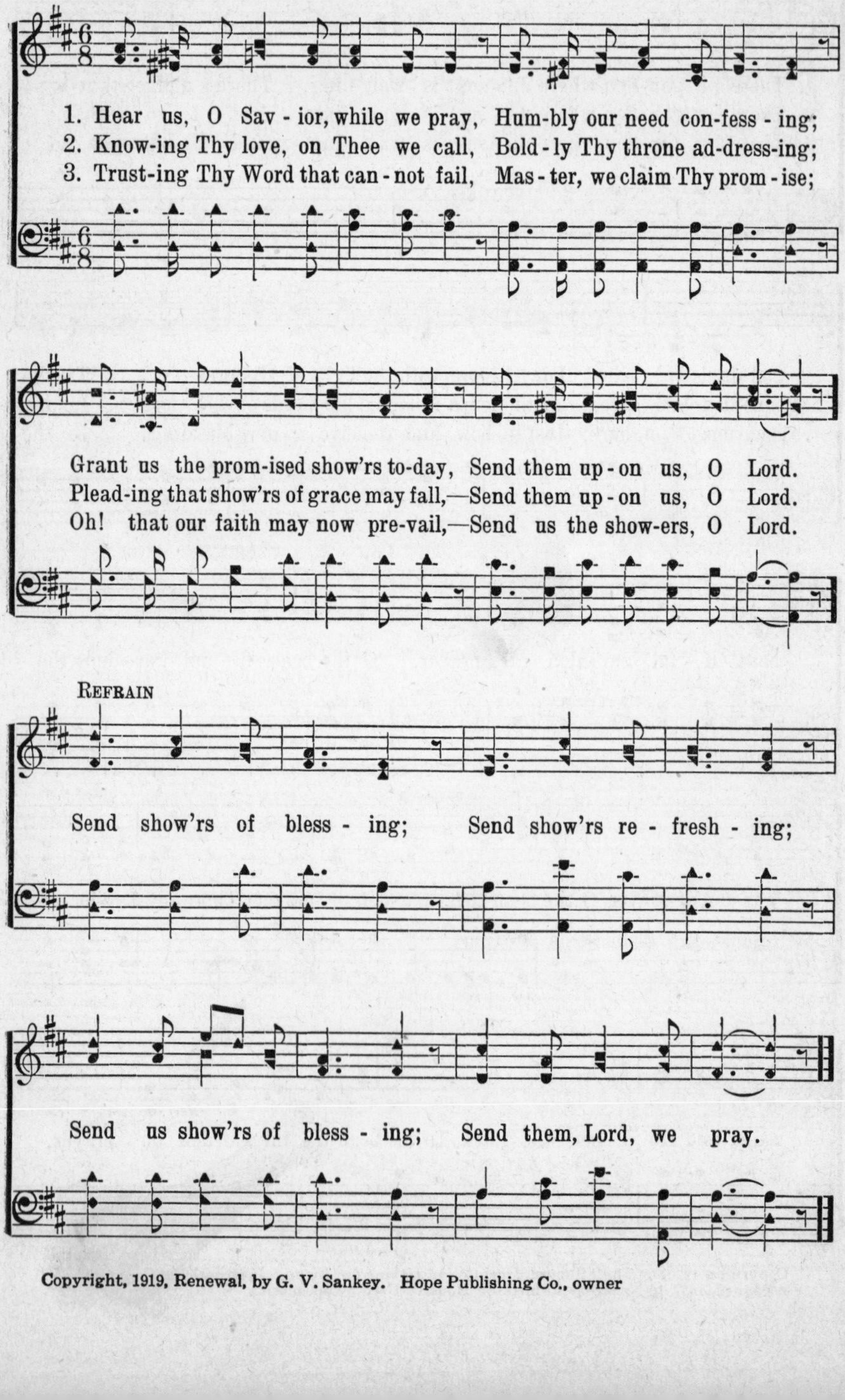
1. Hear us, O Sav - ior, while we pray, Hum-bly our need con-fess - ing;
2. Know-ing Thy love, on Thee we call, Bold - ly Thy throne ad-dress-ing;
3. Trust-ing Thy Word that can - not fail, Mas - ter, we claim Thy prom - ise;
Grant us the prom-ised show'rs to-day, Send them up - on us, O Lord.
Plead-ing that show'rs of grace may fall,—Send them up - on us, O Lord.
Oh! that our faith may now pre-vail,—Send us the show-ers, O Lord.
Refrain
Send show'rs of bless - ing; Send show'rs re - fresh - ing;
Send us show'rs of bless - ing; Send them, Lord, we pray.

Just for Today

EBEN E. REXFORD VICTOR H. BENKE

1. My Fa - ther, this I ask of Thee; Know-ing that Thou wilt
2. I do not ask a lift - ed load, Nor for a smooth and
3. Strength for the pres - ent hour and need— This giv - en, I am
4. Strength for to - day, that I may make Some sad souls glad, for
grant the plea, For this, and on - ly this, I pray,
thorn - less road, Sim - ply for strength e - nough to bear
blest in - deed, For each day, as it comes, will bring
Je - sus' sake, Then they, with me, at eve shall say,
CHORUS
Strength for to - day— just for to - day.
Life's dai - ly bur - dens an - y - where. Strength for each tri - al
Suf - fi - cient strength for an - y - thing.
Thank God for strength He gave to - day.
and each task, What more, my Fa - ther, should I ask? Just as I
need it day by day, Strength for my weak-ness,—this I pray.

65 Be Still

Unknown — J. Duerksen

1. To-night, my soul, be still and sleep; The storms are rag - ing on God's deep— God's deep, not thine; be still and sleep.
2. To-night, my soul, be still and sleep; God's hands shall still the tempt-er's sweep— God's hands, not thine; be still and sleep.
3. To-night, my soul, be still and sleep; God's love is strong, while night hours creep—God's love, not thine; be still and sleep.
4. To-night, my soul, be still and sleep; God's heav'n will com - fort those who weep— God's heav'n, not thine; be still and sleep.

Copyright, 1938, in *Life Songs No. 2.* Mennonite Publishing House, owner

66 God of Our Fathers, Whose Almighty Hand

Daniel C. Roberts — George W. Warren

1. God of our fa - thers, whose al-might - y hand Leads forth in beau - ty all the star - ry band Of shin - ing worlds in splen-dor
2. Thy love di - vine hath led us in the past, In this free land by Thee our lot is cast; Be Thou our rul - er, guard-ian,
3. From war's a - larms, from dead - ly pes - ti - lence, Be Thy strong arm our ev - er strong de - fense; Thy true re - lig - ion in our
4. Re - fresh Thy peo - ple on their toil-some way, Lead us from night to nev - er - end - ing day; Fill all our lives with love and

God of Our Fathers, Whose Almighty Hand

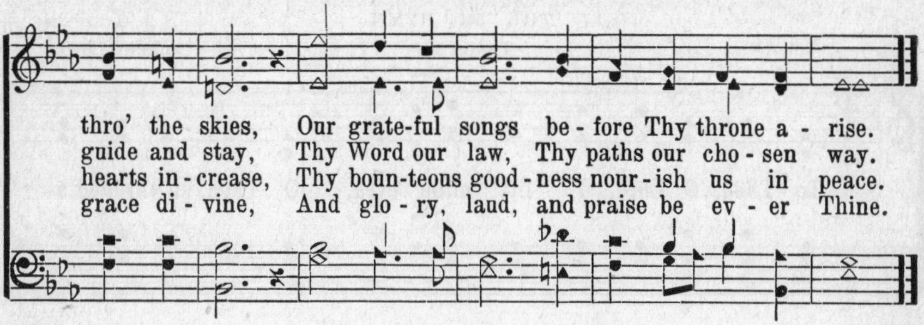
thro' the skies, Our grate-ful songs be-fore Thy throne a-rise.
guide and stay, Thy Word our law, Thy paths our cho-sen way.
hearts in-crease, Thy boun-teous good-ness nour-ish us in peace.
grace di-vine, And glo-ry, laud, and praise be ev-er Thine.

The Hour of Prayer 67

HELEN BOARDMAN KNOX — WALTER E. YODER

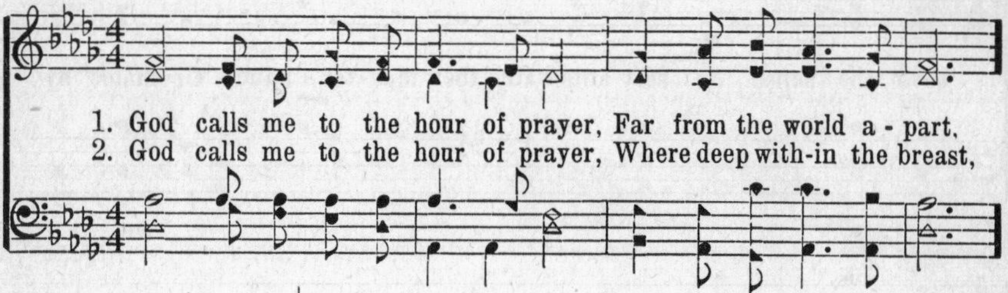
1. God calls me to the hour of prayer, Far from the world a-part,
2. God calls me to the hour of prayer, Where deep with-in the breast,

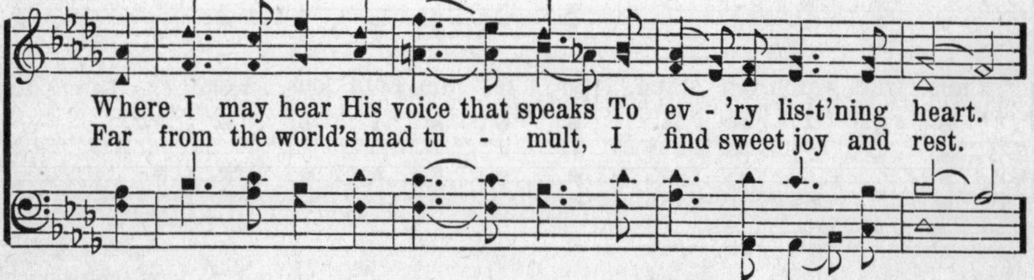
Where I may hear His voice that speaks To ev-'ry lis-t'ning heart.
Far from the world's mad tu-mult, I find sweet joy and rest.

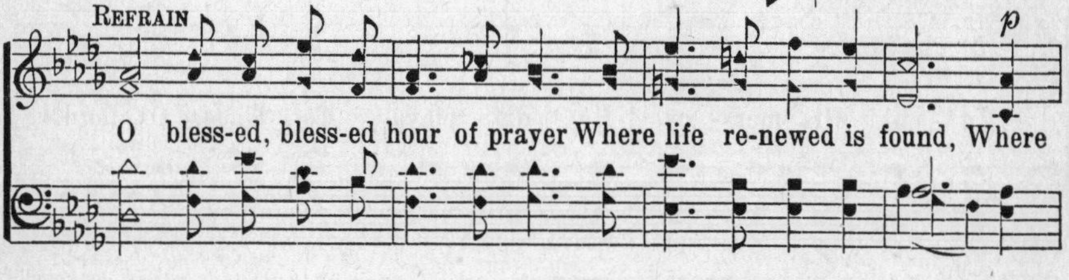
REFRAIN
p
O bless-ed, bless-ed hour of prayer Where life re-newed is found, Where

p For-ev-er-more...... a-bound.
For-ev-er-more a-bound.
peace and love and pow'r di-vine, For-ev-er-more . . . a-bound.

Copyright, 1938, in *Life Songs No. 2.* Mennonite Publishing House, owner

68 To Thee, O Lord, I Lift Mine Eyes

THE "541" HYMN

PSALM 123 ROBERT LOWRY

To Thee, O Lord, I lift mine eyes, O Thou, en-throned a-
bove the skies! As serv-ants watch their mas-ter's hand, Or maids by
mis-tress watch-ing stand, So to the Lord our eyes we raise,
Un - til His mer - cy He dis - plays. To Thee, O Lord,
I lift mine eyes, O Thou, en-throned a - bove the skies!

Open My Eyes That I May See

C. H. S. — Clara H. Scott

1. O - pen my eyes, that I may see Glimps-es of truth Thou hast for me;
2. O - pen my ears, that I may hear Voi - ces of truth Thou send-est clear;
3. O - pen my mouth, and let me bear Glad - ly the warm truth ev-'ry-where;
Place in my hands the won-der-ful key That shall un-clasp, and set me free.
And while the wave-notes fall on my ear, Ev - 'ry-thing false will dis - ap - pear.
O - pen my heart, and let me pre-pare Love with Thy chil-dren thus to share.
Si - lent - ly now I wait for Thee, Read-y, my God, Thy will to see;
Si - lent - ly now I wait for Thee, Read-y, my God, Thy will to see;
Si - lent - ly now I wait for Thee, Read-y, my God, Thy will to see;
O - pen my eyes, il - lu - mine me, Spir - it di - vine!
O - pen my ears, il - lu - mine me, Spir - it di - vine!
O - pen my heart, il - lu - mine me, Spir - it di - vine!

70 Don't Forget to Pray

Mrs. M. A. Kidder — W. O. Perkins

1. Ere you left your room this morn-ing, Did you think to pray? In the name of
2. When you met with great temp-ta-tion, Did you think to pray? By His dy-ing
3. When your heart was filled with an-ger, Did you think to pray? Did you plead for
4. When sore tri-als came up-on you, Did you think to pray? When your soul was

Christ, our Sav-ior, Did you sue for lov-ing fa-vor As a shield to-day?
love and mer-it, Did you claim the Ho-ly Spir-it As your guide and stay?
grace, my broth-er, That you might forgive an-oth-er Who had crossed your way?
bowed in sor-row, Balm of Gil-ead did you bor-row At the gates of day?

D. S.—*So when life seems dark and dreary, Don't for-get to pray.*

Chorus

Oh, how pray-ing rests the wea-ry! Prayer will change the night to day;

71 Prayer Is the Soul's Sincere Desire

James Montgomery — Byefield. C. M. — Thomas Hastings

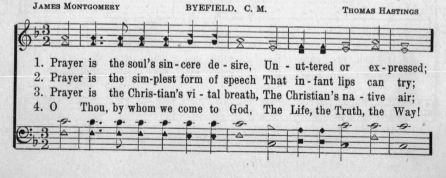

1. Prayer is the soul's sin-cere de-sire, Un-ut-tered or ex-pressed;
2. Prayer is the sim-plest form of speech That in-fant lips can try;
3. Prayer is the Chris-tian's vi-tal breath, The Christian's na-tive air;
4. O Thou, by whom we come to God, The Life, the Truth, the Way!

Prayer Is the Soul's Sincere Desire

The mo-tion of a hid-den fire That trem-bles in the breast.
Prayer the sub-lim-est strains that reach The Maj-es-ty on high.
His watch-word at the gates of death: He en-ters heav'n with prayer.
The path of prayer Thy-self hast trod; Lord, teach us how to pray. A-MEN.

Spirit so Holy

72

D. W. WHITTLE

GEO. C. STEBBINS

1. Spir-it so ho-ly, Spir-it of love, Spir-it so
2. Spir-it of wis-dom, Spir-it of light, Spir-it of
3. Spir-it so hum-ble, Spir-it so meek, Spir-it so
4. Spir-it of pow-er, Spir-it of God, Spir-it of

gen-tle, Sent from a-bove; Price-less pos-ses-sion,
knowl-edge, Show-ing the right; Guide us and teach us,
kind-ly, Help-ing the weak; Work in and thro' us,
burn-ing, Work thro' Thy Word; Search us and sift us,

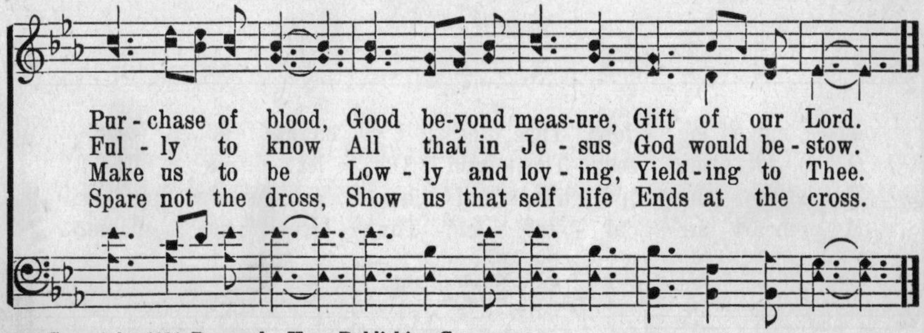
Pur-chase of blood, Good be-yond meas-ure, Gift of our Lord.
Ful-ly to know All that in Je-sus God would be-stow.
Make us to be Low-ly and lov-ing, Yield-ing to Thee.
Spare not the dross, Show us that self life Ends at the cross.

73 Spirit of God, Descend Upon My Heart

GEORGE CROLY FREDERICK C. ATKINSON

1. Spir - it of God, de - scend up - on my heart;
2. Hast Thou not bid us love Thee, God and King?
3. Teach me to feel that Thou art al - ways nigh;
4. Teach me to love Thee as Thine an - gels love,
Wean it from earth, through all its puls - es move;
All, all Thine own, soul, heart and strength and mind;
Teach me the strug - gles of the soul to bear,
One ho - ly pas - sion fill - ing all my frame;
Stoop to my weak - ness, might - y as Thou art,
I see Thy cross— there teach my heart to cling:
To check the ris - ing doubt, the reb - el sigh;
The bap - tism of the heav'n - de - scend - ed Dove,
And make me love Thee as I ought to love.
O let me seek Thee, and O let me find.
Teach me the pa - tience of un - an - swered prayer.
My heart an al - tar, and Thy love the flame.

His Love Cannot Fail

J. M. B. JAMES M. BLACK

1. Since Je - sus my Sav - ior from sin res - cued me, Life's path - way shines
2. My heart o - ver - flows with a won - drous de - light, For Je - sus is
3. There's no one like Je - sus to com - fort and bless, There's no one like
bright - er be - cause I am free; No harm can be - fall me, tho' foes
with me by day and by night; His love ev - er flow - ing, so bound -
Him in the hour of dis - tress; He knows ev - 'ry tri - al on life's
should as - sail, My ref - uge is Je - sus, His love can - not fail.
less and free, It nev - er can fail, 'tis for you and for me.
up - ward way, His love can - not fail, 'tis a joy day by day.
CHORUS
His love can - not fail, His love can - not fail,
can - not fail, can - not fail,
There's no one like Je - sus, His love can - not fail.
can - not fail.

75 Jesus Has Loved Me

J. WAKEFIELD MACGILL — ANTOINE E. BATISTE

1. Je - sus has loved me— won - der - ful Sav - ior! Je - sus has
2. Je - sus has saved me— won - der - ful Sav - ior! Je - sus has
3. Je - sus will lead me— won - der - ful Sav - ior! Je - sus will
loved me, I can - not tell why; He came to res - cue
saved me, I can - not tell how; But this I do know,
lead me, I can - not tell where; So I will fol - low
sin - ners un - wor - thy; My heart He con - quered, for Him I would die.
He came, my ran - som, Dy - ing on Cal - v'ry with thorns on His brow.
thro' joy or sor - row, Sun - shine or tem - pest, since He leads me there.

76 Let Us with a Gladsome Mind

JOHN MILTON — INNOCENTS. 7. 7. 7. 7. — From "The Parish Choir"

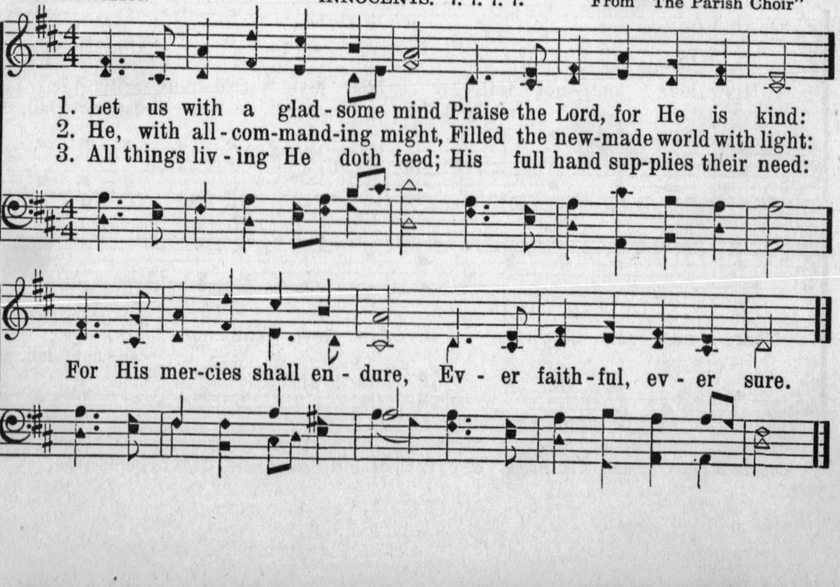
1. Let us with a glad - some mind Praise the Lord, for He is kind:
2. He, with all - com - mand - ing might, Filled the new - made world with light:
3. All things liv - ing He doth feed; His full hand sup - plies their need:
For His mer - cies shall en - dure, Ev - er faith - ful, ev - er sure.

My Savior's Love

C. H. G. — CHAS. H GABRIEL

1. I stand a-mazed in the pres-ence Of Je - sus the Naz - a - rene,
2. For me it was in the gar - den He prayed: "Not My will, but Thine;"
3. In pit - y an - gels be - held Him, And came from the world of light
4. He took my sins and my sor - rows, He made them His ver - y own;
5. When with the ransomed in glo - ry His face I at last shall see,
And won - der how He could love me, A sin-ner, condemned, un-clean.
He had no tears for His own griefs, But sweat-drops of blood for mine.
To com - fort Him in the sor - rows He bore for my soul that night.
He bore the bur - den to Cal - v'ry, And suf-fered, and died a - lone.
'Twill be my joy thro' the a - ges To sing of His love for me.
CHORUS.
How mar-vel-ous! how won-der-ful! And my song shall ev - er be:
Oh, how mar-vel-ous! oh, how won-der-ful!
How mar-vel-ous! how won-der-ful Is my Sav-ior's love for me! A-MEN.
Oh, how mar-vel-ous! oh, how won-der-ful

78 When the Lord of Love Was Here

STOPFORD A. BROOKE ARMSTRONG. 7. 7. 5. 7. 7. 5. GEORGE W. CHADWICK

1. When the Lord of love was here, Hap - py hearts to Him were dear,
2. Meek and low - ly were His ways, From His lov - ing grew His praise,
3. When He walked the fields, He drew From the flow'rs and birds and dew,
4. Fill us with Thy deep de - sire All the sin - ful to in - spire

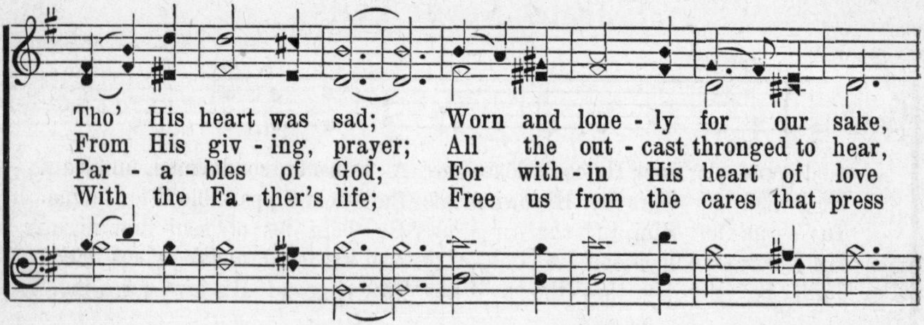
Tho' His heart was sad; Worn and lone - ly for our sake,
From His giv - ing, prayer; All the out - cast thronged to hear,
Par - a - bles of God; For with - in His heart of love
With the Fa - ther's life; Free us from the cares that press

Yet He turned a - side to make All the wea - ry glad.
All the sor - row - ful drew near To en - joy His care.
All the soul of man did move, God had His a - bode.
On the heart of world - li - ness, From the fret and strife.

79 There's Not a Bird with Lonely Nest

BAPTIST W. NOEL FAITHFULNESS. L. M. GEORGE A. MACFARREN

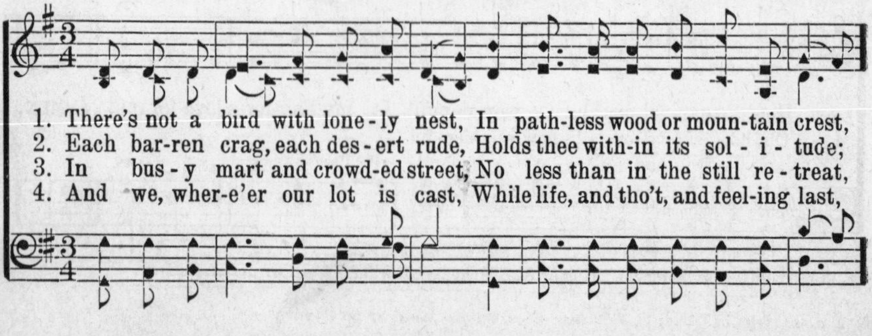
1. There's not a bird with lone - ly nest, In path - less wood or moun - tain crest,
2. Each bar - ren crag, each des - ert rude, Holds thee with - in its sol - i - tude;
3. In bus - y mart and crowd - ed street, No less than in the still re - treat,
4. And we, wher - e'er our lot is cast, While life, and tho't, and feel - ing last,

There's Not a Bird with Lonely Nest

Nor mean-er thing, which does not share, O God, in Thy pa-ter-nal care.
And Thou dost bless the wan-d'rer there, Who makes his sol-i-ta-ry prayer.
Thou, Lord, art near, our souls to bless With all a par-ent's ten-der-ness.
Thro' all the years, in ev-'ry place, Will bless Thee for Thy boundless grace.

Jesus Never Fails

80

A. A. L. A. A. LUTHER

1. Earth-ly friends may prove un-true, Doubts and fears as-sail;
2. Tho' the sky be dark and drear, Fierce and strong the gale,
3. In life's dark and bit-ter hour Love will still pre-vail;

One still loves and cares for you: Je-sus nev-er fails. nev-er fails.
Just re-mem-ber He is near, And He will not fail. will not fail.
Trust His ev-er-last-ing pow'r, Je-sus will not fail. will not fail.

CHORUS

Je-sus nev-er fails, Je-sus nev-er fails;

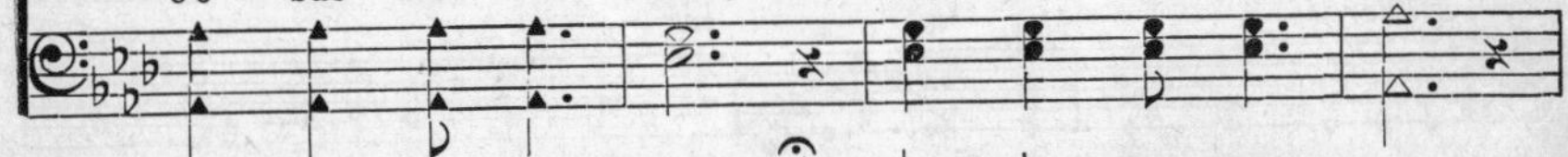

Heav'n and earth may pass a-way But Je-sus nev-er fails.

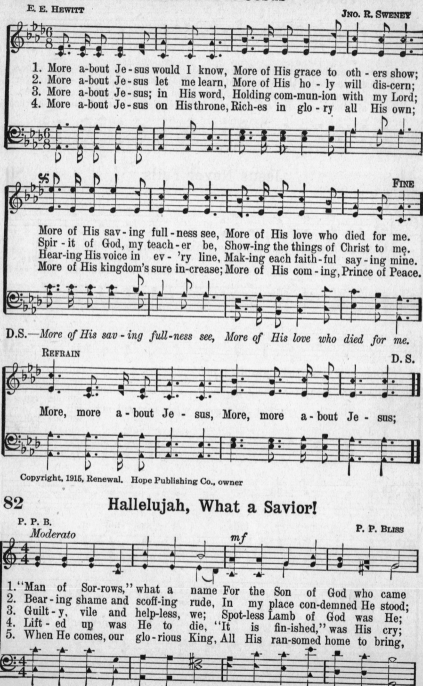

81 More About Jesus

E. E. HEWITT

JNO. R. SWENEY

1. More a-bout Je-sus would I know, More of His grace to oth-ers show;
2. More a-bout Je-sus let me learn, More of His ho-ly will dis-cern;
3. More a-bout Je-sus; in His word, Holding com-mun-ion with my Lord;
4. More a-bout Je-sus on His throne, Rich-es in glo-ry all His own;

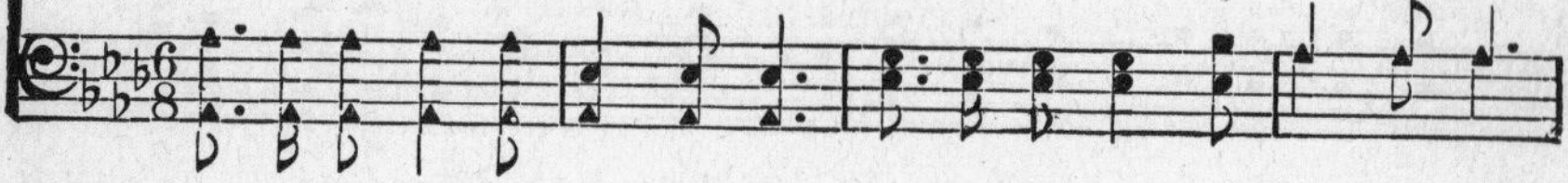

FINE

More of His sav-ing full-ness see, More of His love who died for me.
Spir-it of God, my teach-er be, Show-ing the things of Christ to me.
Hear-ing His voice in ev-'ry line, Mak-ing each faith-ful say-ing mine.
More of His kingdom's sure in-crease; More of His com-ing, Prince of Peace.

D.S.—*More of His sav-ing full-ness see, More of His love who died for me.*

REFRAIN

D. S.

More, more a-bout Je-sus, More, more a-bout Je-sus;

Copyright, 1915, Renewal. Hope Publishing Co., owner

82 Hallelujah, What a Savior!

P. P. B.

P. P. BLISS

Moderato

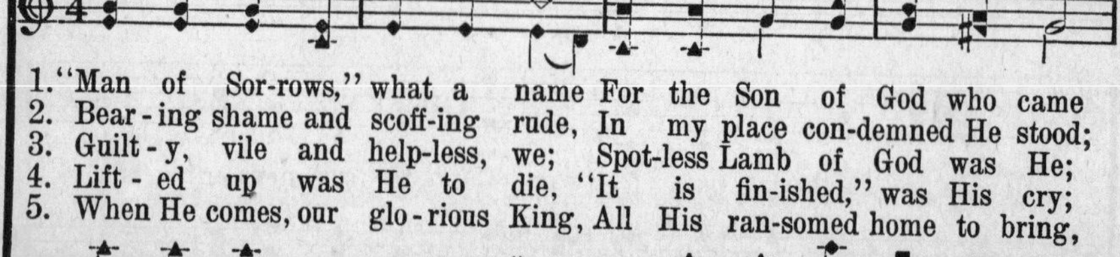

1. "Man of Sor-rows," what a name For the Son of God who came
2. Bear-ing shame and scoff-ing rude, In my place con-demned He stood;
3. Guilt-y, vile and help-less, we; Spot-less Lamb of God was He;
4. Lift-ed up was He to die, "It is fin-ished," was His cry;
5. When He comes, our glo-rious King, All His ran-somed home to bring,

Hallelujah, What a Savior!

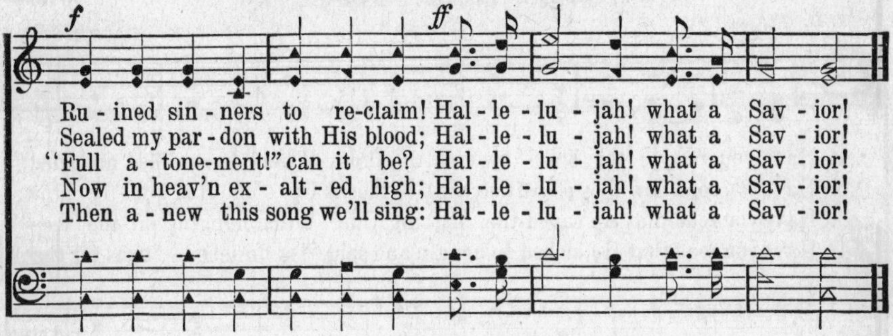

Ru - ined sin - ners to re-claim! Hal - le - lu - jah! what a Sav - ior!
Sealed my par - don with His blood; Hal - le - lu - jah! what a Sav - ior!
"Full a - tone-ment!" can it be? Hal - le - lu - jah! what a Sav - ior!
Now in heav'n ex - alt - ed high; Hal - le - lu - jah! what a Sav - ior!
Then a - new this song we'll sing: Hal - le - lu - jah! what a Sav - ior!

O Love That Wilt Not Let Me Go 83

GEORGE MATHESON — A. L. PEACE

1. O Love that wilt not let me go, I rest my wea - ry
2. O Light that fol - low'st all my way, I yield my flick-'ring
3. O Joy that seek - est me thro' pain, I can - not close my
4. O Cross that lift - est up my head, I dare not ask to

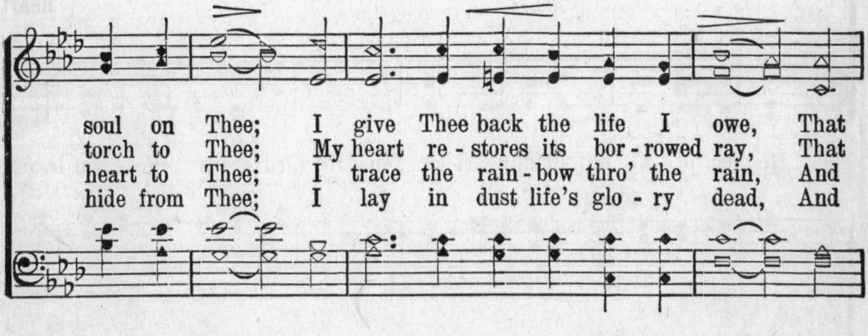

soul on Thee; I give Thee back the life I owe, That
torch to Thee; My heart re - stores its bor - rowed ray, That
heart to Thee; I trace the rain - bow thro' the rain, And
hide from Thee; I lay in dust life's glo - ry dead, And

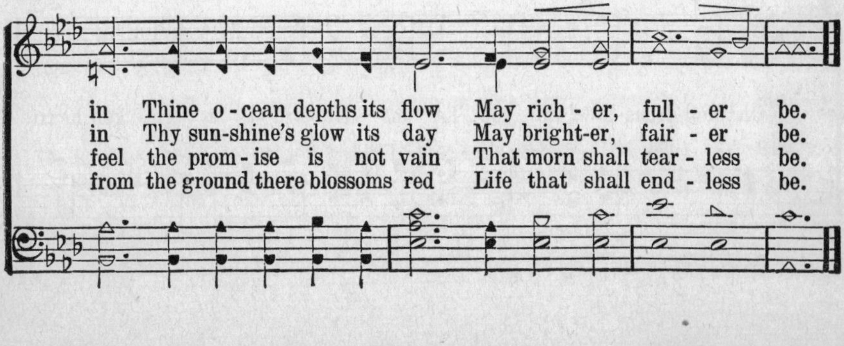

in Thine o - cean depths its flow May rich - er, full - er be.
in Thy sun-shine's glow its day May bright-er, fair - er be.
feel the prom - ise is not vain That morn shall tear - less be.
from the ground there blossoms red Life that shall end - less be.

84 The Broken Heart

T. D. T. DENNIS

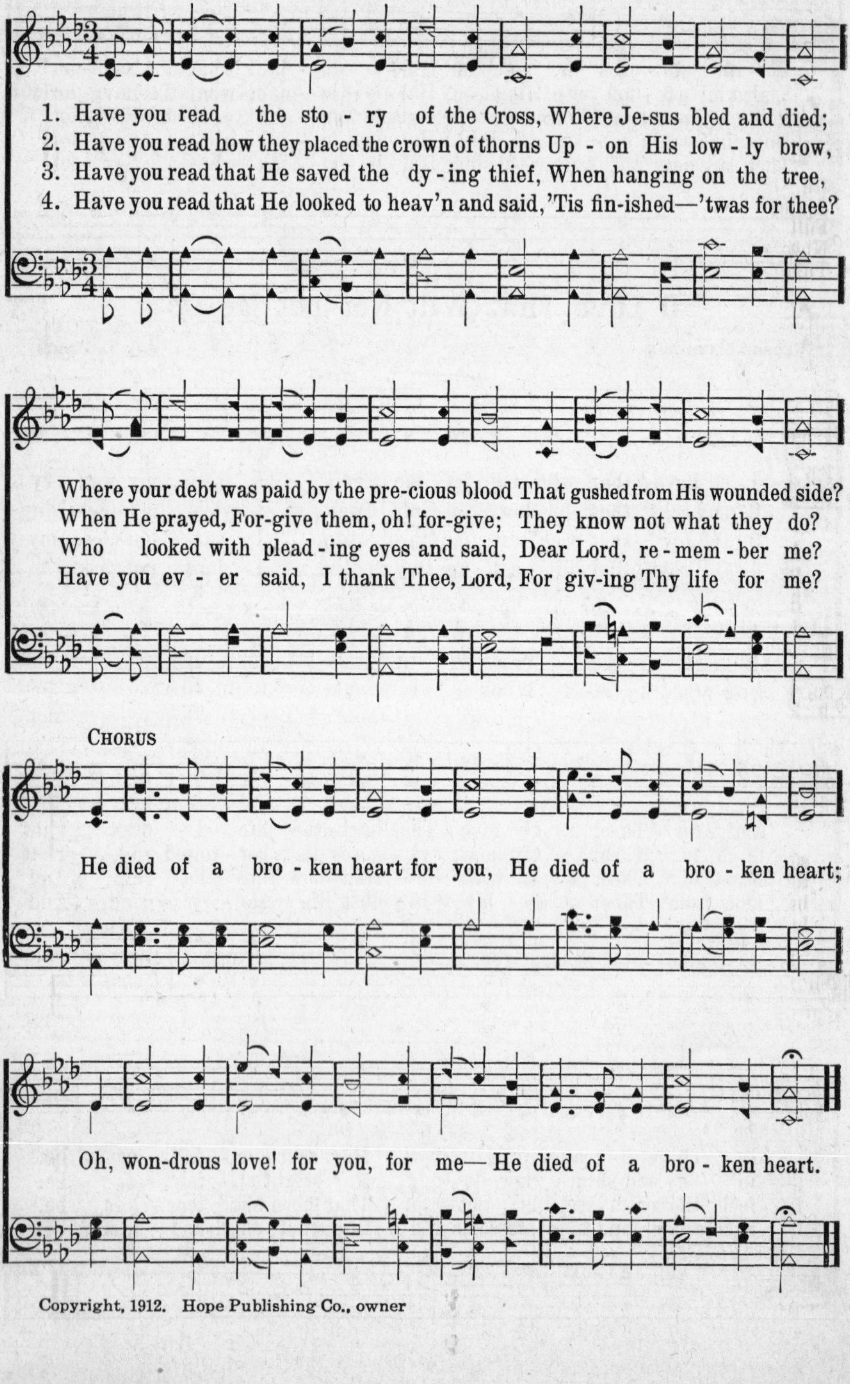

1. Have you read the sto - ry of the Cross, Where Je-sus bled and died;
2. Have you read how they placed the crown of thorns Up - on His low - ly brow,
3. Have you read that He saved the dy - ing thief, When hanging on the tree,
4. Have you read that He looked to heav'n and said, 'Tis fin-ished—'twas for thee?
Where your debt was paid by the pre-cious blood That gushed from His wounded side?
When He prayed, For-give them, oh! for-give; They know not what they do?
Who looked with plead - ing eyes and said, Dear Lord, re - mem - ber me?
Have you ev - er said, I thank Thee, Lord, For giv-ing Thy life for me?
CHORUS
He died of a bro - ken heart for you, He died of a bro - ken heart;
Oh, won-drous love! for you, for me— He died of a bro - ken heart.

Jesus Loves Even Me

P. P. B. P. P. Bliss

1. I am so glad that our Fa-ther in heav'n Tells of His
2. Tho' I for-get Him and wan-der a-way, Still He doth
3. Oh, if there's on-ly one song I can sing, When in His
love in the Book He has giv'n, Won-der-ful things in the
love me wher-ev-er I stray; Back to His dear lov-ing
beau-ty I see the great King, This shall my song in e-
Bi-ble I see; This is the dear-est, that Je-sus loves me.
arms would I flee, When I re-mem-ber that Je-sus loves me.
ter-ni-ty be: "Oh, what a won-der that Je-sus loves me."
CHORUS
I am so glad that Je-sus loves me, Je-sus loves me, Je-sus loves me,
I am so glad that Je-sus loves me, Je-sus loves e-ven me.

86 **It's Just Like His Great Love**

EDNA R. WORRELL — DEKOVEN

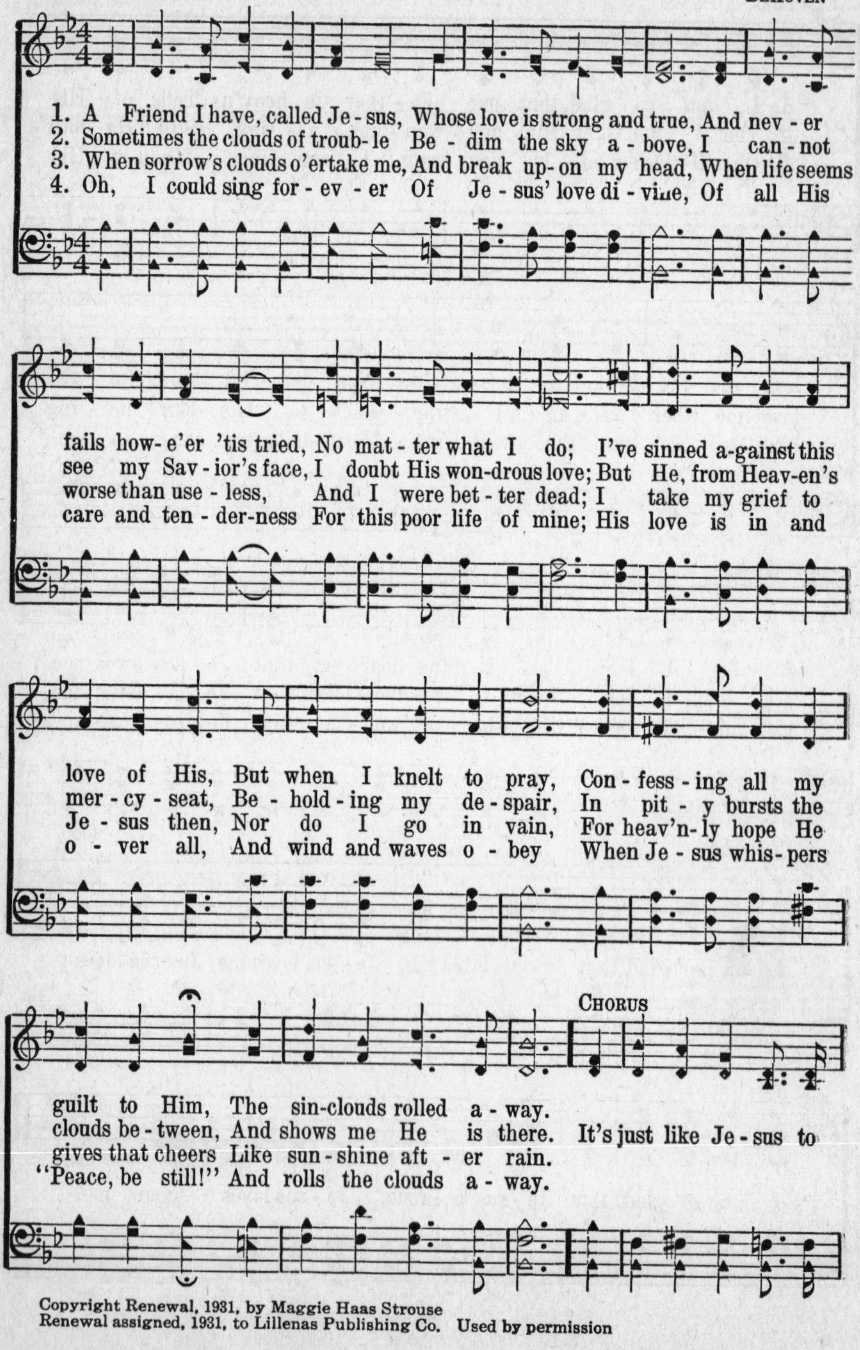
1. A Friend I have, called Je-sus, Whose love is strong and true, And nev-er
2. Sometimes the clouds of troub-le Be-dim the sky a-bove, I can-not
3. When sorrow's clouds o'ertake me, And break up-on my head, When life seems
4. Oh, I could sing for-ev-er Of Je-sus' love di-vine, Of all His
fails how-e'er 'tis tried, No mat-ter what I do; I've sinned a-gainst this
see my Sav-ior's face, I doubt His won-drous love; But He, from Heav-en's
worse than use-less, And I were bet-ter dead; I take my grief to
care and ten-der-ness For this poor life of mine; His love is in and
love of His, But when I knelt to pray, Con-fess-ing all my
mer-cy-seat, Be-hold-ing my de-spair, In pit-y bursts the
Je-sus then, Nor do I go in vain, For heav'n-ly hope He
o-ver all, And wind and waves o-bey When Je-sus whis-pers
guilt to Him, The sin-clouds rolled a-way.
clouds be-tween, And shows me He is there. It's just like Je-sus to
gives that cheers Like sun-shine aft-er rain.
"Peace, be still!" And rolls the clouds a-way.
CHORUS

It's Just Like His Great Love

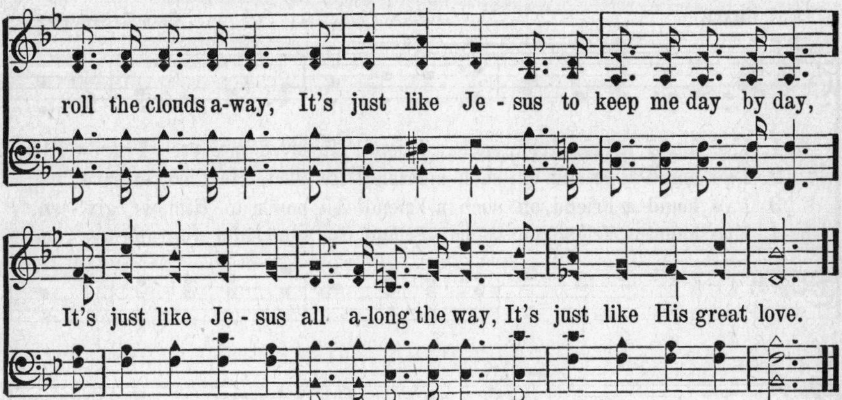
roll the clouds a-way, It's just like Je - sus to keep me day by day,
It's just like Je - sus all a-long the way, It's just like His great love.

Unsearchable Riches

87

F. J. C. — Jno. R. Sweney

1. O the un-search-a-ble rich- es of Christ!–Wealth that can nev-er be told;—
2. O the un-search-a-ble rich- es of Christ! Who shall their greatness de-clare!
3. O the un-search-a-ble rich- es of Christ! Free- ly, how free - ly they flow;
4. O the un-search-a-ble rich- es of Christ! Who would not glad-ly en - dure
FINE
Rich- es ex-haust-less of mer- cy and grace, Precious, more precious than gold!
Jew-els whose lus-ter our lives may a - dorn, Pearls that the poor-est may wear.
Mak-ing the souls of the faith-ful and true Hap - py wher-ev - er they go.
Tri - als, af-flic-tions, and cross-es on earth, Rich - es like these to se - cure!
D.S.—O the un-search-a - ble rich - es of Christ! Precious, more precious than gold.
CHORUS
D. S.
Pre - cious, more pre - cious;—Wealth that can nev - er be told;

88 I've Found a Friend

J. G. SMALL GEO. C. STEBBINS

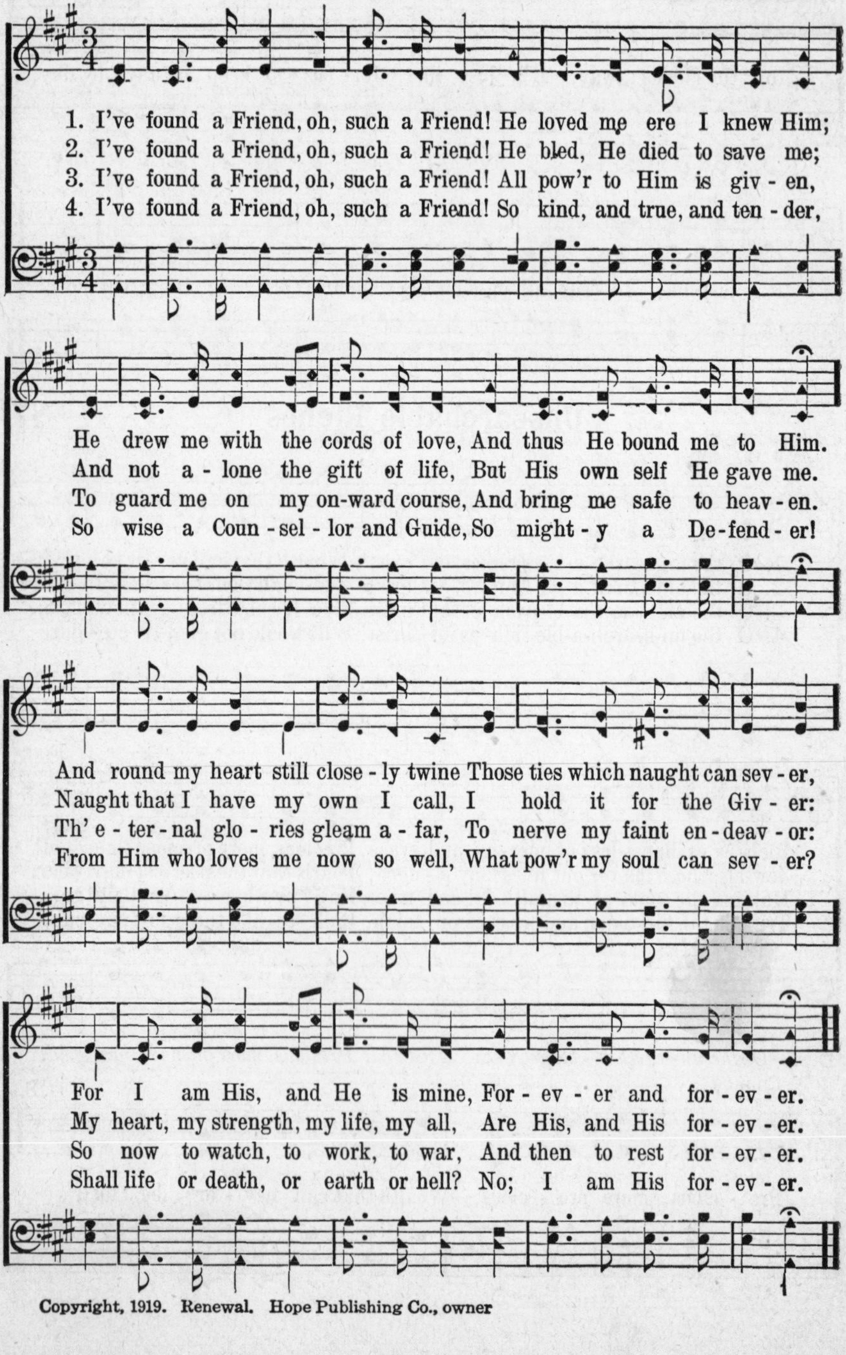
1. I've found a Friend, oh, such a Friend! He loved me ere I knew Him;
2. I've found a Friend, oh, such a Friend! He bled, He died to save me;
3. I've found a Friend, oh, such a Friend! All pow'r to Him is giv - en,
4. I've found a Friend, oh, such a Friend! So kind, and true, and ten - der,
He drew me with the cords of love, And thus He bound me to Him.
And not a - lone the gift of life, But His own self He gave me.
To guard me on my on-ward course, And bring me safe to heav - en.
So wise a Coun - sel - lor and Guide, So might - y a De-fend - er!
And round my heart still close - ly twine Those ties which naught can sev - er,
Naught that I have my own I call, I hold it for the Giv - er:
Th' e - ter - nal glo - ries gleam a - far, To nerve my faint en - deav - or:
From Him who loves me now so well, What pow'r my soul can sev - er?
For I am His, and He is mine, For - ev - er and for - ev - er.
My heart, my strength, my life, my all, Are His, and His for - ev - er.
So now to watch, to work, to war, And then to rest for - ev - er.
Shall life or death, or earth or hell? No; I am His for - ev - er.

Savior, Teach Me, Day by Day

EMMELAR. 7. 7. 7. 7. D.

JANE E. LEESON

Arranged from ARTHUR S. SULLIVAN

1. Sav - ior, teach me, day by day, Love's sweet les - son to o - bey;
2. Teach me all Thy steps to trace, Strong to fol - low in Thy grace,

Sweet - er les - son can - not be,— Lov - ing Him who first loved me.
Learn - ing how to love from Thee, Lov - ing Him who first loved me.

With a child - like heart of love, At Thy bid - ding may I move;
Thus may I re - joice to show That I feel the love I owe;

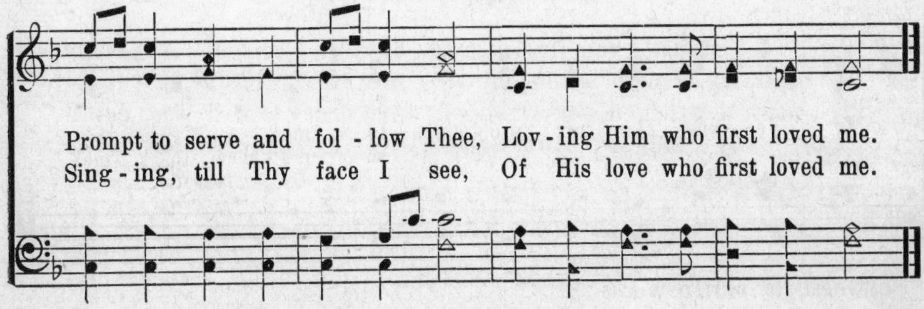
Prompt to serve and fol - low Thee, Lov - ing Him who first loved me.
Sing - ing, till Thy face I see, Of His love who first loved me.

My Jesus, Thou Art Precious

SADIE A. HARTZLER

H. D. WEAVER

1. My Je - sus, Thou art pre - cious! Thy love has won my soul;
2. My Je - sus, Thou art pre - cious! Thy fel - low - ship is sweet;
3. My Je - sus, Thou art pre - cious! Thy joy fills up my day;
4. My Je - sus, Thou art pre - cious! Thy pres - ence is so near;
Thy good-ness marks my go - ing; Each day take Thou con - trol.
Thy friend-ship is my com - fort; Each day be my re - treat.
Thy peace gives full - est pleas - ures; Each day lead Thou the way.
Thy truth is dear - est treas - ure; Each day keep Thou from fear.
CHORUS
Thou art pre - cious to me! Pre - cious to me. My Je - sus, Thou art
pre - cious to me! Pre - cious to me, Pre - cious to me,
so pre-cious to me!
ritard.
My Je - sus, Thou art pre - cious to me!
so pre - cious to me!

Sitting at the Feet of Jesus

J. H. 8s. 7s. D. Arr.

1. {Sit-ting at the feet of Je-sus, Oh, what words I hear Him say!
 {Hap-py place! so near, so pre-cious! May it find me there each . . . . day.
2. {Sit-ting at the feet of Je-sus, Where can mor-tal be more blest?
 {There I lay my sins and sor-rows, And, when wea-ry, find sweet . . . rest.
3. {Bless me, O my Sav-ior, bless me, As I sit low at Thy feet;
 {Oh, look down in love up-on me, Let me see Thy face so . . . . sweet.

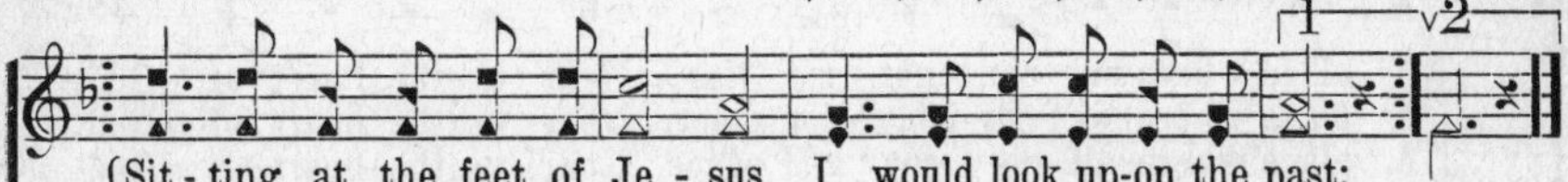

{Sit-ting at the feet of Je-sus, I would look up-on the past:
{For His love has been so gra-cious, It has won my heart at . . . . last.
{Sit-ting at the feet of Je-sus, There I love to weep and pray,
{While I from His full-ness gath-er Grace and comfort ev-'ry . . . . day.
{Give me, Lord, the mind of Je-sus, Make me ho-ly as He is;
{May I prove I've been with Je-sus, Who is all my right-eous- . . . ness.

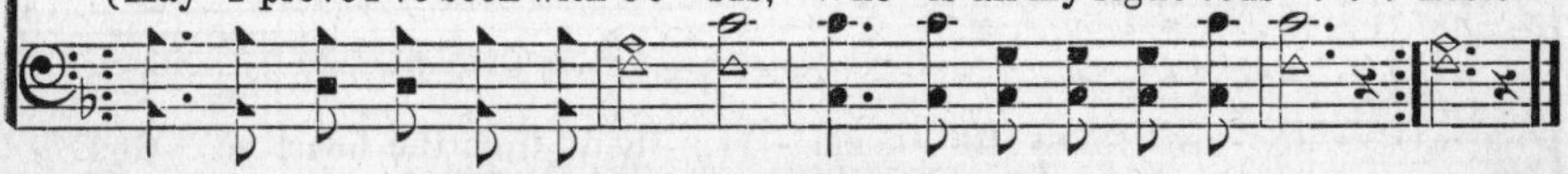

There Is a Name I Love

F. WHITFIELD GEER. C. M. H. W. GREATOREX

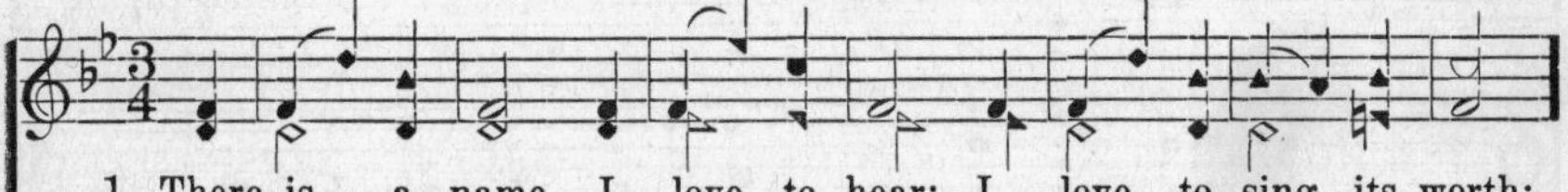

1. There is a name I love to hear; I love to sing its worth;
2. It tells me of a Sav-ior's love Who died to set me free;
3. It tells of One whose lov-ing heart Can feel my small-est woe—
4. It bids my trem-bling soul re-joice, And dries each ris-ing tear;

It sounds like mu-sic in mine ear— The sweet-est Name on earth.
It tells me of His pre-cious blood—The sin-ner's per-fect plea.
Who in each sor-row bears a part That none can bear be-low.
It tells me in a "still small voice," To trust, and not to fear.

93 Near to the Heart of God

C. B. McA. P. M. With Chorus CLELAND B. MCAFEE

In moderate time, with expression

1. There is a place of qui - et rest, Near to the heart of God,
2. There is a place of com - fort sweet, Near to the heart of God,
3. There is a place of full re - lease, Near to the heart of God,
A place where sin can - not mo - lest, Near to the heart of God.
A place where we our Sav - ior meet, Near to the heart of God.
A place where all is joy and peace, Near to the heart of God.
CHORUS
O Je - sus, blest Re - deem - er, Sent from the heart of God,
Hold us, who wait be - fore Thee, Near to the heart of God.

94 Jesus Calls Us; O'er the Tumult

CECIL F. ALEXANDER GALILEE. 8. 7. 8. 7. WILLIAM H. JUDD

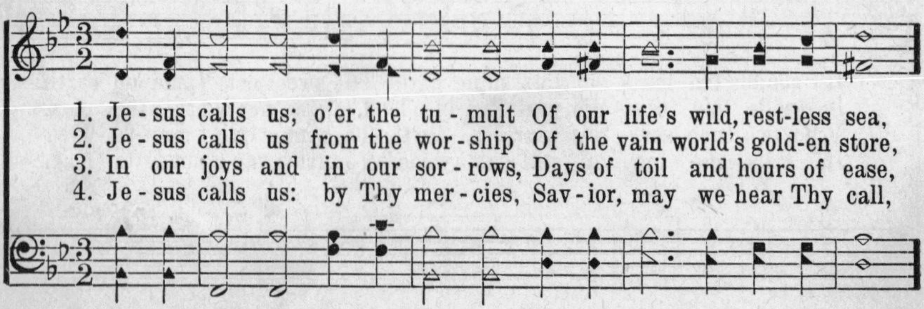
1. Je - sus calls us; o'er the tu - mult Of our life's wild, rest-less sea,
2. Je - sus calls us from the wor - ship Of the vain world's gold-en store,
3. In our joys and in our sor - rows, Days of toil and hours of ease,
4. Je - sus calls us: by Thy mer - cies, Sav - ior, may we hear Thy call,

Jesus Calls Us; O'er the Tumult

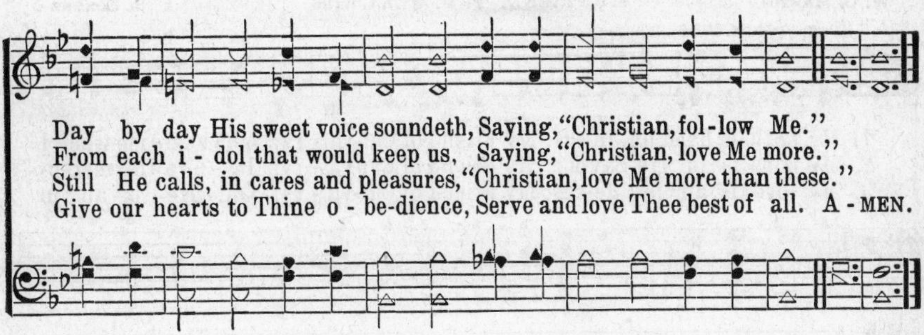
Day by day His sweet voice soundeth, Saying, "Christian, fol-low Me."
From each i - dol that would keep us, Saying, "Christian, love Me more."
Still He calls, in cares and pleasures, "Christian, love Me more than these."
Give our hearts to Thine o - be-dience, Serve and love Thee best of all. A - MEN.

My Jesus, I Love Thee 95

WILLIAM RALF FEATHERSTONE — A. J. GORDON

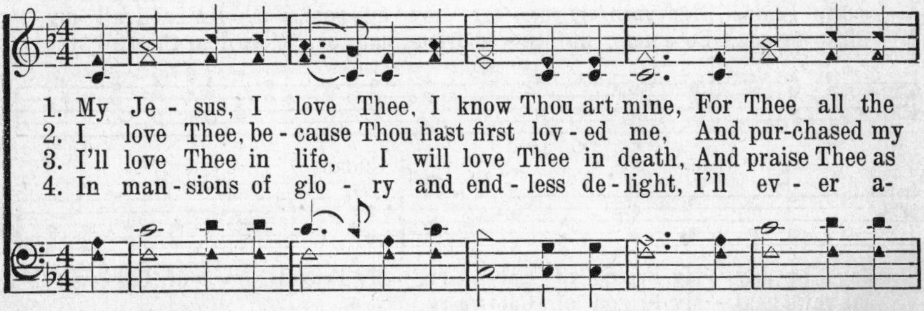
1. My Je - sus, I love Thee, I know Thou art mine, For Thee all the
2. I love Thee, be - cause Thou hast first lov - ed me, And pur-chased my
3. I'll love Thee in life, I will love Thee in death, And praise Thee as
4. In man - sions of glo - ry and end - less de - light, I'll ev - er a-

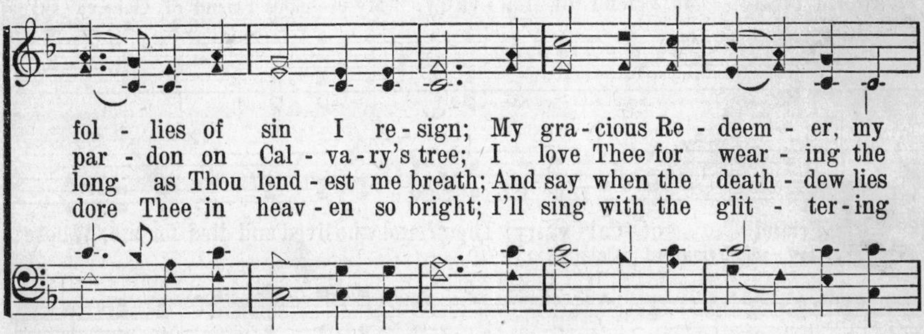
fol - lies of sin I re - sign; My gra - cious Re - deem - er, my
par - don on Cal - va - ry's tree; I love Thee for wear - ing the
long as Thou lend - est me breath; And say when the death - dew lies
dore Thee in heav - en so bright; I'll sing with the glit - ter - ing

Sav - ior art Thou; If ev - er I loved Thee, my Je - sus, 'tis now.
thorns on Thy brow: If ev - er I loved Thee, my Je - sus, 'tis now.
cold on my brow, If ev - er I loved Thee, my Je - sus, 'tis now.
crown on my brow, If ev - er I loved Thee, my Je - sus, 'tis now.

96 My Friend of Calvary

W. C. Martin — MY FRIEND. P. M. With Chorus — E. S. Lorenz

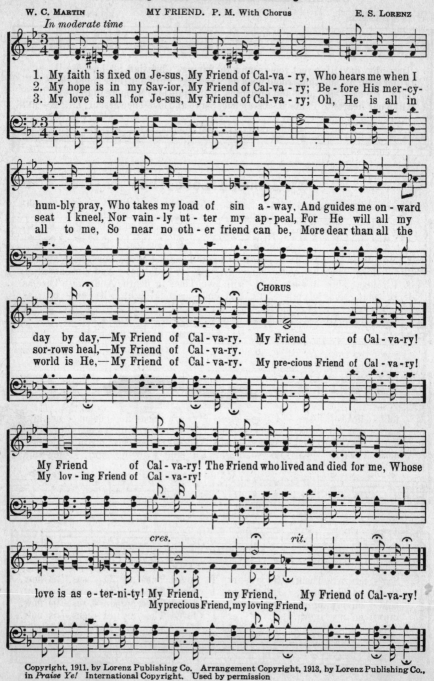

In moderate time
1. My faith is fixed on Je-sus, My Friend of Cal-va - ry, Who hears me when I
2. My hope is in my Sav-ior, My Friend of Cal-va - ry; Be - fore His mer-cy-
3. My love is all for Je-sus, My Friend of Cal-va - ry; Oh, He is all in
hum-bly pray, Who takes my load of sin a - way, And guides me on - ward
seat I kneel, Nor vain - ly ut - ter my ap - peal, For He will all my
all to me, So near no oth - er friend can be, More dear than all the
Chorus
day by day,—My Friend of Cal-va-ry. My Friend of Cal-va-ry!
sor-rows heal,—My Friend of Cal - va-ry.
world is He,—My Friend of Cal - va-ry. My pre-cious Friend of Cal - va - ry!
My Friend of Cal - va-ry! The Friend who lived and died for me, Whose
My lov - ing Friend of Cal - va - ry!
cres.
rit.
love is as e - ter-ni-ty! My Friend, my Friend, My Friend of Cal-va-ry!
My precious Friend, my loving Friend,

The Banner of the Cross

D. W. Whittle

James McGranahan

1. There's a roy - al ban - ner giv - en for dis - play To the sol - diers of the King;
2. Though the foe may rage and gath - er as the flood, Let the stand - ard be dis - played;
3. O - ver land and sea, wher - ev - er man may dwell, Make the glo - rious ti - dings known;
4. When the glo - ry dawns—'tis draw - ing ver - y near—It is has - t'ning day by day—
As an en - sign fair we lift it up to - day, While as ran - somed ones we sing.
And be - neath its folds, as sol - diers of the Lord, For the truth be not dis - mayed!
Of the crim - son ban - ner now the sto - ry tell, While the Lord shall claim His own!
Then be - fore our King the foe shall dis - ap - pear, And the cross the world shall sway!
Chorus
March - ing on, . . . march - ing on, . . For Christ count ev - 'ry - thing but loss! . . . . And to crown Him King, toil and sing 'Neath the ban - ner of the cross!
on, on, on, on, ev - 'ry - thing, ev - 'ry - thing but loss! we'll Be - neath

Copyright, 1912, Renewal. Hope Publishing Co., owner

98 Oh, Wonderful Word!

FANNY J. CROSBY — IRA D. SANKEY

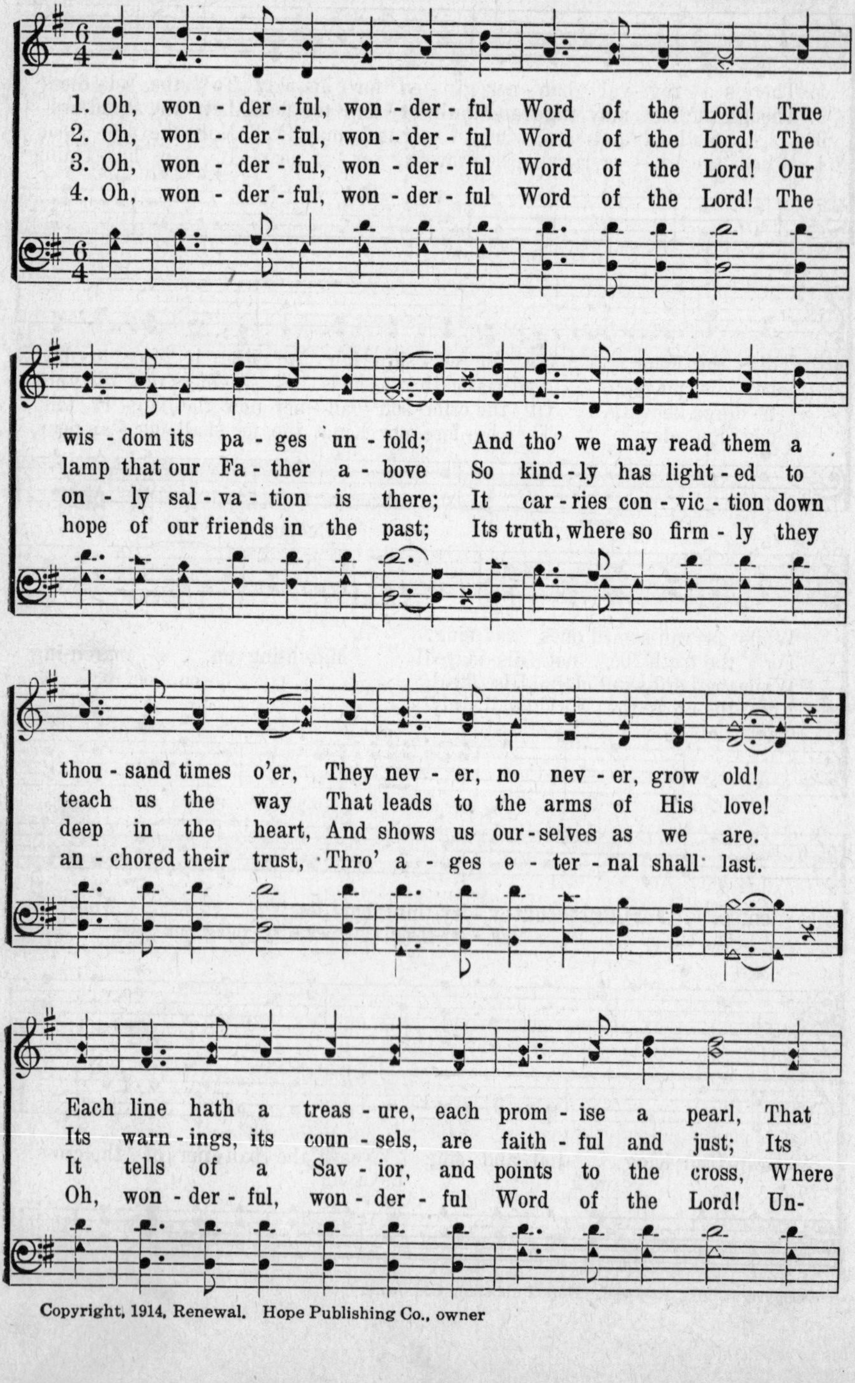
1. Oh, won - der - ful, won - der - ful Word of the Lord! True
2. Oh, won - der - ful, won - der - ful Word of the Lord! The
3. Oh, won - der - ful, won - der - ful Word of the Lord! Our
4. Oh, won - der - ful, won - der - ful Word of the Lord! The
wis - dom its pa - ges un - fold; And tho' we may read them a
lamp that our Fa - ther a - bove So kind - ly has light - ed to
on - ly sal - va - tion is there; It car - ries con - vic - tion down
hope of our friends in the past; Its truth, where so firm - ly they
thou - sand times o'er, They nev - er, no nev - er, grow old!
teach us the way That leads to the arms of His love!
deep in the heart, And shows us our - selves as we are.
an - chored their trust, Thro' a - ges e - ter - nal shall last.
Each line hath a treas - ure, each prom - ise a pearl, That
Its warn - ings, its coun - sels, are faith - ful and just; Its
It tells of a Sav - ior, and points to the cross, Where
Oh, won - der - ful, won - der - ful Word of the Lord! Un-

Copyright, 1914, Renewal. Hope Publishing Co., owner

Oh, Wonderful Word!

all if they will may se - cure; And we know that when time and the
judg-ments are per - fect and pure; And we know that when time and the
par - don we now may se - cure; For we know that when time and the
chang-ing, a - bid - ing and sure; For we know that when time and the

world pass a - way, God's Word shall for - ev - er en - dure.

Lamp of Our Feet, Whereby We Trace 99

LAMBETH. C. M.

BERNARD D. BARTON | A. SCHULTHES

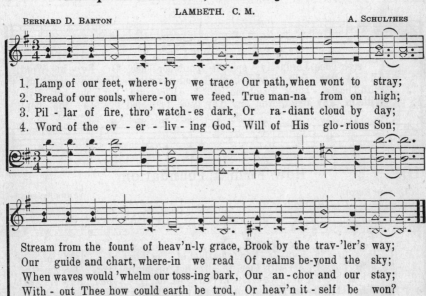

1. Lamp of our feet, where - by we trace Our path, when wont to stray;
2. Bread of our souls, where - on we feed, True man-na from on high;
3. Pil - lar of fire, thro' watch - es dark, Or ra - diant cloud by day;
4. Word of the ev - er - liv - ing God, Will of His glo - rious Son;

Stream from the fount of heav'n-ly grace, Brook by the trav-'ler's way;
Our guide and chart, where-in we read Of realms be-yond the sky;
When waves would 'whelm our toss-ing bark, Our an - chor and our stay;
With - out Thee how could earth be trod, Or heav'n it - self be won?

100 Break Thou the Bread of Life

MARY ANN LATHBURY WILLIAM F. SHERWIN

1. Break Thou the bread of life, Dear Lord, to me, As Thou didst
2. Bless Thou the truth, dear Lord, To me— to me— As Thou didst
3. Thou art the bread of life, O Lord, to me, Thy ho - ly
4. O send Thy Spir - it, Lord, Now un - to me, That He may
break the loaves Be - side the sea; Be - yond the sa - cred page
bless the bread By Gal - i - lee; Then shall all bond-age cease,
Word the truth That sav - eth me; Give me to eat and live
touch my eyes, And make me see: Show me the truth con-cealed
I seek Thee, Lord; My spir - it pants for Thee, O liv - ing Word.
All fet-ters fall; And I shall find my peace, My All in all.
With Thee a - bove; Teach me to love Thy truth, For Thou art love.
With-in Thy Word, And in Thy book re-vealed I see the Lord.

101 How Firm a Foundation

GEORGE KEITH ANNE STEELE

1. How firm a foun-da - tion, ye saints of the Lord, Is laid for your
2. "Fear not, I am with thee, O be not dis-mayed, For I am thy
3. "When thro' the deep wa-ters I call thee to go, The riv - ers of
4. "When thro' fi - ery tri - als thy path-way shall lie, My grace, all - suf-

How Firm a Foundation

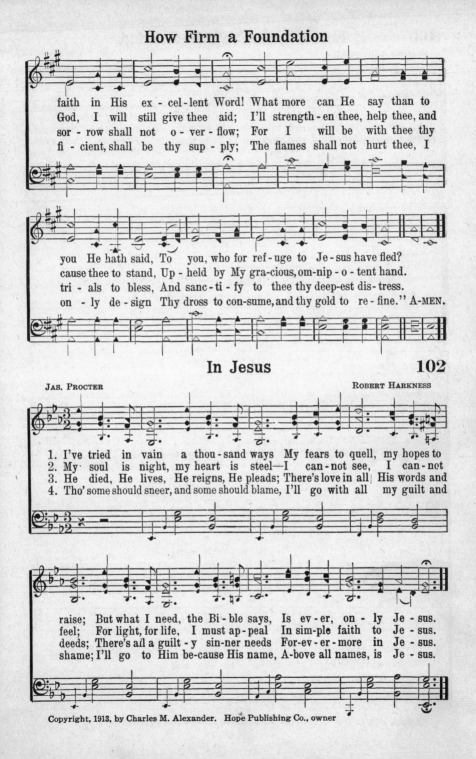

faith in His ex - cel - lent Word! What more can He say than to
God, I will still give thee aid; I'll strength - en thee, help thee, and
sor - row shall not o - ver - flow; For I will be with thee thy
fi - cient, shall be thy sup - ply; The flames shall not hurt thee, I

you He hath said, To you, who for ref - uge to Je - sus have fled?
cause thee to stand, Up - held by My gra - cious, om - nip - o - tent hand.
tri - als to bless, And sanc - ti - fy to thee thy deep - est dis - tress.
on - ly de - sign Thy dross to con - sume, and thy gold to re - fine." A-MEN.

In Jesus 102

JAS. PROCTER ROBERT HARKNESS

1. I've tried in vain a thou - sand ways My fears to quell, my hopes to
2. My soul is night, my heart is steel—I can - not see, I can - not
3. He died, He lives, He reigns, He pleads; There's love in all His words and
4. Tho' some should sneer, and some should blame, I'll go with all my guilt and

raise; But what I need, the Bi - ble says, Is ev - er, on - ly Je - sus.
feel; For light, for life, I must ap - peal In sim - ple faith to Je - sus.
deeds; There's all a guilt - y sin - ner needs For - ev - er - more in Je - sus.
shame; I'll go to Him be - cause His name, A - bove all names, is Je - sus.

103 True-Hearted, Whole-Hearted

FRANCES R. HAVERGAL GEO. C. STEBBINS

1. True-hearted, whole-hearted, faith-ful and loy - al, King of our lives, by Thy
2. True-hearted, whole-hearted, full - est al - le-giance Yielding henceforth to our
3. True-hearted, whole-hearted, Sav - ior all - glo-rious! Take Thy great pow-er and
grace we will be; Un-der the standard ex - alt - ed and roy - al, Strong in Thy
glo - ri - ous King; Val-iant en-deav-or and lov - ing o-be-dience, Free - ly and
reign there a - lone, O - ver our wills and af-fec-tions vic-to-rious, Free - ly sur-
CHORUS
strength we will bat-tle for Thee. Peal out the watch-word! si - lence it nev-er!
joy - ous - ly now would we bring.
ren-dered and whol-ly Thine own. Peal out the watch-word! si - lence it nev-er!
Song of our spir-its, re - joic - ing and free; Peal out the watch-word!
Song of our spir - its, re - joic-ing and free; Peal out the watch-word!
loy - al for - ev - er, King of our lives, by Thy grace we will be.
loy - al for - ev - er, King of our lives, by Thy grace we will be.

Grace, Enough For Me

E. O. E. E. O. EXCELL

1. In look-ing thro' my tears one day, I saw Mount Cal-va-
2. While standing there, my trem-bling heart, Once full of ag-o-
3. When I be-held my ev-'ry sin Nailed to the cru-el
4. When I am safe with-in the veil, My por-tion there will
ry; Be-neath the cross there flowed a stream Of grace, e-nough for
ny, Could scarce be-lieve the sight I saw Of grace, e-nough for
tree, I felt a flood go thro' my soul Of grace, e-nough for
be, To sing thro' all the years to come Of grace, e-nough for
CHORUS.
me. Grace is flow-ing from Cal-va-ry, . . .
e-nough for me. Grace is flow-ing from Cal-va-ry for me,
Grace as fath-om-less as the sea, . . Grace for time and e-
Grace as fath-om-less as the roll-ing sea, Grace for time and e-
ter-ni-ty, . . . Grace, . . e-nough for me. A-MEN.
ter-ni-ty, His a-bun-dant grace I see, e-nough for me.

105 Hallelujah, 'Tis Done

P. P. B. — P. P. Bliss

1. 'Tis the prom - ise of God, full sal - va - tion to give
2. Tho' the path - way be lone - ly, and dan - ger - ous too,
3. Man - y loved ones have I in yon heav - en - ly throng,
4. There's a part in that cho - rus for you and for me,
Un - to him who on Je - sus, His Son, will be - lieve.
Sure - ly Je - sus is a - ble to car - ry me through.
They are safe now in glo - ry, and this is their song:
And the theme of our prais - es for - ev - er will be:
Refrain
Hal - le - lu - jah, 'tis done! I be-lieve on the Son; I am
saved by the blood of the cru - ci - fied One; cru - ci - fied One.
1
2

106 Jesus Paid It All

Mrs. H. M. Hall — John T. Grape

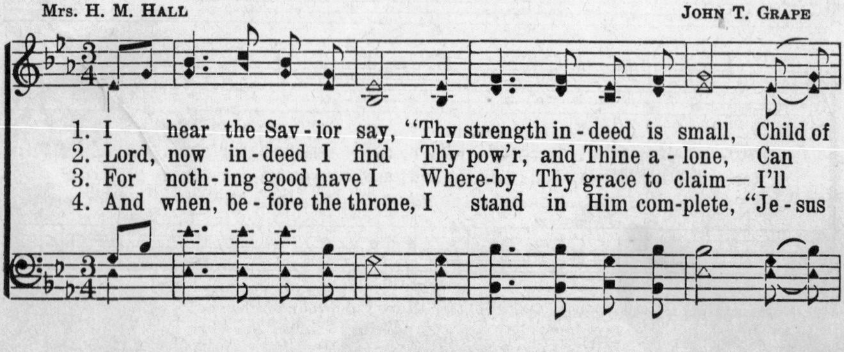

1. I hear the Sav-ior say, "Thy strength in - deed is small, Child of
2. Lord, now in - deed I find Thy pow'r, and Thine a - lone, Can
3. For noth - ing good have I Where-by Thy grace to claim— I'll
4. And when, be - fore the throne, I stand in Him com-plete, "Je - sus

Jesus Paid It All

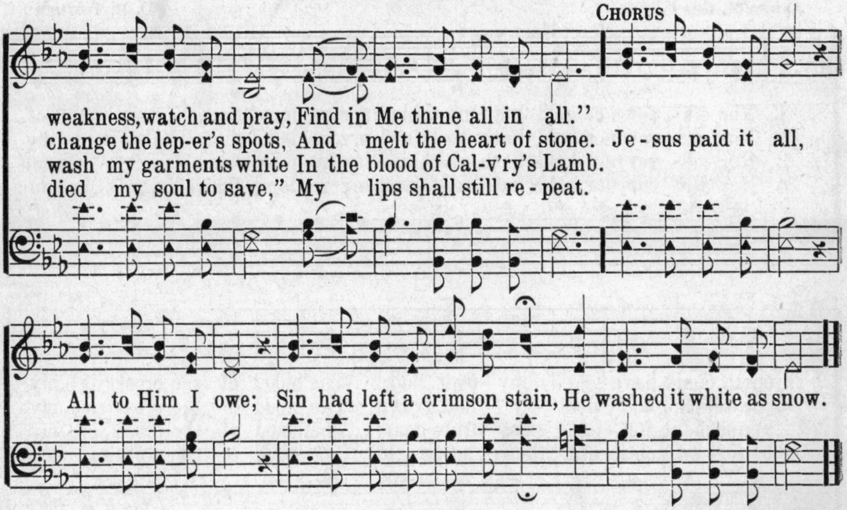
CHORUS
weakness, watch and pray, Find in Me thine all in all."
change the lep-er's spots, And melt the heart of stone. Je - sus paid it all,
wash my garments white In the blood of Cal-v'ry's Lamb.
died my soul to save," My lips shall still re - peat.
All to Him I owe; Sin had left a crimson stain, He washed it white as snow.

For Me

107

J. B. COMMUNION MEDITATION JOHN BIERI

1. O why, O why, In dark Geth-sem-a - ne, Did Je - sus, glo - rious
2. O why, O why, In court of eq - ui - ty, Did Je - sus, Mak - er
3. O why, O why, On cru - el Cal - va - ry, Did Je - sus, might - y
Prince of Peace, Pray long in ag - o - ny? For me, for me, In dark Geth-
of Man-kind, En - dure hu - mil - i - ty? For me, for me, In court of
King of kings, Hang on the shame-ful tree? For me, for me, On cru - el
sem - a - ne, He knelt, He prayed, He bled, He cried In ag - o - ny for me.
eq - ui - ty, He took the lash, the shame, the scorn In si-lence all for me.
Cal - va - ry, The nails, the spear, the thirst, the thorns, He suf-fered all for me.

108 Nor Silver Nor Gold

JAMES M. GRAY D. B. TOWNER

1. Nor sil - ver nor gold hath ob-tained my re-demp-tion, Nor rich - es of
2. Nor sil - ver nor gold hath ob-tained my re-demp-tion, The guilt on my
3. Nor sil - ver nor gold hath ob-tained my re-demp-tion, The ho - ly com-
4. Nor sil - ver nor gold hath ob-tained my re-demp-tion, The way in - to
earth could have saved my poor soul; The blood of the cross is my
con-science too heav - y had grown; The blood of the cross is my
mand-ment for - bade me draw near; The blood of the cross is my
heav - en could not thus be bought; The blood of the cross is my
on - ly foun - da-tion, The death of my Sav-ior now mak - eth me whole.
on - ly foun - da-tion, The death of my Sav - ior could on - ly a - tone.
on - ly foun - da-tion, The death of my Sav - ior re - mov - eth my fear.
on - ly foun - da-tion, The death of my Sav-ior re-demp-tion hath wrought
CHORUS
I am re - deemed, ... but not with sil - ver;
I am re-deemed, I am re-deemed, but not with sil - ver;
I am bought, . but not with gold; Bought with a
I am bought, I am bought, but not with gold;

Nor Silver Nor Gold

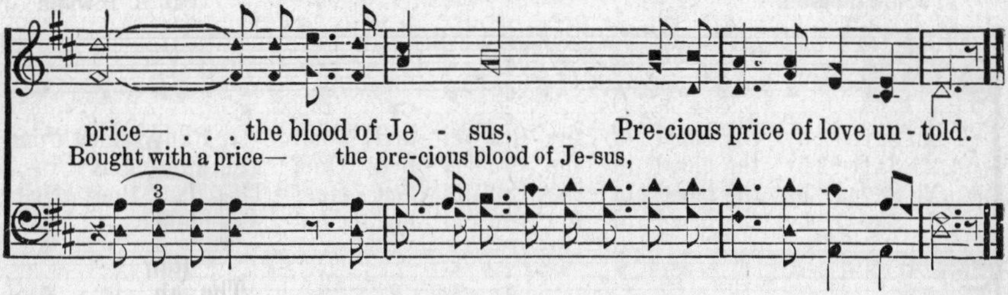
price— . . . the blood of Je - sus, Pre-cious price of love un-told.
Bought with a price— the pre-cious blood of Je-sus,
3

Christ Liveth in Me

Maj. D. W. Whittle (El Nathan) JAMES McGRANAHAN

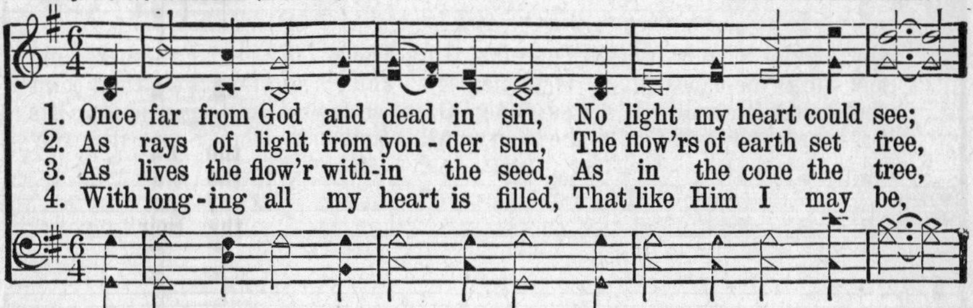
1. Once far from God and dead in sin, No light my heart could see;
2. As rays of light from yon-der sun, The flow'rs of earth set free,
3. As lives the flow'r with-in the seed, As in the cone the tree,
4. With long-ing all my heart is filled, That like Him I may be,

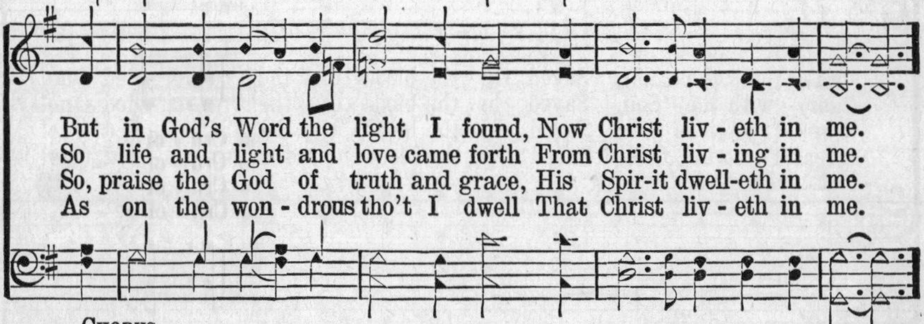
But in God's Word the light I found, Now Christ liv-eth in me.
So life and light and love came forth From Christ liv-ing in me.
So, praise the God of truth and grace, His Spir-it dwell-eth in me.
As on the won-drous tho't I dwell That Christ liv-eth in me.

CHORUS.

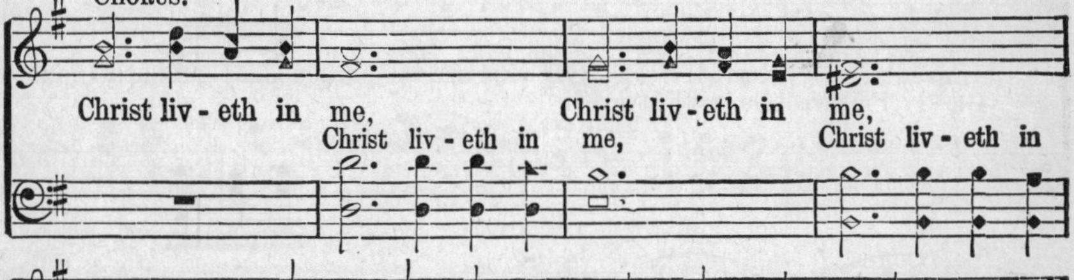
Christ liv-eth in me, Christ liv-eth in me,
Christ liv-eth in me, Christ liv-eth in

Oh! what a sal-va-tion this, That Christ liv-eth in me.
me, Oh!

110 Saved By the Blood

S. J. HENDERSON — D. B. TOWNER

1. Saved by the blood of the Cru-ci-fied One! Ran-somed from sin and a new work be-gun, Sing praise to the Fa-ther and praise to the Son, Saved by the blood of the Cru-ci-fied One!
2. Saved by the blood of the Cru-ci-fied One! The an-gels re-joic-ing be-cause it is done; A child of the Fa-ther joint-heir with the Son, Saved by the blood of the Cru-ci-fied One!
3. Saved by the blood of the Cru-ci-fied One! The Fa-ther He spake, and His will it was done; Great price of my par-don, His own pre-cious Son; Saved by the blood of the Cru-ci-fied One!
4. Saved by the blood of the Cru-ci-fied One! All hail to the Fa-ther, all hail to the Son, All hail to the Spir-it, the great Three in One! Saved by the blood of the Cru-ci-fied One!
CHORUS
Saved! . . saved! . . My sins are all pardoned my guilt is all gone!
Glo-ry, I'm saved! glo-ry, I'm saved!
Saved! . . saved! . . I am saved by the blood of the Cru-ci-fied One!
Glo-ry, I'm saved! glo-ry, I'm saved!

I Will Pass Over You

El Nathan — James McGranahan

1. When God of old the way of life Would teach to all His own,
2. By Christ, the sin - less Lamb of God, The pre-cious blood was shed,
3. O soul, for thee sal - va - tion thus By God is free - ly giv'n;
4. The wrath of God that was our due, Up - on the lamb was laid;
5. How calm the judg-ment hour shall pass To all who do o - bey

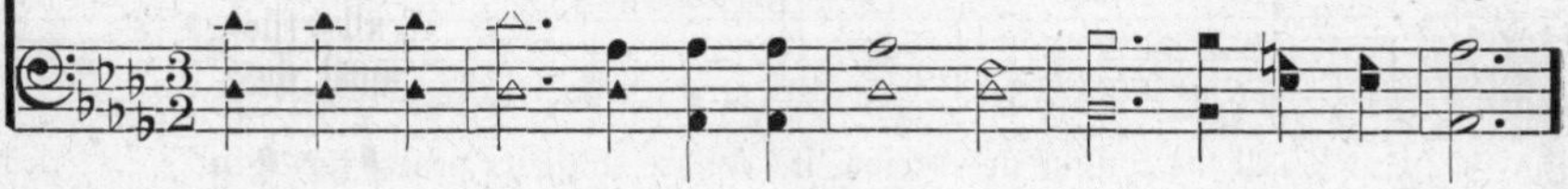

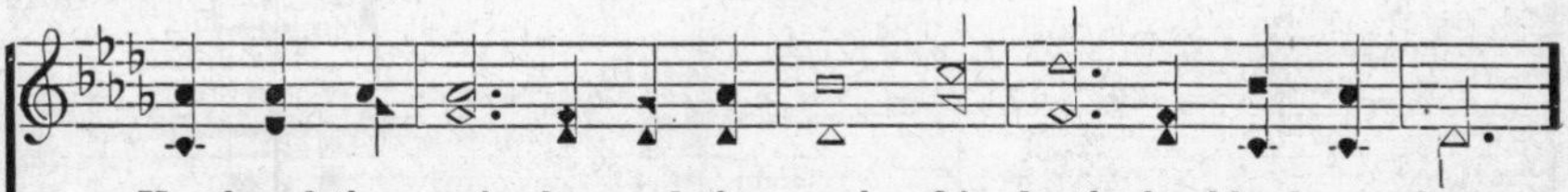

He placed them safe be-yond the reach Of death, by blood a - lone.
When He ful-filled God's ho - ly Word, And suf - fered in our stead.
The blood of Christ a-tones for sin, And makes us meet for heav'n.
And by the shed - ding of His blood, The debt for us was paid.
The Word of God, and trust the blood, And make that Word their stay!

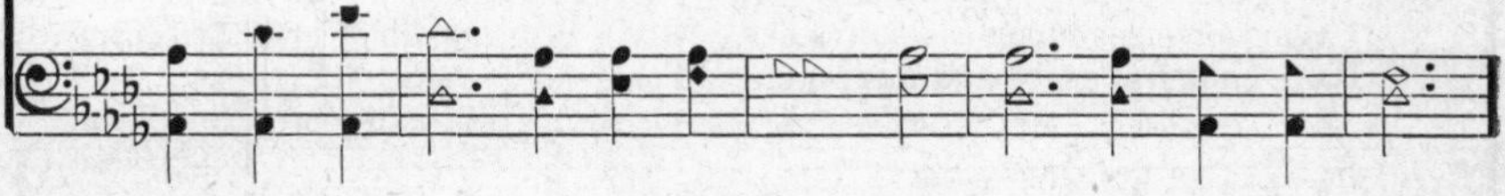

Chorus

It is His Word, God's precious Word, It stands for - ev - er true:
It is His Word, God's pre-cious Word,

"When I the Lord shall see the blood, I will pass o - ver you."
"When I the Lord shall see the blood,

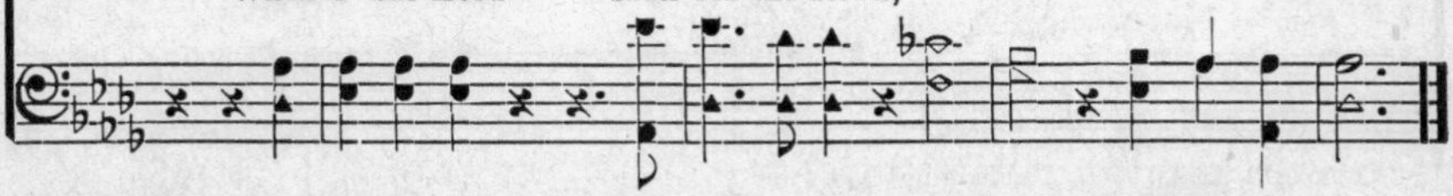

112 Wonderful Grace of Jesus

H. L. HALDOR LILLENAS

1. Won - der - ful grace of Je - sus, Great - er than all my sin; . .
2. Won - der - ful grace of Je - sus, Reach-ing to all the lost, . .
3. Won - der - ful grace of Je - sus, Reach-ing the most de - filed, . .
How shall my tongue de - scribe it, Where shall its praise be - gin? . . .
By it I have been pardoned, Saved to the ut - ter - most, . . .
By its trans-form-ing pow - er, Mak - ing him God's dear child, . .
Tak - ing a - way my bur - den, Set - ting my spir - it free; . .
Chains have been torn a - sun - der, Giv - ing me lib - er - ty; . . .
Pur - chas-ing peace and heav - en, For all e - ter - ni - ty; . . .
For the won - der - ful grace of Je - sus reach - es me.
For the won - der - ful grace of Je - sus reach - es me.
And the won - der - ful grace of Je - sus reach - es me.
CHORUS
the matchless grace of Je-sus,
Won-der-ful the matchless grace of Je - - - sus, Deep-er than the

Wonderful Grace of Jesus

the roll-ing sea; Won - - - der - ful
might - y roll - ing sea;............... Higher than the mountain,
grace, all - suf - fi - - - cient for
spar-kling like a foun - tain, All - suf - fi - cient grace for e - ven
me, for e - ven me, Broad - er than the scope of my trans-
me,...............
gres - sions, Great - er far than all my sin and shame..........
gres-sions, sing it! my sin and shame,
O mag - ni - fy the pre-cious name of Je - sus, Praise His name!

113 Transformed

Mrs. F. G. Burroughs | B. D. Ackley

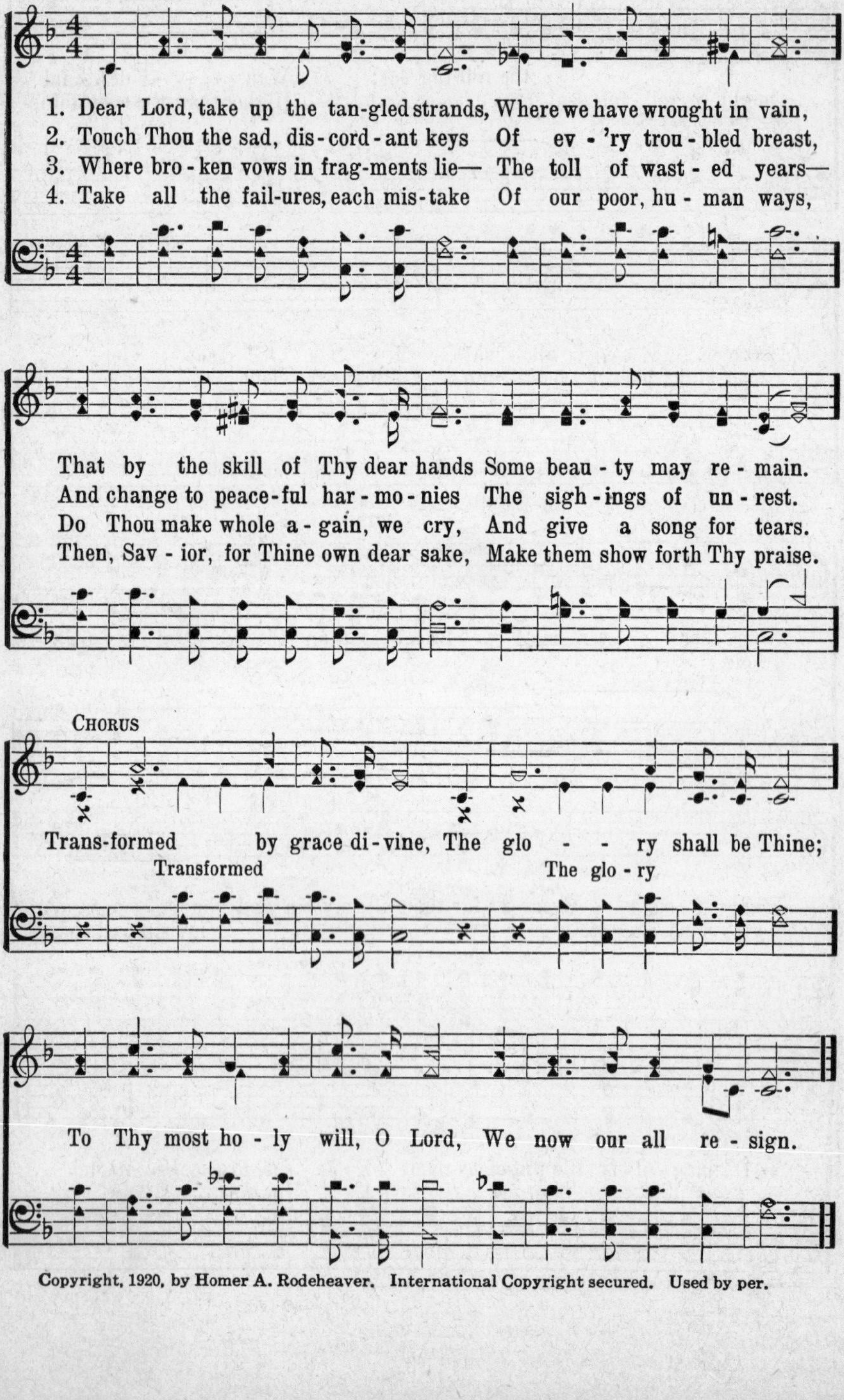
1. Dear Lord, take up the tan-gled strands, Where we have wrought in vain,
2. Touch Thou the sad, dis-cord-ant keys Of ev - 'ry trou - bled breast,
3. Where bro - ken vows in frag-ments lie— The toll of wast - ed years—
4. Take all the fail-ures, each mis-take Of our poor, hu - man ways,
That by the skill of Thy dear hands Some beau - ty may re - main.
And change to peace-ful har - mo - nies The sigh - ings of un - rest.
Do Thou make whole a - gain, we cry, And give a song for tears.
Then, Sav - ior, for Thine own dear sake, Make them show forth Thy praise.
CHORUS
Trans-formed by grace di - vine, The glo - - ry shall be Thine;
Transformed
The glo - ry
To Thy most ho - ly will, O Lord, We now our all re - sign.

Glory Ever Be to Jesus

FANNY J. CROSBY

IRA D. SANKEY

1. Glo - ry ev - er be to Je - sus, God's own well - be - lov - ed Son;
2. Oh, the wea - ry days of wand'ring, Long-ing, hop - ing for the light;
3. In His safe and ho - ly keep-ing, 'Neath the shad - ow of His wing,
By His grace He hath redeemed us, "It is fin - ished," all is done.
These at last lie all be - hind us, Je - sus is our strength and might.
Glad - ly in His love con-fid - ing, May our souls His prais - es sing.
CHORUS
Saved by grace thro' faith in Je - sus, Saved by His own pre - cious blood,
May we in His love a - bid - ing, Fol - low on to know the Lord.

115 On Calvary's Brow

W. M'K. Darwood | CALVARY | Jno. R. Sweney

1. On Cal-v'ry's brow . . . . my Sav - ior died, ... 'Twas there my
2. 'Mid rend-ing rocks . . . . and dark'ning skies, ... My Sav - ior
3. O Je - sus, Lord, ... how can it be, ... That Thou shouldst
1. On Cal-v'ry's brow
my Sav-ior died,
Lord . . . . was cru-ci - fied; . . . 'Twas on the cross . . . . He bled for
bows . . . . His head and dies; . . . The opening vail . . . . re-veals the
give . . . . Thy life for me, . . . To bear the cross . . . . and ag - o-
'Twas there my Lord
was cru-ci-fied;
'Twas on the cross
me, ... And pur-chased there . . . . my par - don free.
way . . . . . To heav-en's joys . . . . and end-less day.
ny, ... In that dread hour . . . . on Cal - va - ry!
He bled for me,
And pur-chased there,
Chorus mf p m p pp
O Cal - va - ry! dark Cal - va - ry! Where Je-sus shed His blood for me (for me);
mf ff mf rit. p
O Cal - va - ry! blest Cal - va - ry! 'Twas there my Sav - ior died for me.

There is a Green Hill Far Away

Cecil F. Alexander — Geo. C. Stebbins

1. There is a green hill far a-way, With-out a cit-y wall,
2. We may not know, we can-not tell, What pains He had to bear;
3. He died that we might be for-giv'n, He died to make us good,
4. There was no oth-er good e-nough, To pay the price of sin;

Where the dear Lord was cru-ci-fied, Who died to save us all.
But we be-lieve it was for us He hung and suf-fered there.
That we might go at last to Heav'n, Saved by His pre-cious blood.
He on-ly could un-lock the gate Of Heav'n and let us in.

Chorus

Oh, dear-ly, dear-ly has He loved, And we must love Him, too,

And trust in His re-deem-ing blood, And try His works to do.

117 Wounded for Me

GLADYS WATKIN ROBERTS — Music and first verse by Rev. W. G. OVENS

1. Wound-ed for me, wound-ed for me, There on the cross
2. Dy - ing for me, dy - ing for me, There on the cross
3. Ris - en for me, ris - en for me, Up from the grave
4. Liv - ing for me, liv - ing for me, Up in the skies
5. Com - ing for me, com - ing for me, One day to earth
He was wound - ed for me; Gone my trans - gres - sions, and
He was dy - ing for me; Now in His death my re-
He has ris - en for me; Now ev - er - more from death's
He is liv - ing for me; Dai - ly He's plead - ing and
He is com - ing for me; Then with what joy His dear
dim.
now I am free, All be - cause Je - sus was wound-ed for me.
demp-tion I see, All be - cause Je - sus was dy - ing for me.
sting I am free, All be - cause Je - sus has ris - en for me.
pray - ing for me, All be - cause Je - sus is liv - ing for me.
face I shall see, Oh, how I praise Him! He's com - ing for me.

118 Not All the Blood of Beasts

ISAAC WATTS — BOYLSTON. S. M. — Dr. LOWELL MASON

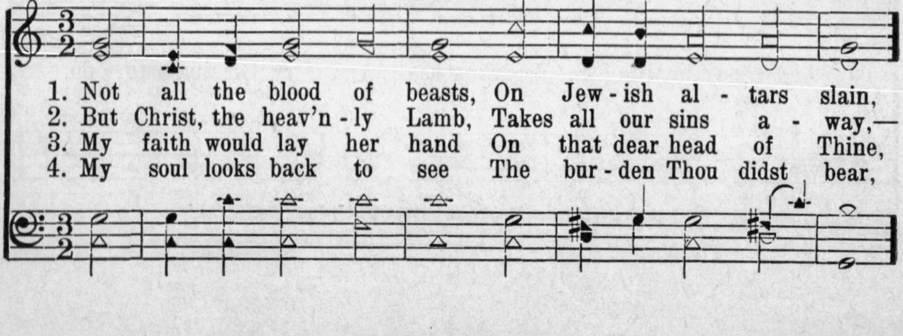
1. Not all the blood of beasts, On Jew - ish al - tars slain,
2. But Christ, the heav'n - ly Lamb, Takes all our sins a - way,—
3. My faith would lay her hand On that dear head of Thine,
4. My soul looks back to see The bur - den Thou didst bear,

Not All the Blood of Beasts

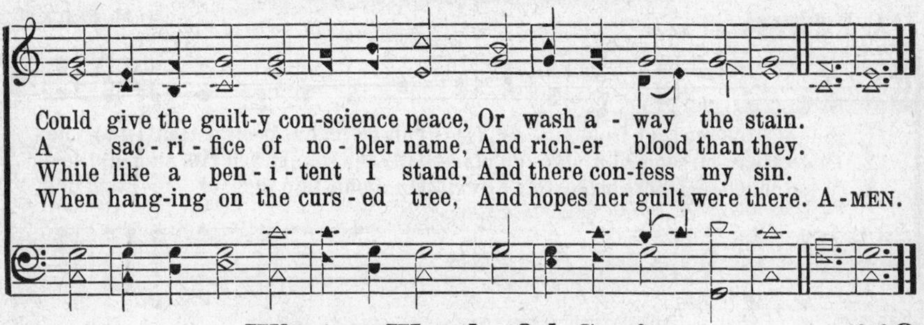
Could give the guilt-y con-science peace, Or wash a - way the stain.
A sac - ri - fice of no - bler name, And rich-er blood than they.
While like a pen - i - tent I stand, And there con-fess my sin.
When hang-ing on the curs - ed tree, And hopes her guilt were there. A - MEN.

What a Wonderful Savior 119

E. A. H. ELISHA A. HOFFMAN

1. Christ has for sin a - tone-ment made, What a won - der - ful Sav - ior!
2. I praise Him for the cleans-ing blood, What a won - der - ful Sav - ior!
3. He cleansed my heart from all its sin, What a won - der - ful Sav - ior!
4. He walks be - side me in the way, What a won - der - ful Sav - ior!
We are redeemed! the price is paid! What a won - der - ful Sav - ior!
That rec - on-ciled my soul to God; What a won - der - ful Sav - ior!
And now He reigns and rules there - in, What a won - der - ful Sav - ior!
And keeps me faith- ful day by day; What a won - der - ful Sav - ior!
CHORUS
What a won - der - ful Sav - ior is Je - sus, my Je - sus!
What a won - der - ful Sav - ior is Je - sus, my Lord!

120 Where Jesus Is, 'Tis Heaven

C. F. BUTLER — J. M. BLACK

1. Since Christ my soul from sin set free, This world has been a Heav'n to me;
2. Once Heav-en seemed a far-off place, Till Je-sus showed His smil-ing face;
3. What mat-ters where on earth we dwell? On moun-tain top, or in the dell,

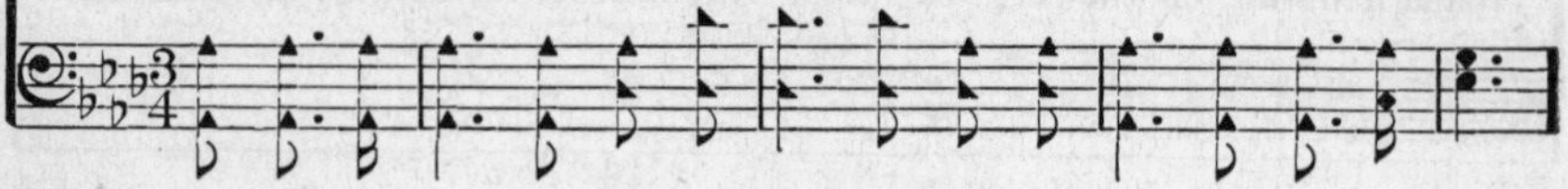

And 'mid earth's sorrows and its woe, 'Tis Heav'n my Je-sus here to know.
Now it's be-gun with-in my soul, 'Twill last while end-less a-ges roll.
In cot-tage, or a man-sion fair, Where Je-sus is, 'tis Heav-en there.

CHORUS

O hal-le-lu-jah, yes, 'tis Heav'n, 'Tis Heav'n to know my sins for-giv'n;

On land or sea, what matters where? Where Je-sus is, 'tis Heav-en there.

121 Eternal Source of Joys Divine

ST. NICHOLAS. C. M. — Dr. HAVERGAL

1. E-ter-nal Source of joys di-vine, To Thee my soul as-pires;
2. My Hope, my Trust, my Life, my Lord, As-sures me of Thy love;
3. Then shall my thank-ful pow'rs re-joice, And tri-umph in my God,

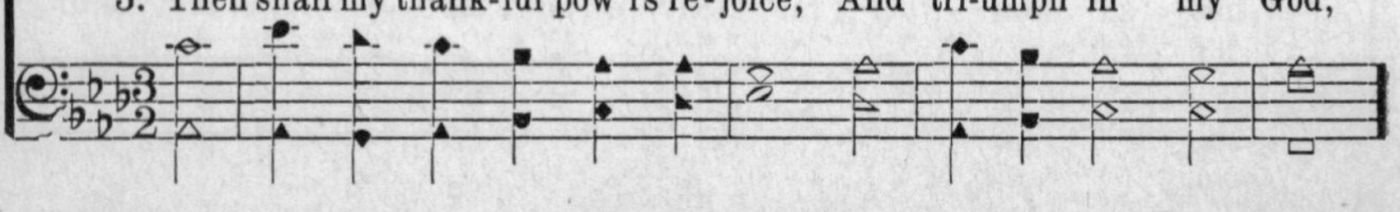

Eternal Source of Joys Divine

Oh, could I say, "The Lord is mine," 'Tis all my soul de - sires.
Oh, speak the kind, trans-port-ing word, And bid my fears re - move.
Till heav'n-ly rap - ture tune my voice, To spread Thy praise a - broad.

Hiding In Thee 122

WM. O. CUSHING

IRA D. SANKEY

1. O safe to the Rock that is high-er than I, My soul in its con - flicts and sor - rows would fly; So sin - ful, so wea - ry, Thine, Thine would I be; Thou blest "Rock of A - ges," I'm hid - ing in Thee.
2. In the calm of the noon-tide, in sor-row's lone hour, In times when temp - ta - tion casts o'er me its pow'r; In the tem - pests of life, on its wide, heaving sea, Thou blest "Rock of A - ges," I'm hid - ing in Thee.
3. How oft in the con-flict, when pressed by the foe, I have fled to my Ref - uge and breathed out my woe; How oft - en, when tri - als like sea - bil - lows roll, Have I hid - den in Thee, O Thou Rock of my soul.
CHORUS
Hid-ing in Thee, Hiding in Thee, Thou blest "Rock of Ages," I'm hid-ing in Thee.

123 Saved to the Uttermost

W. J. K. — Wm. J. Kirkpatrick

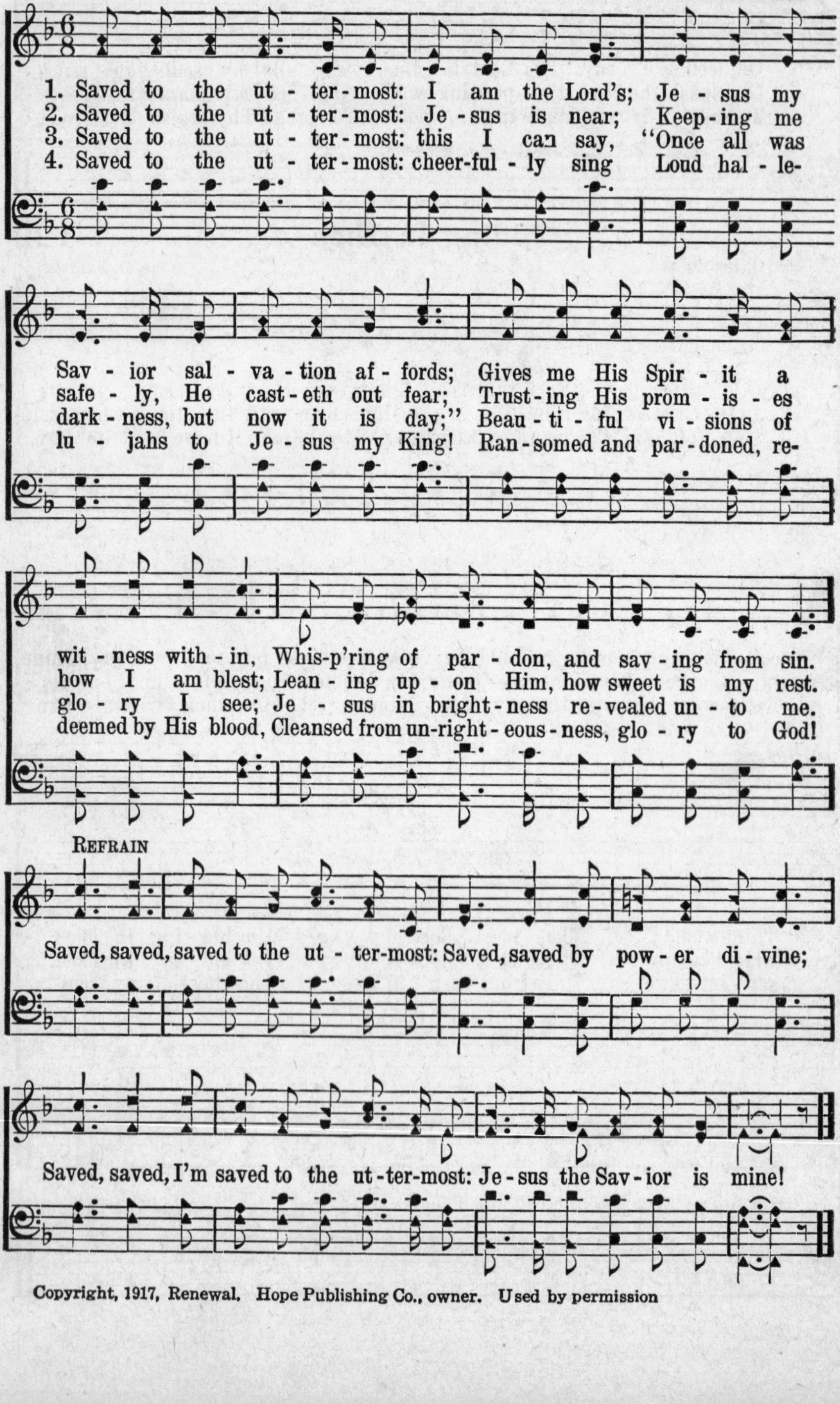

1. Saved to the ut - ter-most: I am the Lord's; Je - sus my Sav - ior sal - va - tion af - fords; Gives me His Spir - it a wit - ness with - in, Whis-p'ring of par - don, and sav - ing from sin.
2. Saved to the ut - ter-most: Je - sus is near; Keep-ing me safe - ly, He cast-eth out fear; Trust-ing His prom - is - es how I am blest; Lean - ing up - on Him, how sweet is my rest.
3. Saved to the ut - ter-most: this I can say, "Once all was dark - ness, but now it is day;" Beau - ti - ful vi - sions of glo - ry I see; Je - sus in bright - ness re - vealed un - to me.
4. Saved to the ut - ter-most: cheer-ful - ly sing Loud hal - le - lu - jahs to Je - sus my King! Ran-somed and par-doned, re - deemed by His blood, Cleansed from un-right - eous - ness, glo - ry to God!
Refrain
Saved, saved, saved to the ut - ter-most: Saved, saved by pow - er di - vine;
Saved, saved, I'm saved to the ut - ter-most: Je - sus the Sav - ior is mine!

I Am Happy in Him

E. O. E. — E. O. Excell

1. My soul is so happy in Je - sus, For He is so precious to me; . . . .
2. He sought me so long ere I knew Him, When wand'ring afar from the fold; . .
3. His love and His mercy surround me, His grace like a riv-er doth flow; . . .
4. They say I shall some day be like Him, My cross and my burden lay down; . .

His voice it is mu-sic to hear it, His face it is heav-en to see. . . .
Safe home in His arms He hath bro't me, To where there are pleasures untold.
His Spir - it, to guide and to com-fort, Is with me wher-ev-er I go. . . .
Till then I will ev-er be faith - ful, In gath - er-ing gems for His crown.

CHORUS

I am hap-py in Him, ... I am hap-py in Him; . . . .
I . . . . am hap-py in Him, I . . . . am hap-py in Him;

My soul with de-light He fills day and night, For I am hap-py in Him.

125 Since I Found My Savior

E. E. Hewitt — Jno. R. Sweney

1. Life wears a dif - f'rent phase to me, Since I found my Sav - ior;
2. He sought me in His wondrous love, So I found my Sav - ior;
3. The pass-ing clouds may in - ter-vene, Since I found my Sav - ior;
4. A strong hand kind - ly holds my own, Since I found my Sav - ior;
Rich mer - cy at the cross I see, My dy - ing, liv - ing Sav - ior.
He brought sal - va - tion from a - bove, My dear, al-might - y Sav - ior.
But He is with me, tho' un-seen, My ev - er - pres-ent Sav - ior.
It leads me on-ward to the throne; O there I'll see my Sav - ior.
Chorus
Gold - en sun-beams 'round me play, Je - sus turns my night to day,
Heav - en seems not far a - way, Since I found my Sav - ior.
3

126 Depth of Mercy

Charles Wesley — SEYMOUR. 7s. — C. M. Von Weber

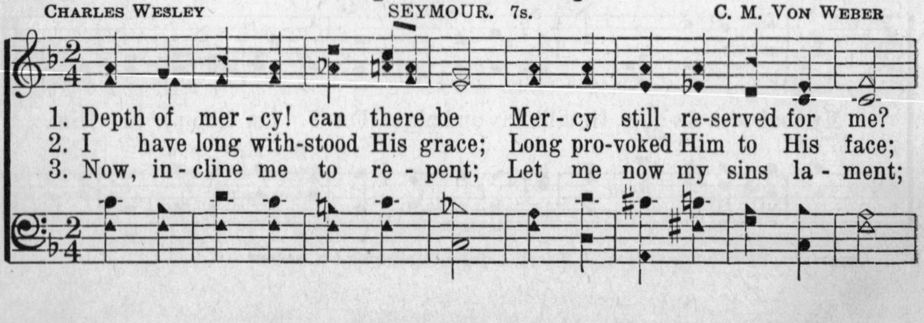
1. Depth of mer - cy! can there be Mer - cy still re-served for me?
2. I have long with-stood His grace; Long pro-voked Him to His face;
3. Now, in - cline me to re - pent; Let me now my sins la - ment;

Depth of Mercy

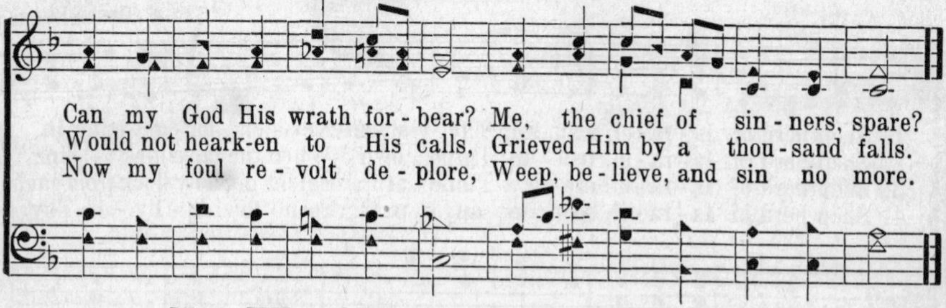
Can my God His wrath for - bear? Me, the chief of sin - ners, spare?
Would not heark-en to His calls, Grieved Him by a thou - sand falls.
Now my foul re - volt de - plore, Weep, be - lieve, and sin no more.

Not What These Hands Have Done 127

HORATIUS BONAR

JAMES MCGRANAHAN

1. Not what these hands have done, Can save this guilt - y soul;
2. Not what I feel or do, Can give me peace with God;
3. Thy love to me, O God, Not mine, O Lord, to Thee,
4. No oth - er work save Thine, No mean - er blood, will do;
5. I praise the God of grace, I trust His love and might;
Not what this toil - ing flesh has borne, Can make my spir - it whole.
Not all my prayers, or sigh, or tears, Can ease my aw - ful load.
Can rid me of this dark un - rest, And set my spir - it free.
No strength, save that which is di - vine, Can bear me safe - ly through.
He calls me His, I call Him mine; My God, my joy, my light!
REFRAIN
Thy work a - lone, my Sav - ior, Can ease this weight of sin;
Thy blood a - lone, O Lamb of God, Can give me peace with - in.

128 Shepherd of Israel

A. A. P. | Geo. C. Stebbins

1. Shep-herd of Is-ra-el, keep-ing Thy sheep—Nev-er for-get-ting in
2. Shep-herd of Is-ra-el, true to Thine own When the false hire-ling
3. Shep-herd of Is-ra-el! strong is Thine arm, Shield-ing Thy flock from each
4. Shep-herd of Is-ra-el, soon to ap-pear, Soon to de-liv-er Thy
slum-ber or sleep; Fold-ing them gen-tly when night com-eth on,
serv-ant hath flown; Lay-ing Thy life down their par-don to win,
threat-en-ing harm; Gath'ring the lambs as they fal-ter and fall,
"lit-tle flock" here! Just to be-hold Thee their rich-est re-ward—
CHORUS
Go-ing be-fore them at break of the dawn!
Shed-ding Thy blood to re-deem them from sin! Shep-herd of Is-ra-el!
Safe in Thy bos-om en-fold-ing them all!
Shep-herd of Is-ra-el, Je-sus, their Lord!
Shep-herd of love! Watching Thy flock from the glo-ry a-bove! Know-ing how
wea-ry their wil-der-ness way; Pray-ing for them—ev-er liv-ing to pray!

The Lord is My Shepherd

23rd Psalm

Arr. from KOSCHAT by E. O. E.

1. The Lord is my Shep-herd, no want shall I know; I feed in green pas - tures, safe-fold - ed I rest; He lead - eth my soul where the still wa - ters flow, Re - stores me when wan-d'ring, re-deems when op-pressed; Re - stores me when wan-d'ring, re - deems when op-pressed.
2. Thro' the valley and shad- ow of death tho' I stray, Since Thou art my Guard-ian, no e - vil I fear; Thy rod shall de-fend me, Thy staff be my stay; No harm can be - fall with my Com-fort - er near; No harm can be - fall with my Com - fort - er near.
3. In the midst of af - flic - tion my ta - ble is spread; With blessings un-meas-ured my cup run-neth o'er; With per-fume and oil Thou a-noint-est my head; O what shall I ask of Thy prov - i - dence more? O what shall I ask of Thy prov - i - dence more?
4. Let good-ness and mer - cy, my boun - ti - ful God, Still fol - low my steps till I meet Thee a - bove: I seek by the path which my fore - fa-thers trod, Thro' the land of their so - journ, Thy king-dom of love; Thro' the land of their so - journ, Thy king-dom of love.

130 Welcome for Me

FANNY J. CROSBY — WM J. KIRKPATRICK

1. Like a bird on the deep, far a-way from its nest, I had wandered, my
2. I am safe in the ark; I have fold-ed my wings On the bos-om of
3. I am safe in the ark, and I dread not the storm, Tho' a-round me the
Sav-ior, from Thee; But Thy dear lov-ing voice called me home to Thy breast,
mer-cy di-vine; I am filled with the light of Thy pres-ence so bright,
sur-ges may roll; I will look to the skies, where the day nev-er dies,
CHORUS
And I knew there was wel-come for me.
And the joy that will ev-er be mine. Wel-come for me,
I will sing of the joy in my soul.
Sav-ior, from Thee; A smile and a wel-come for me; Now, like a dove,
I rest in Thy love, And find a sweet ref-uge in Thee. . . .
in Thee.

Yield Not to Temptation

H. R. P. — Dr. H. R. Palmer

1. Yield not to temp-ta-tion, For yield-ing is sin; Each vic-t'ry will help you Some oth-er to win; Fight man-ful-ly on-ward, Dark pas-sions sub-due; Look ev-er to Je-sus, He'll car-ry you through.
2. Shun e-vil com-pan-ions, Bad lan-guage dis-dain; God's name hold in rev-'rence, Nor take it in vain; Be thought-ful and ear-nest, Kind-heart-ed and true; Look ev-er to Je-sus, He'll car-ry you through.
3. To him that o'er-com-eth, God giv-eth a crown; Thro' faith we will con-quer, Tho' oft-en cast down; He who is our Sav-ior, Our strength will re-new; Look ev-er to Je-sus, He'll car-ry you through.
Chorus
Ask the Sav-ior to help you, Com-fort, strength-en, and keep you;
He is will-ing to aid you, He will car-ry you through.

132 If Thou Shalt Confess

JOHN R. CLEMENTS

B. D. ACKLEY

1. O lost one in the wilds of sin, So long from God a - way;
2. So man - y roads a - cross the marsh But lead to vales of night;
3. How man - y paths at first seem fair, That lead to loss and pain!
Be - fore thee lies an o - pen path, Where thou canst walk to - day.
This one, "the true and liv - ing way," Ends in the fade - less light.
This one yields com - fort all the way, The end e - ter - nal gain.
CHORUS
For if thou shalt con - fess the Lord, . . . And in thine
the Lord,
heart be - lieve; . . . . His Word is sure, it stands se-
thine heart,
And in thine heart be - lieve,
rit.
cure, . . . "Thou shalt be saved," . . . . "Thou shalt be saved."
se - cure,
"Thou shalt be saved,"

There Shall Be Showers of Blessing

El Nathan James McGranahan

1. "There shall be show-ers of bless-ing:" This is the prom-ise of love;
2. "There shall be show-ers of bless-ing"–Pre-cious re-viv-ing a-gain:
3. "There shall be show-ers of bless-ing:" Send them up-on us, O Lord;
4. "There shall be show-ers of bless-ing:" Oh, that to-day they might fall,
There shall be sea-sons re-fresh-ing, Sent from the Sav-ior a-bove.
O-ver the hills and the val-leys, Sound of a-bun-dance of rain.
Grant to us now a re-fresh-ing, Come, and now hon-or Thy Word.
Now as to God we're con-fess-ing, Now as on Je-sus we call!
Chorus
Show - - ers of bless-ing, Show-ers of bless-ing we need:
Show-ers, show-ers of bless-ing,
Mer-cy-drops round us are fall-ing, But for the show-ers we plead.

Have You Sought?

FANNY J. CROSBY | IRA D. SANKEY

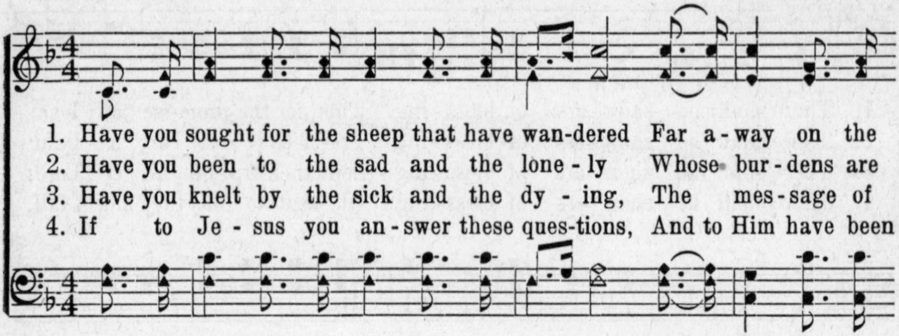
1. Have you sought for the sheep that have wan-dered Far a-way on the
2. Have you been to the sad and the lone-ly Whose bur-dens are
3. Have you knelt by the sick and the dy-ing, The mes-sage of
4. If to Je-sus you an-swer these ques-tions, And to Him have been

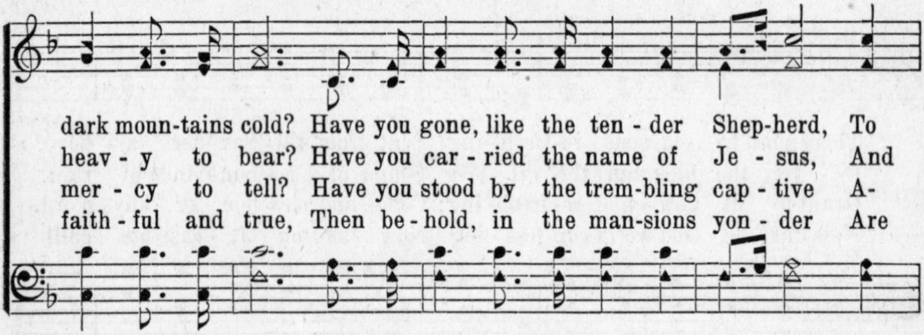
dark moun-tains cold? Have you gone, like the ten-der Shep-herd, To
heav-y to bear? Have you car-ried the name of Je-sus, And
mer-cy to tell? Have you stood by the trem-bling cap-tive A-
faith-ful and true, Then be-hold, in the man-sions yon-der Are

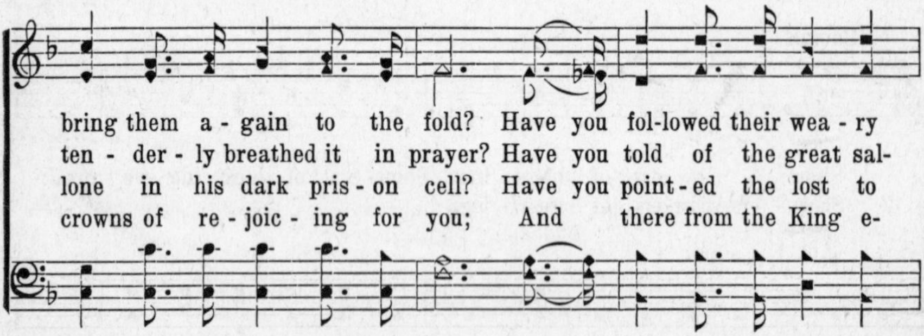
bring them a-gain to the fold? Have you fol-lowed their wea-ry
ten-der-ly breathed it in prayer? Have you told of the great sal-
lone in his dark pris-on cell? Have you point-ed the lost to
crowns of re-joic-ing for you; And there from the King e-

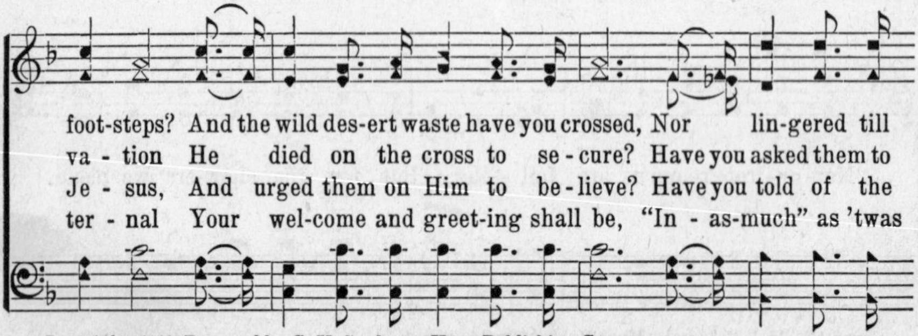
foot-steps? And the wild des-ert waste have you crossed, Nor lin-gered till
va-tion He died on the cross to se-cure? Have you asked them to
Je-sus, And urged them on Him to be-lieve? Have you told of the
ter-nal Your wel-come and greet-ing shall be, "In-as-much" as 'twas

Have You Sought?

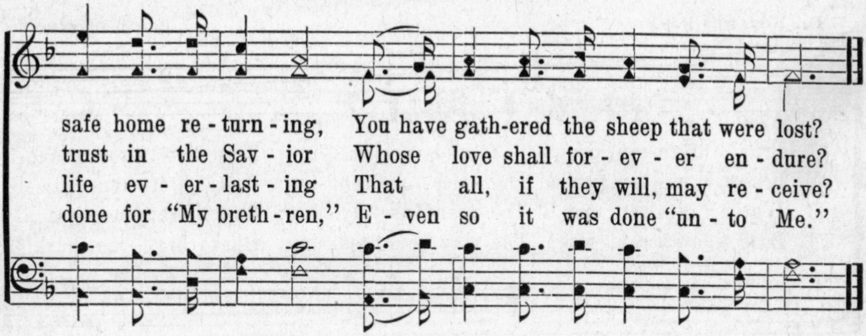
safe home re - turn - ing, You have gath-ered the sheep that were lost?
trust in the Sav - ior Whose love shall for - ev - er en - dure?
life ev - er - last - ing That all, if they will, may re - ceive?
done for "My breth - ren," E - ven so it was done "un - to Me."

Pray for the Wanderer

135

C. M. HOTT

A. S. KIEFFER

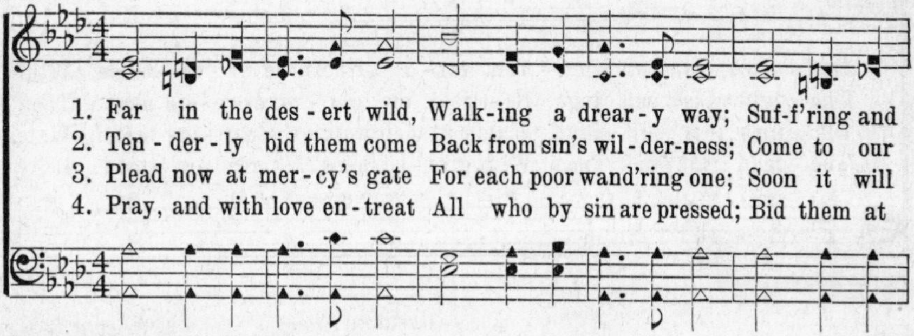
1. Far in the des - ert wild, Walk-ing a drear - y way; Suf-f'ring and
2. Ten - der - ly bid them come Back from sin's wil - der-ness; Come to our
3. Plead now at mer - cy's gate For each poor wand'ring one; Soon it will
4. Pray, and with love en - treat All who by sin are pressed; Bid them at

CHORUS

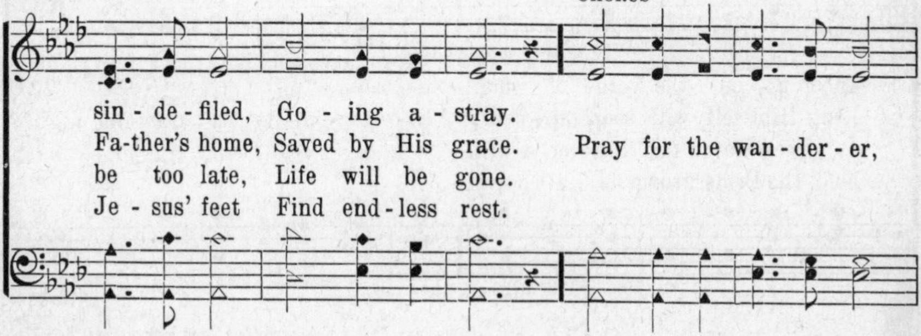
sin - de - filed, Go - ing a - stray.
Fa-ther's home, Saved by His grace.
be too late, Life will be gone.
Je - sus' feet Find end - less rest.
Pray for the wan - der - er,

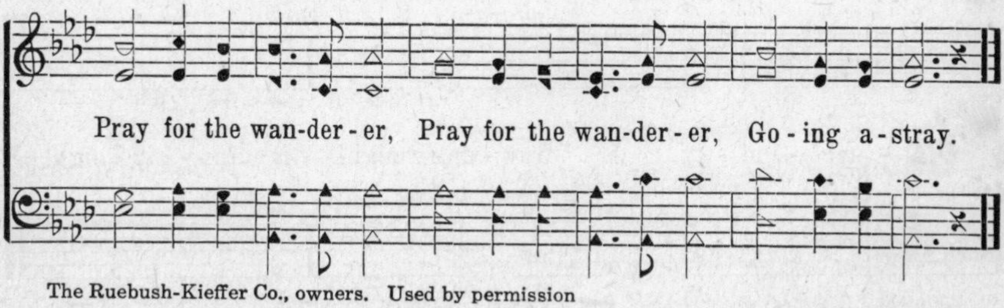
Pray for the wan-der - er, Pray for the wan-der - er, Go - ing a - stray.

Pray, Brethren, Pray!

Dr. Horatius Bonar | Philip Phillips

Moderato
1. Pray, breth-ren, pray! The sands are fall-ing; Pray, breth-ren, pray!
2. Praise, breth-ren, praise! The skies are rend-ing; Praise, breth-ren, praise!
3. Watch, breth-ren, watch! The years are dy-ing; Watch, breth-ren, watch!
4. Look, breth-ren, look! The day is break-ing; Hark, breth-ren, hark!
Allegro
God's voice is call-ing. Yon tur-ret strikes the dy-ing chime; We
The fight is end-ing. Be-hold, the glo-ry draw-eth near, The
Old time is fly-ing! Watch as men watch the part-ing breath, Watch
The dead are wak-ing, With gird-ed loins all read-y stand; Be-
kneel up-on the verge of time:
King Him-self will soon ap-pear:
as men watch for life or death:
hold, the Bride-groom is at hand!
Refrain Slow
E-ter-ni-ty is draw-ing nigh!
ritard.
After last verse only.
adagio
E-ter-ni-ty is draw-ing nigh! is draw-ing nigh!

Throw Out the Life-Line

EDWARD S. UFFORD

E. S. UFFORD
Arr. by GEORGE C. STEBBINS

1. Throw out the Life-Line a - cross the dark wave, There is a broth - er whom
2. Throw out the Life-Line with hand quick and strong: Why do you tar - ry, why
3. Throw out the Life-Line to dan-ger-fraught men, Sink-ing in an-guish where
4. Soon will the sea - son of res - cue be o'er, Soon will they drift to e-
some one should save; Somebody's broth-er! oh, who then, will dare To throw out the
lin - ger so long? See! he is sink ing; oh; has-ten to-day—And out with the
you've nev-er been: Winds of temp-ta-tion and bil-lows of woe Will soon hurl them
ter - ni - ty's shore, Haste then, my brother, no time for de-lay, But throw out the
CHORUS.
Life-Line, his per - il to share?
Life-Boat! a-way, then, a-way! Throw out the Life-Line! Throw out the Life-Line!
out where the dark wa-ters flow.
Life-Line and save them to-day.
1
2
Some one is drift-ing a - way; Some one is sink-ing to - day. A - MEN.

138 Galilee, Bright Galilee

William F. Sherwin — William F. Sherwin

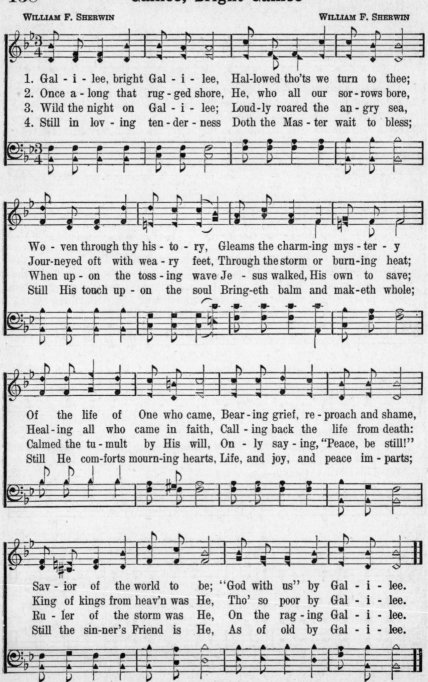

1. Gal - i - lee, bright Gal - i - lee, Hal-lowed tho'ts we turn to thee;
2. Once a - long that rug - ged shore, He, who all our sor - rows bore,
3. Wild the night on Gal - i - lee; Loud-ly roared the an - gry sea,
4. Still in lov - ing ten - der - ness Doth the Mas - ter wait to bless;

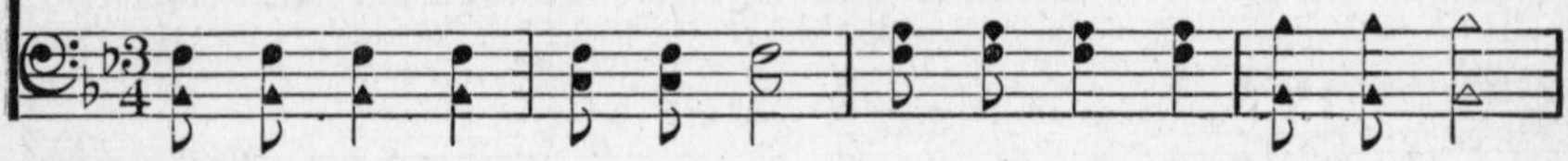

Wo - ven through thy his - to - ry, Gleams the charm-ing mys - ter - y
Jour-neyed oft with wea - ry feet, Through the storm or burn-ing heat;
When up - on the toss - ing wave Je - sus walked, His own to save;
Still His touch up - on the soul Bring-eth balm and mak-eth whole;

Of the life of One who came, Bear - ing grief, re - proach and shame,
Heal - ing all who came in faith, Call - ing back the life from death:
Calmed the tu - mult by His will, On - ly say - ing, "Peace, be still!"
Still He com-forts mourn-ing hearts, Life, and joy, and peace im - parts;

Sav - ior of the world to be; "God with us" by Gal - i - lee.
King of kings from heav'n was He, Tho' so poor by Gal - i - lee.
Ru - ler of the storm was He, On the rag - ing Gal - i - lee.
Still the sin-ner's Friend is He, As of old by Gal - i - lee.

Verily, Verily

JAMES McGRANAHAN — JAMES McGRANAHAN

1. Oh, what a Sav - ior, that He died for me! From con - dem-
2. All my in - iq - ui - ties on Him were laid, All my in-
3. Though poor and need - y I can trust my Lord, Though weak and
4. Though all un - wor - thy, yet I will not doubt, For him that
na - tion He hath made me free; "He that be - liev - eth on the
debt - ed - ness by Him was paid; All who be - lieve on Him, the
sin - ful I be - lieve His Word; Oh, glad mes - sage! ev - 'ry
com - eth, He will not cast out; "He that be - liev - eth," oh, the
Son," saith He, "Hath ev - er - last - ing life."
Lord hath said, "Hath ev - er - last - ing life."
child of God "Hath ev - er - last - ing life."
good news shout, "Hath ev - er - last - ing life!"
CHORUS
"Ver - i - ly, ver - i - ly,
I say un - to you," "Ver - i - ly, ver - i - ly," mes - sage ev - er new;
"He that be - liev - eth on the Son," 'tis true, "Hath ev - er - last - ing life."

"Whosoever Will"

P. P. B. | P. P. Bliss

1. "Who-so-ev-er hear - eth," shout, shout the sound! Spread the bless-ed ti-dings
2. Who-so-ev-er com - eth, need not de - lay, Now the door is o - pen,
3. "Who-so-ev-er will!" the prom-ise is se-cure; "Who-so-ev - er will," for-
all the world a-round; Tell the joy-ful news wher - ev - er man is found,
en - ter while you may; Je - sus is the true, the on - ly Liv - ing Way:
ev - er must en-dure; "Who-so - ev - er will!" 'tis life for - ev - er - more;
Chorus
"Who-so-ev - er will may come." "Who-so-ev - er will, who - so-ev - er will!"
Send the proc - la - ma - tion o - ver vale and hill; 'Tis a lov - ing
Fa - ther calls the wan-d'rer home: "Who - so - ev - er will may come."

Jesus Will!

Ina Duley Ogdon — B. D. Ackley

1. Who will o-pen mer-cy's door? Je-sus will! Je-sus will!
2. Who can take a-way my sin? Je-sus will! Je-sus will!
3. Who can conquer doubts and fears? Je-sus will! Je-sus will!
4. Who will be my dear-est Friend? Je-sus will! Je-sus will!
Je-sus will! Je-sus will!
As for par-don I im-plore? Je-sus, bless-ed Je-sus will!
Make me pure, with-out, with-in? Je-sus, bless-ed Je-sus will!
Share my joys and dry my tears? Je-sus, bless-ed Je-sus will!
Love and keep me to the end? Je-sus, bless-ed Je-sus will!
Refrain
Je-sus will, Je-sus will! Yes, your lov-ing Sav-ior will;
sure-ly will;
He will each and ev'ry need ful-fill, Je-sus, bless-ed Je-sus will!

Into My Heart

H. D. C. HARRY D. CLARKE

1. Come in - to my heart, blessed Je - sus, Come in - to my heart, I pray;
2. Come in - to my heart, blessed Je - sus, I need Thee thro' life's dreary way;
3. Come in - to my heart, blessed Je - sus, And take all my guilt a - way;
4. Come in - to my heart, blessed Je - sus, O cleanse and il - lu-mine my soul;
My soul is so trou-bled and wea - ry, Come in - to my heart to - day.
The bur-den of sin is so heav - y, Come in - to my heart to stay.
Then spotless I'll stand in Thy pres-ence, When breaks Thine e-ter-nal day.
Fill me with Thy won-der-ful Spir - it, Come in and take full con-trol.
CHORUS
In - to my heart, in - to my heart, Come in - to my heart, Lord Je - sus;
Come in to-day, Come in to stay, Come in-to my heart, Lord Je - sus.

Jesus of Nazareth Passeth By

Miss Etta Campbell — T. E. Perkins

1. What means this ea - ger, anxious throng, Which moves with bus-y haste a-long—
2. Who is this Je - sus? Why should He The cit - y move so might - i - ly?
3. Je - sus! 'tis He who once be - low Man's pathway trod,'mid pain and woe;
4. A - gain He comes! from place to place His ho - ly foot-prints we can trace.
5. Ho! all ye heav - y - la - den, come! Here's par-don, comfort, rest, and home!
6. But if you still this call re - fuse, And all His won-drous love a - buse,

These wondrous gath'rings day by day? What means this strange commotion, pray?
A pass - ing stran-ger, has He skill To move the mul - ti - tude at will?
And bur-dened ones, wher-e'er He came, Bro't out their sick, and deaf, and lame.
He paus - eth at our threshold—nay, He en - ters—con - de-scends to stay.
Ye wan-d'rers from a Fa-ther's face! Re - turn, ac - cept His pro-ffered grace.
Soon will He sad - ly from you turn, Your bit - ter prayer for par - don spurn.

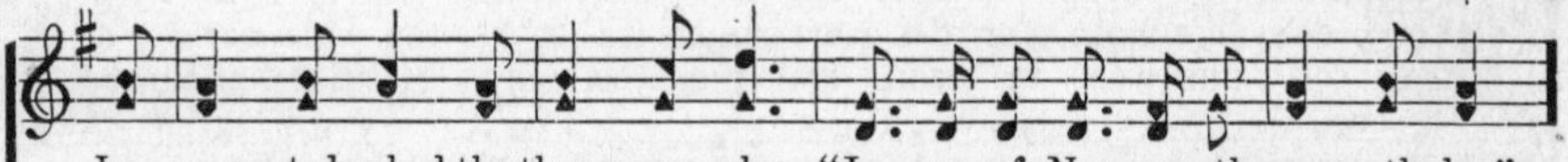

In ac-cents hushed the throng re - ply: "Je - sus of Naz - a-reth pass - eth by,"
A - gain the stir-ring notes re - ply: "Je - sus of Naz - a-reth pass - eth by,"
The blind re-joiced to hear the cry: "Je - sus of Naz - a-reth pass - eth by,"
Shall we not glad - ly raise the cry—"Je - sus of Naz - a-reth pass - eth by,"
Ye tempt - ed ones, there's ref-uge nigh: "Je - sus of Naz - a-reth pass - eth by,"
"Too late! too late!" will be the cry—"Je - sus of Naz - a-reth *has passed by,*"

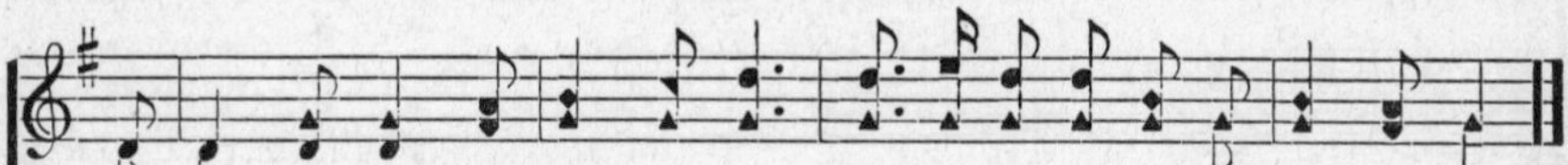

In ac-cents hushed the throng re - ply: "Je - sus of Naz - a-reth pass - eth by."
A - gain the stir - ring notes re - ply: "Je - sus of Naz - a-reth pass - eth by."
The blind re-joiced to hear the cry: "Je - sus of Naz - a-reth pass - eth by."
Shall we not glad - ly raise the cry—"Je - sus of Naz - a-reth pass - eth by."
Ye tempt - ed ones, there's ref-uge nigh: "Je - sus of Naz - a-reth pass - eth by."
"Too late! too late!" will be the cry—"Je - sus of Naz - a-reth *has passed by.*"

144 He Seeks His Wandering Sheep Today

Mrs. Martha Mills Newton — J. Henry Showalter

1. The Shep-herd's heart is sad-dened, His sheep have gone a-stray;
2. Thro' bri-ers, thorns, and bram-bles, He seeks with anx-ious heart,
3. He's call-ing for thee, lost one, Can you not hear His voice?
Thro' sum-mer's heat, and win-ter's cold, He seeks His sheep al-way.
O'er moun-tain, vale, or for-est wild, Or in the crowd-ed mart.
Then an-swer to His lov-ing call, Go meet Him and re-joice.
Some wan-d'ring sheep He's seek-ing now, Say broth-er, is it you?
O'er o-cean's main, o'er des-ert sands, He seeks the wide world o'er;
Are you not wea-ry wan-der-ing Out in the storm and cold?
Are you safe shel-tered in the fold, Or are you wan-d'ring too?
In gild-ed pal-ace of the rich; In cot-tage of the poor.
A-rise, and seek your Shep-herd's face, Re-turn un-to the fold.
Refrain
He seeks His wand'ring sheep, Out in the storm and cold;
He seeks His wan-d'ring, wan-d'ring sheep to-day, Out in the storm and cold;

He Seeks His Wandering Sheep Today

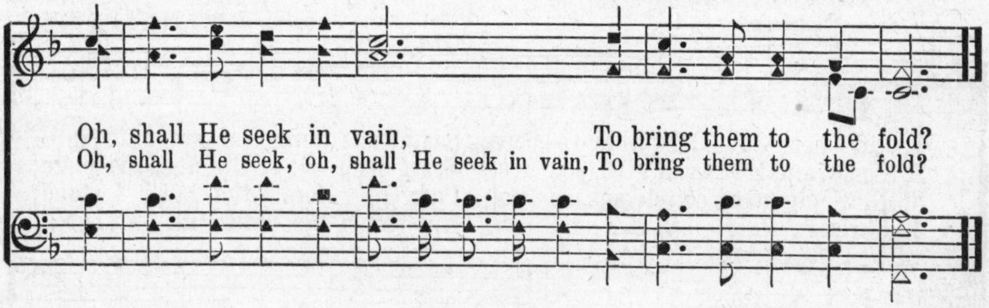
Oh, shall He seek in vain, To bring them to the fold?
Oh, shall He seek, oh, shall He seek in vain, To bring them to the fold?

At Calvary

145

WM. R. NEWELL

D. B. TOWNER

1. Years I spent in van - i - ty and pride, Car - ing not my Lord was
2. By God's Word at last my sin I learned; Then I trem-bled at the
3. Now I've giv'n to Je - sus ev - 'ry - thing, Now I glad - ly own Him
4. Oh, the love that drew sal - va - tion's plan! Oh, the grace that bro't it
cru - ci - fied, Know-ing not it was for me He died On Cal - va - ry.
law I'd spurned, Till my guilt-y soul im-plor-ing turned To Cal - va - ry.
as my King, Now my raptured soul can on - ly sing Of Cal - va - ry.
down to man! Oh, the might-y gulf that God did span At Cal - va - ry!
CHORUS
Mer - cy there was great, and grace was free; Par - don there was mul - ti -
plied to me; There my burdened soul found lib-er - ty, At Cal - va - ry.

146 Christ Receiveth Sinful Men

Arr. from NEUMASTER, 1671

JAMES MCGRANAHAN

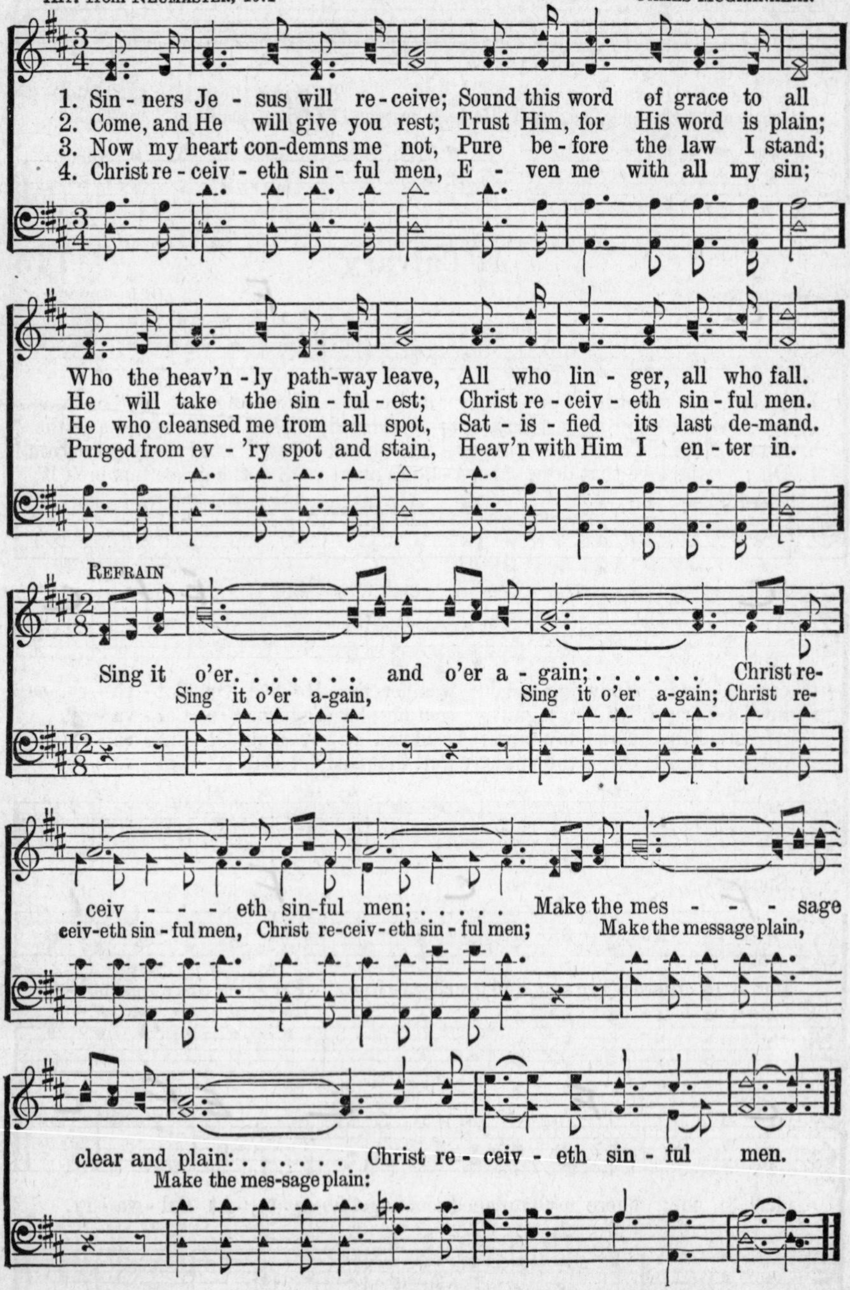
3/4
1. Sin-ners Je - sus will re-ceive; Sound this word of grace to all
2. Come, and He will give you rest; Trust Him, for His word is plain;
3. Now my heart con-demns me not, Pure be-fore the law I stand;
4. Christ re-ceiv - eth sin - ful men, E - ven me with all my sin;
Who the heav'n-ly path-way leave, All who lin - ger, all who fall.
He will take the sin - ful - est; Christ re - ceiv - eth sin - ful men.
He who cleansed me from all spot, Sat - is - fied its last de-mand.
Purged from ev - 'ry spot and stain, Heav'n with Him I en - ter in.
REFRAIN
12/8
Sing it o'er. . . . . . . and o'er a - gain; . . . . . . Christ re-
Sing it o'er a-gain, Sing it o'er a-gain; Christ re-
ceiv - - - eth sin-ful men; . . . . . Make the mes - - - sage
ceiv-eth sin - ful men, Christ re-ceiv - eth sin - ful men; Make the message plain,
clear and plain: . . . . Christ re - ceiv - eth sin - ful men.
Make the mes-sage plain:

What Will You Do With Jesus? 147

Anon. M. L. Stocks

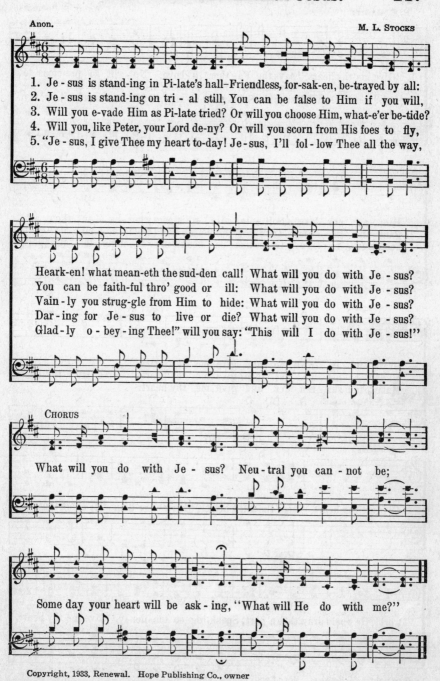

1. Je - sus is stand-ing in Pi-late's hall–Friendless, for-sak-en, be-trayed by all:
2. Je - sus is stand-ing on tri - al still, You can be false to Him if you will,
3. Will you e-vade Him as Pi-late tried? Or will you choose Him, what-e'er be-tide?
4. Will you, like Peter, your Lord de-ny? Or will you scorn from His foes to fly,
5. "Je - sus, I give Thee my heart to-day! Je - sus, I'll fol - low Thee all the way,

Heark-en! what mean-eth the sud-den call! What will you do with Je - sus?
You can be faith-ful thro' good or ill: What will you do with Je - sus?
Vain-ly you strug-gle from Him to hide: What will you do with Je - sus?
Dar - ing for Je - sus to live or die? What will you do with Je - sus?
Glad - ly o - bey - ing Thee!" will you say: "This will I do with Je - sus!"

CHORUS

What will you do with Je - sus? Neu - tral you can - not be;

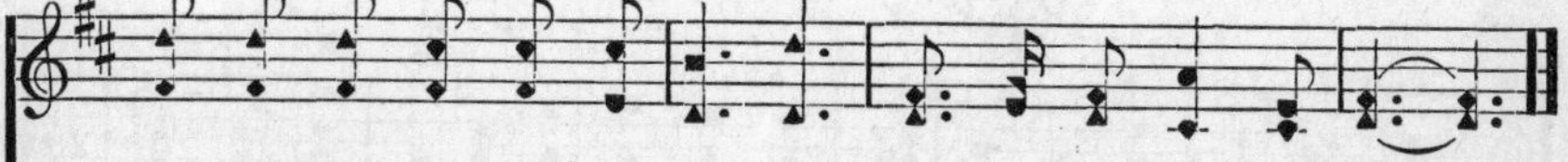

Some day your heart will be ask - ing, "What will He do with me?"

148 Give Me Thy Heart

E. E. HEWITT ANNIE F. BOURNE

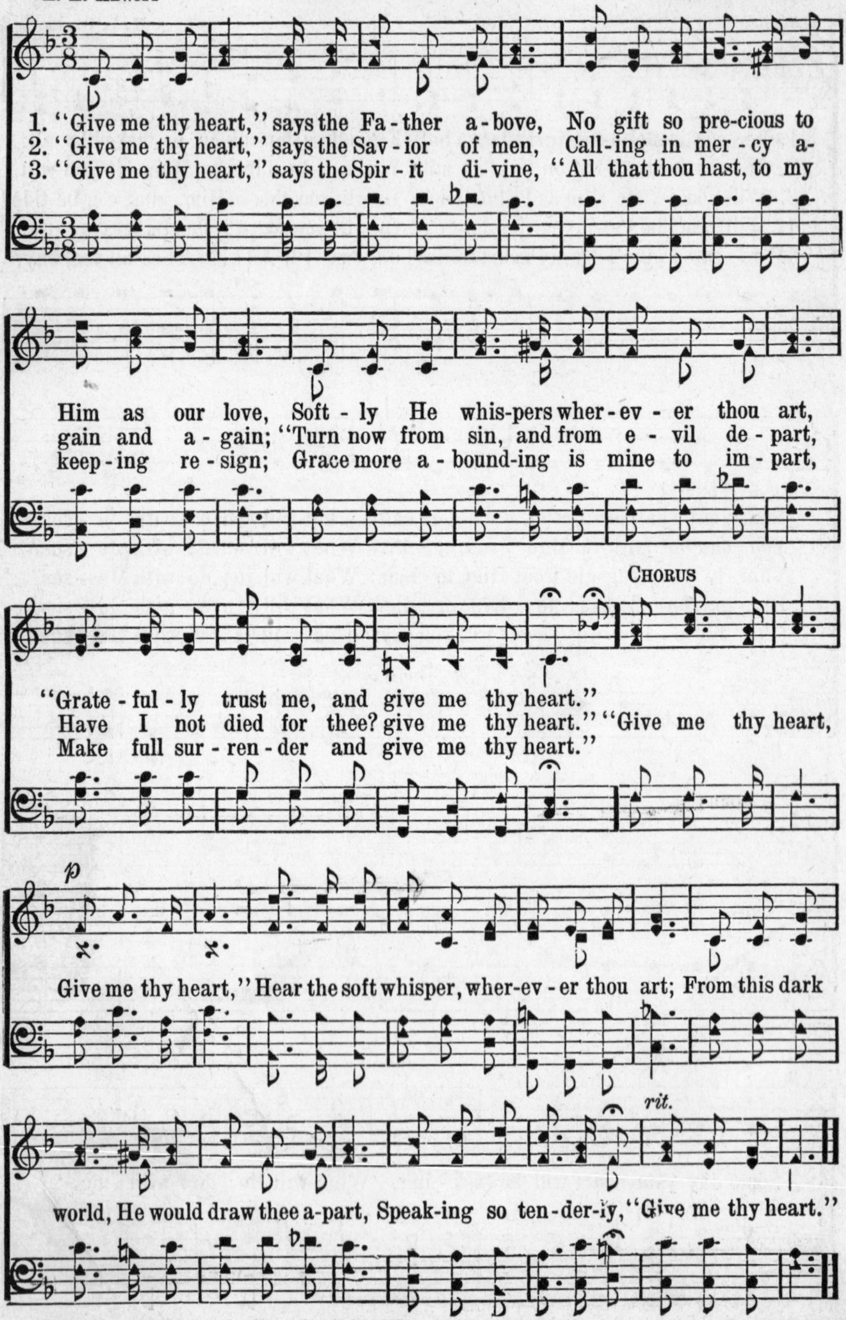
1. "Give me thy heart," says the Fa-ther a-bove, No gift so pre-cious to
2. "Give me thy heart," says the Sav-ior of men, Call-ing in mer-cy a-
3. "Give me thy heart," says the Spir-it di-vine, "All that thou hast, to my
Him as our love, Soft-ly He whis-pers wher-ev-er thou art,
gain and a-gain; "Turn now from sin, and from e-vil de-part,
keep-ing re-sign; Grace more a-bound-ing is mine to im-part,
CHORUS
"Grate-ful-ly trust me, and give me thy heart."
Have I not died for thee? give me thy heart." "Give me thy heart,
Make full sur-ren-der and give me thy heart."
p
Give me thy heart," Hear the soft whisper, wher-ev-er thou art; From this dark
rit.
world, He would draw thee a-part, Speak-ing so ten-der-ly, "Give me thy heart."

Only a Sinner

JAMES M. GRAY — D. B. TOWNER

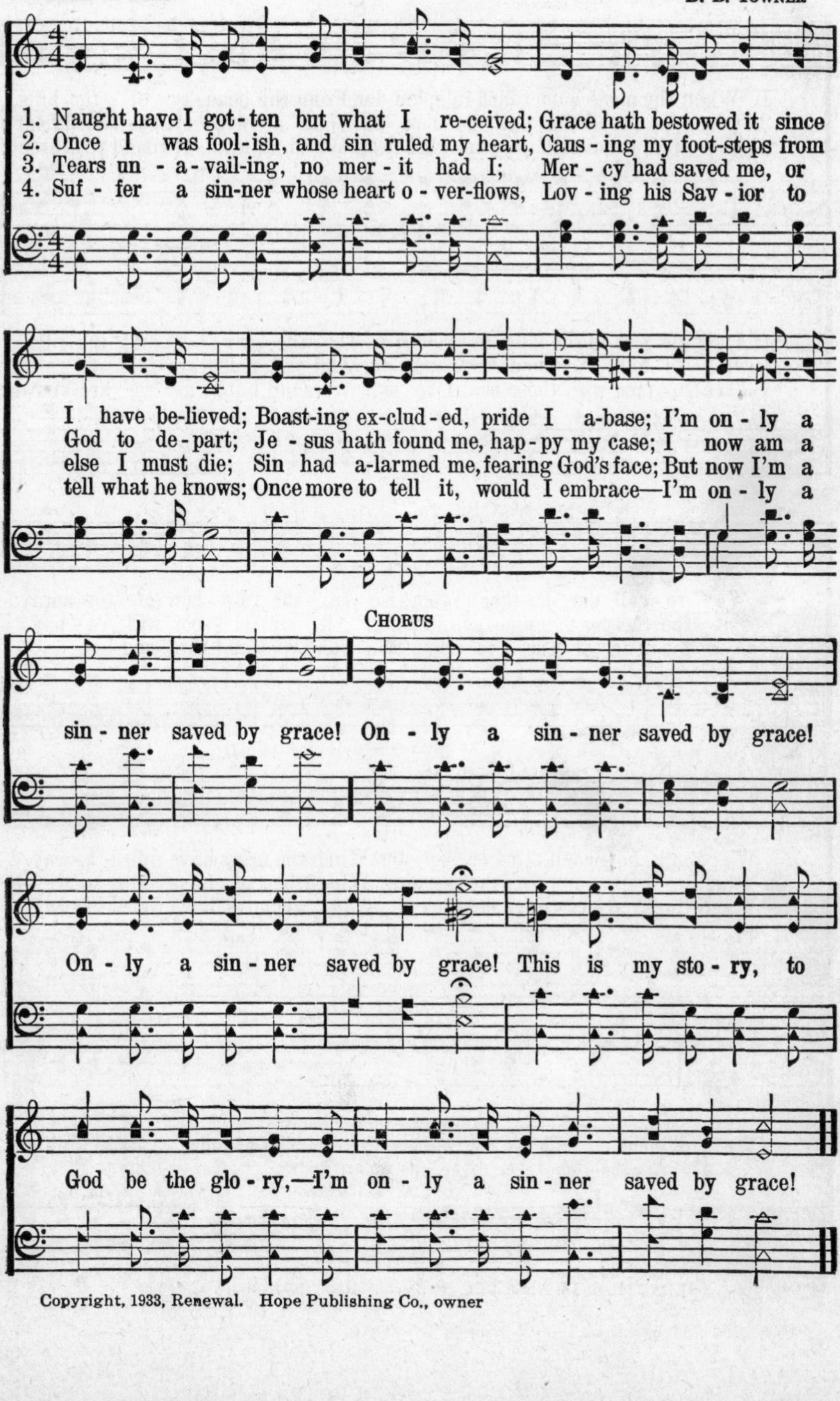
1. Naught have I got-ten but what I re-ceived; Grace hath bestowed it since
2. Once I was fool-ish, and sin ruled my heart, Caus-ing my foot-steps from
3. Tears un-a-vail-ing, no mer-it had I; Mer-cy had saved me, or
4. Suf-fer a sin-ner whose heart o-ver-flows, Lov-ing his Sav-ior to
I have be-lieved; Boast-ing ex-clud-ed, pride I a-base; I'm on-ly a
God to de-part; Je-sus hath found me, hap-py my case; I now am a
else I must die; Sin had a-larmed me, fearing God's face; But now I'm a
tell what he knows; Once more to tell it, would I embrace—I'm on-ly a
sin-ner saved by grace!
CHORUS
On-ly a sin-ner saved by grace!
On-ly a sin-ner saved by grace! This is my sto-ry, to
God be the glo-ry,—I'm on-ly a sin-ner saved by grace!

150 When the Mists Have Rolled Away

ANNIE HERBERT. Arr. IRA D. SANKEY

1. When the mists have rolled in splen-dor From the beau-ty of the hills,
2. Oft we tread the path be-fore us With a wea-ry, bur-dened heart;
3. We shall come with joy and glad-ness, We shall gath-er round the throne;
And the sun-light falls in glad-ness On the riv-er and the rills,
Oft we toil a-mid the shad-ows, And our fields are far a-part:
Face to face with those that love us, We shall know as we are known:
We re-call our Fa-ther's prom-ise In the rain-bow of the spray:
But the Sav-ior's "Come, ye bless-ed," All our la-bor will re-pay,
And the song of our re-demp-tion Shall re-sound thro' end-less day,
rit.
We shall know each oth-er bet-ter When the mists have rolled a-way.
When we gath-er in the morning Where the mists have rolled a-way.
When the shad-ows have de-part-ed, And the mists have rolled a-way.
CHORUS
known, as we are known,
We shall know . . . as we are known, . . . Nev-er-more . . . to walk a-
We shall know as we are known, Nev-er-more to walk a-

When the Mists Have Rolled Away

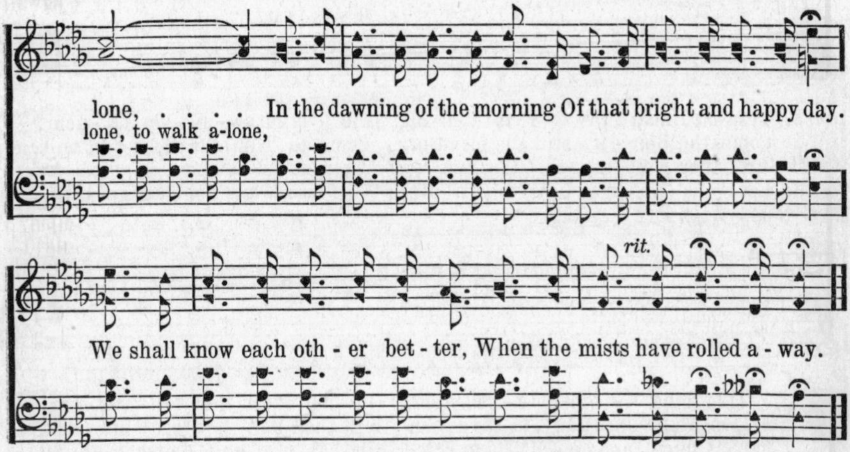
lone, ... In the dawning of the morning Of that bright and happy day.
lone, to walk a-lone,
rit.
We shall know each oth - er bet - ter, When the mists have rolled a - way.

Almost Persuaded

151

P. P. B.

P. P. Bliss

1. "Al - most per-suad - ed," now to be - lieve; "Al - most per-suad - ed,"
2. "Al - most per-suad - ed," come, come to - day; "Al - most per-suad - ed,"
3. "Al - most per-suad - ed," har - vest is past! "Al - most per-suad - ed,"
Christ to re - ceive; Seems now some soul to say, "Go, Spir - it,
turn not a - way; Je - sus in - vites you here, An - gels are
doom comes at last! "Al - most" can - not a - vail; "Al - most" is
go Thy way, Some more con - ven - ient day On.. Thee I'll call."
ling'ring near, Prayers rise from hearts so dear, O... wan - d'rer, come.
but to fail! Sad, sad, that bit - ter wail, "Al - most," but lost.

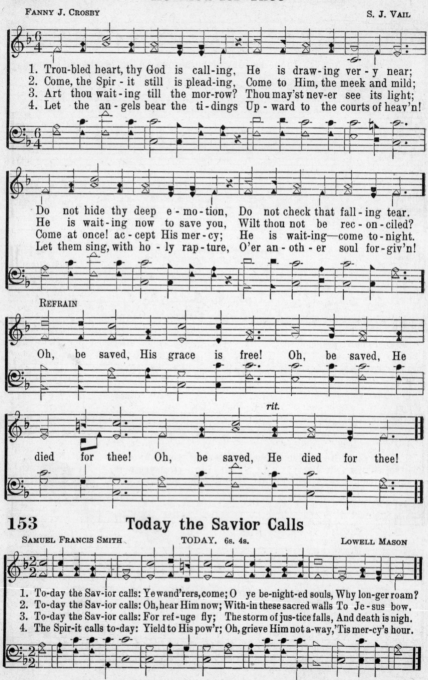

152 He Died for Thee

FANNY J. CROSBY — S. J. VAIL

1. Trou-bled heart, thy God is call-ing, He is draw-ing ver - y near;
2. Come, the Spir - it still is plead-ing, Come to Him, the meek and mild;
3. Art thou wait - ing till the mor-row? Thou may'st nev-er see its light;
4. Let the an-gels bear the ti-dings Up - ward to the courts of heav'n!

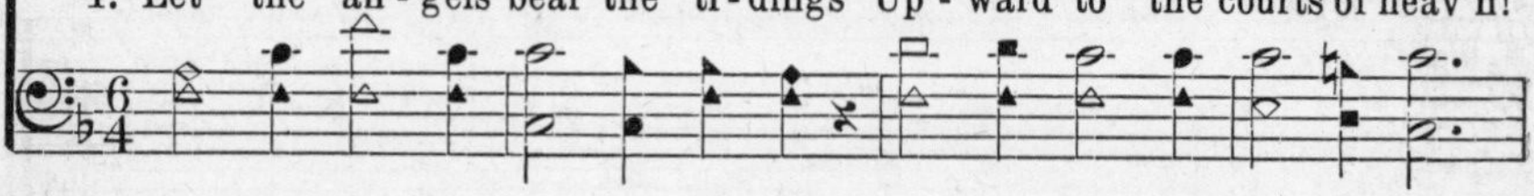

Do not hide thy deep e - mo - tion, Do not check that fall - ing tear.
He is wait - ing now to save you, Wilt thou not be rec - on - ciled?
Come at once! ac - cept His mer - cy; He is wait-ing—come to - night.
Let them sing, with ho - ly rap - ture, O'er an - oth - er soul for - giv'n!

REFRAIN

Oh, be saved, His grace is free! Oh, be saved, He

rit.

died for thee! Oh, be saved, He died for thee!

153 Today the Savior Calls

SAMUEL FRANCIS SMITH — TODAY. 6s. 4s. — LOWELL MASON

1. To-day the Sav-ior calls: Ye wand'rers, come; O ye be-night-ed souls, Why lon-ger roam?
2. To-day the Sav-ior calls: Oh, hear Him now; With-in these sacred walls To Je - sus bow.
3. To-day the Sav-ior calls: For ref - uge fly; The storm of jus-tice falls, And death is nigh.
4. The Spir-it calls to-day: Yield to His pow'r; Oh, grieve Him not a-way, 'Tis mer-cy's hour.

The Ninety and Nine

ELIZABETH C. CLEPHANE · IRA D. SANKEY

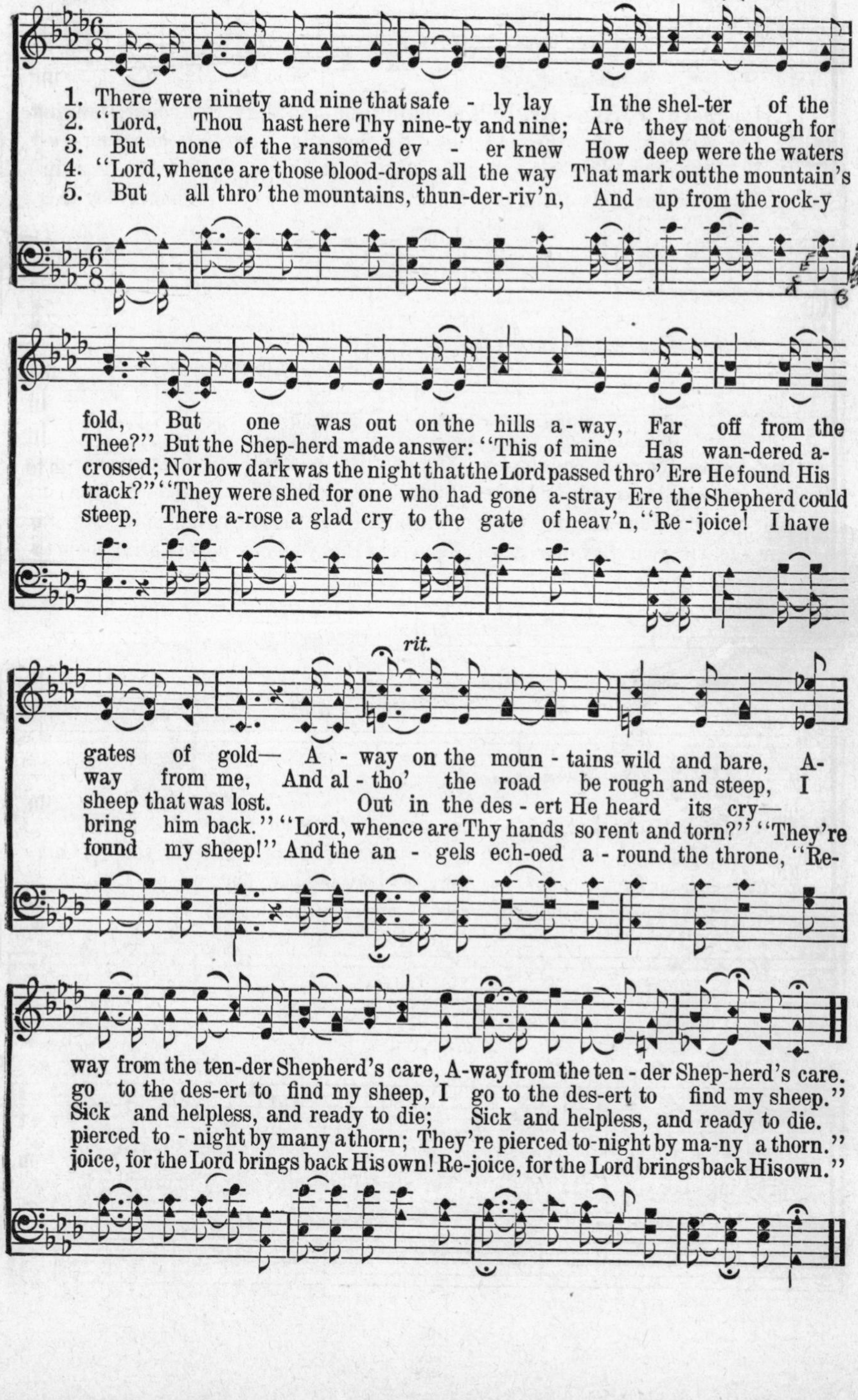

1. There were ninety and nine that safe - ly lay In the shel-ter of the
2. "Lord, Thou hast here Thy nine-ty and nine; Are they not enough for
3. But none of the ransomed ev - er knew How deep were the waters
4. "Lord, whence are those blood-drops all the way That mark out the mountain's
5. But all thro' the mountains, thun-der-riv'n, And up from the rock-y
fold, But one was out on the hills a - way, Far off from the
Thee?" But the Shep-herd made answer: "This of mine Has wan-dered a-
crossed; Nor how dark was the night that the Lord passed thro' Ere He found His
track?" "They were shed for one who had gone a-stray Ere the Shepherd could
steep, There a-rose a glad cry to the gate of heav'n, "Re - joice! I have
rit.
gates of gold— A - way on the moun - tains wild and bare, A-
way from me, And al - tho' the road be rough and steep, I
sheep that was lost. Out in the des - ert He heard its cry—
bring him back." "Lord, whence are Thy hands so rent and torn?" "They're
found my sheep!" And the an - gels ech-oed a - round the throne, "Re-
way from the ten-der Shepherd's care, A-way from the ten - der Shep-herd's care.
go to the des-ert to find my sheep, I go to the des-ert to find my sheep."
Sick and helpless, and ready to die; Sick and helpless, and ready to die.
pierced to - night by many a thorn; They're pierced to-night by ma-ny a thorn."
joice, for the Lord brings back His own! Re-joice, for the Lord brings back His own."

155 I Am Praying for You

S. O'Maley Cluff | Ira D. Sankey

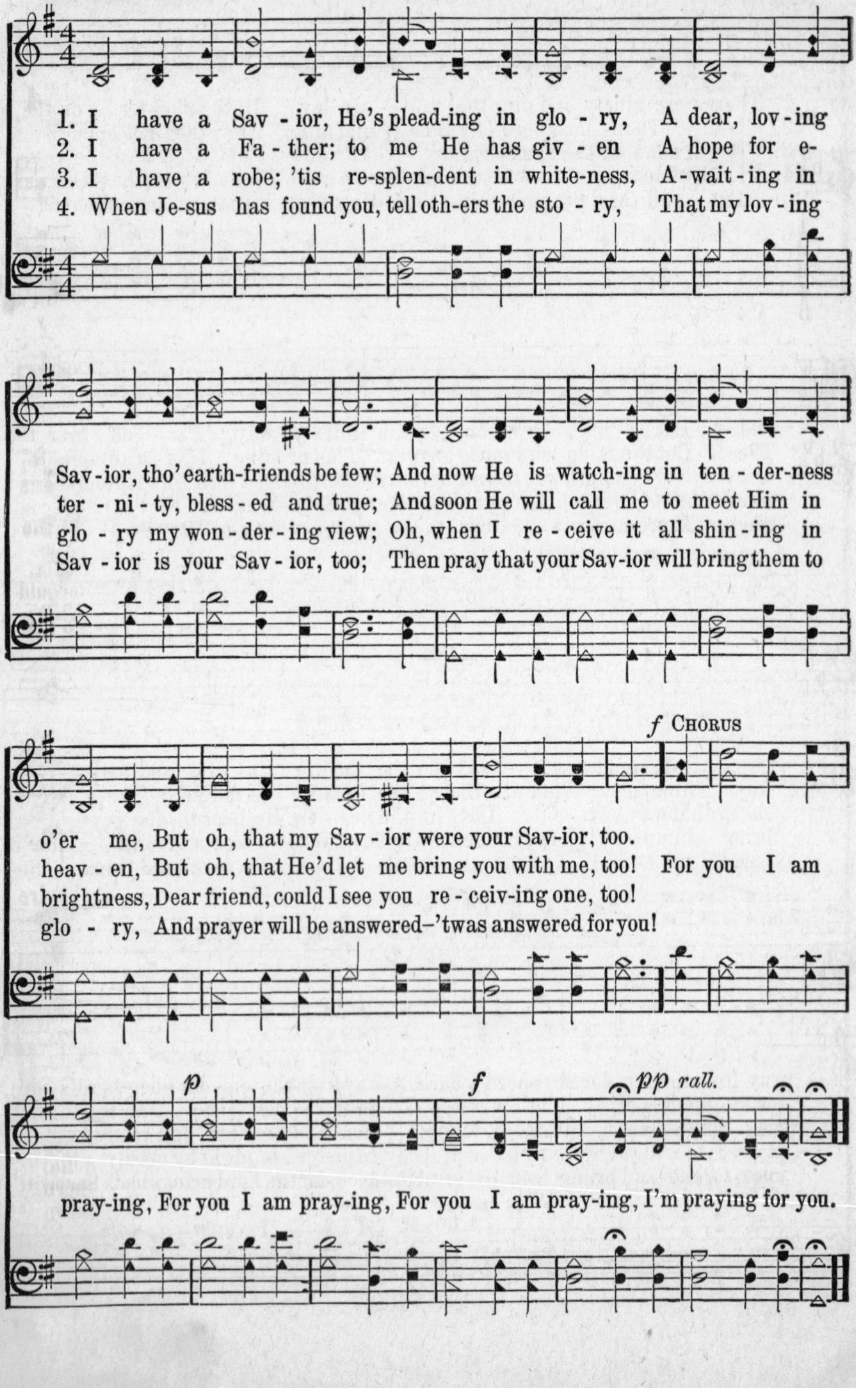
1. I have a Sav - ior, He's plead-ing in glo - ry, A dear, lov-ing
2. I have a Fa - ther; to me He has giv - en A hope for e-
3. I have a robe; 'tis re-splen-dent in white-ness, A-wait-ing in
4. When Je-sus has found you, tell oth-ers the sto - ry, That my lov-ing
Sav-ior, tho' earth-friends be few; And now He is watch-ing in ten - der-ness
ter - ni - ty, bless - ed and true; And soon He will call me to meet Him in
glo - ry my won - der - ing view; Oh, when I re - ceive it all shin - ing in
Sav - ior is your Sav - ior, too; Then pray that your Sav-ior will bring them to
f Chorus
o'er me, But oh, that my Sav - ior were your Sav-ior, too.
heav - en, But oh, that He'd let me bring you with me, too! For you I am
brightness, Dear friend, could I see you re - ceiv-ing one, too!
glo - ry, And prayer will be answered—'twas answered for you!
p
f
pp
rall.
pray-ing, For you I am pray-ing, For you I am pray-ing, I'm praying for you.

Softly and Tenderly

W. L. T. WILL L. THOMPSON

Very slow pp
m
1. Soft - ly and ten-der - ly Je - sus is call-ing, Call - ing for you and for me;
2. Why should we tarry when Jesus is plead-ing, Pleading for you and for me?
3. Time is now fleeting, the moments are passing, Passing from you and from me;
4. Oh! for the won-der-ful love He has promised, Promised for you and for me;
See, on the portals He's waiting and watching, Watching for you and for me.
Why should we linger and heed not His mercies, Mer-cies for you and for me?
Shadows are gathering, death-beds are coming, Com-ing for you and for me.
Tho' we have sinned, He has mercy and pardon, Par-don for you and for me.
CHORUS m
cresc.
Come home,.. come home,..... Ye who are wear-y, come home;...
Come home, come home,
pp ppp
rit.
pp
Ear-nest-ly, ten-der-ly, Je-sus is call-ing, Call-ing, O sin-ner, come home!

157 Open Wide Thy Heart

H. H. Pierson — R. T. Owen

1. O-pen wide thy heart to-day At Je - sus' call; Bid Him en - ter and a-
2. O-pen wide thy heart to-day To Him who pleads; Heed His voice and fol-low
3. O-pen wide thy heart to-day To love di - vine, And a wealth of grace un-
4. O-pen wide thy heart to-day With all its need, And the hun-ger of the
bide, Thy life, thy all.
on Wher-e'er He leads.
told May all be thine.
soul His love will feed.
Refrain
On-ly trust Him, and be still; Let Him work in
be still;
thee His will, For the heart that's opened wide His love shall fill.
His will,
o-pened wide His love, His love shall fill.

158 Behold a Stranger At the Door

BERA. L. M.

Joseph Grigg — John E. Gould

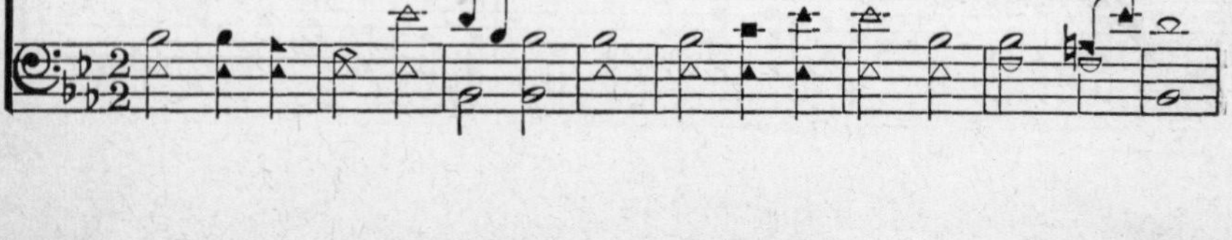
1. Be - hold a Stran-ger at the door! He gen-tly knocks, has knocked be-fore,
2. O love-ly at - ti - tude! He stands With melting heart and la - den hands:
3. But will He prove a friend in - deed? He will; the ver - y friend you need;
4. Rise, touched with grat-i-tude di-vine; Turn out His en - e - my and thine,

Behold a Stranger at the Door

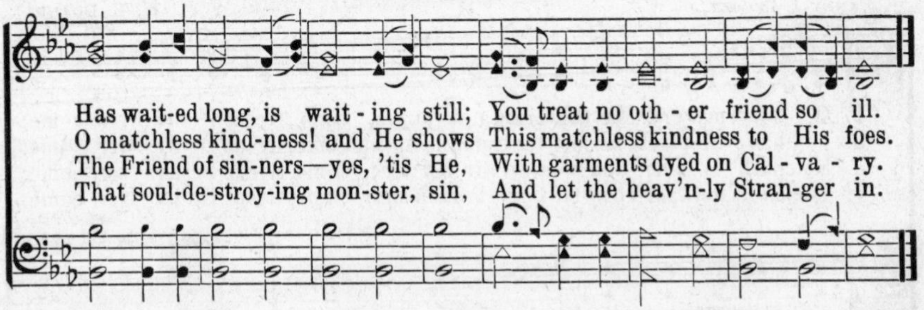
Has wait-ed long, is wait - ing still; You treat no oth - er friend so ill.
O matchless kind-ness! and He shows This matchless kindness to His foes.
The Friend of sin-ners—yes, 'tis He, With garments dyed on Cal - va - ry.
That soul-de-stroy-ing mon-ster, sin, And let the heav'n-ly Stran-ger in.

Sinners, Turn; Why Will Ye Die? 159

CHAS. WESLEY HOLLINGSIDE. 7s. D. JOHN B. DYKES

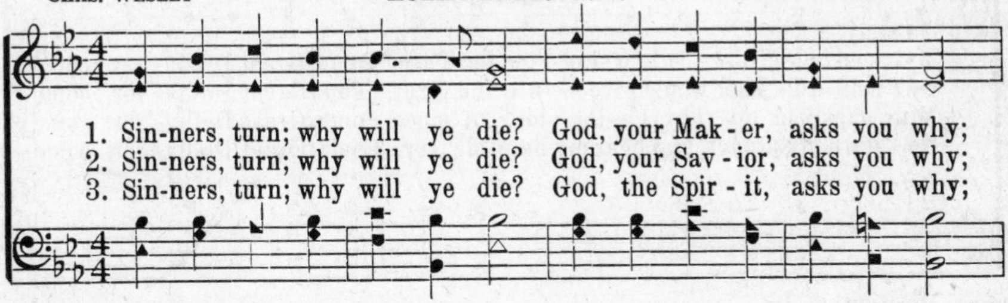
1. Sin-ners, turn; why will ye die? God, your Mak - er, asks you why;
2. Sin-ners, turn; why will ye die? God, your Sav - ior, asks you why;
3. Sin-ners, turn; why will ye die? God, the Spir - it, asks you why;

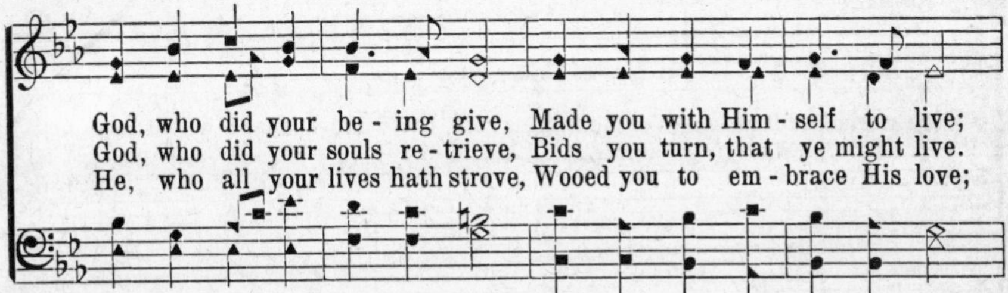
God, who did your be - ing give, Made you with Him - self to live;
God, who did your souls re - trieve, Bids you turn, that ye might live.
He, who all your lives hath strove, Wooed you to em - brace His love;

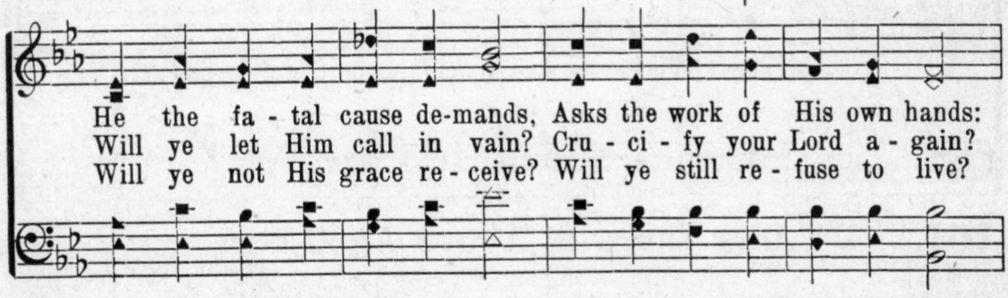
He the fa - tal cause de-mands, Asks the work of His own hands:
Will ye let Him call in vain? Cru - ci - fy your Lord a - gain?
Will ye not His grace re - ceive? Will ye still re - fuse to live?

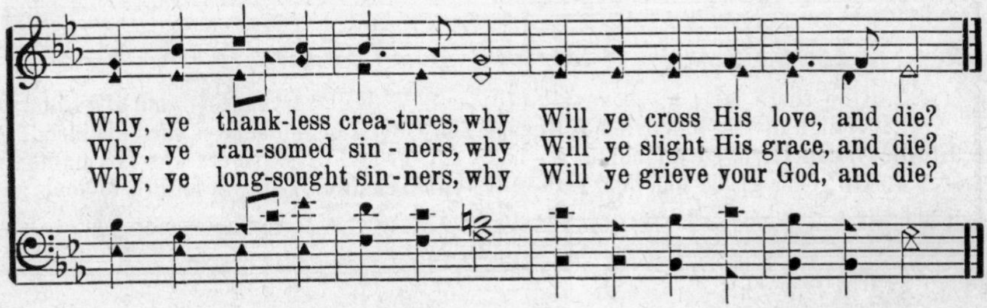
Why, ye thank-less crea-tures, why Will ye cross His love, and die?
Why, ye ran-somed sin - ners, why Will ye slight His grace, and die?
Why, ye long-sought sin - ners, why Will ye grieve your God, and die?

160 Come, Great Deliverer, Come

FANNY J. CROSBY W. H. DOANE

1. O, hear my cry, be gra-cious now to me, Come, Great De-liv-'rer, come;
2. I have no place, no shel-ter from the night, Come, Great De-liv-'rer, come;
3. My path is lone, and wea-ry are my feet, Come, Great De-liv-'rer, come;
4. Thou wilt not spurn con-tri-tion's broken sigh, Come, Great De-liv-'rer, come;
My soul bowed down is long-ing now for Thee, Come, Great De-liv-'rer, come.
One look from Thee would give me life and light, Come, Great De-liv-'rer, come.
Mine eyes look up Thy lov-ing smile to meet, Come, Great De-liv-'rer, come.
Re-gard my prayer, and hear my hum-ble cry, Come, Great De-liv-'rer, come.
REFRAIN
I've wandered far a-way o'er mountains cold, I've wandered far a-way from home;
O take me now, and bring me to Thy fold, Come, Great De-liv-'rer, come.

161 One There Is Above All Others

OVIO. 8s. 7s.

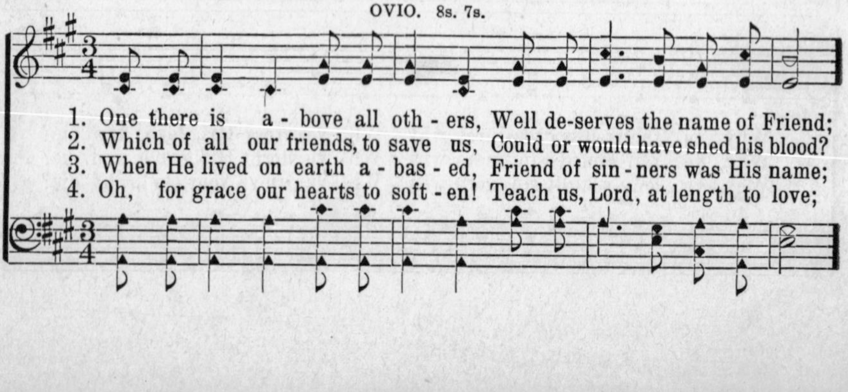
1. One there is a-bove all oth-ers, Well de-serves the name of Friend;
2. Which of all our friends, to save us, Could or would have shed his blood?
3. When He lived on earth a-bas-ed, Friend of sin-ners was His name;
4. Oh, for grace our hearts to soft-en! Teach us, Lord, at length to love;

One There Is Above All Others

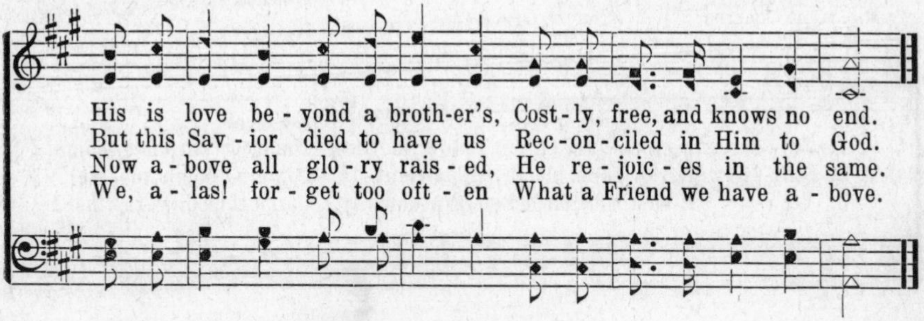
His is love be - yond a broth-er's, Cost - ly, free, and knows no end.
But this Sav - ior died to have us Rec - on - ciled in Him to God.
Now a - bove all glo - ry rais - ed, He re - joic - es in the same.
We, a - las! for - get too oft - en What a Friend we have a - bove.

Whiter Than Snow 162

James Nicholson — Wm. G. Fischer

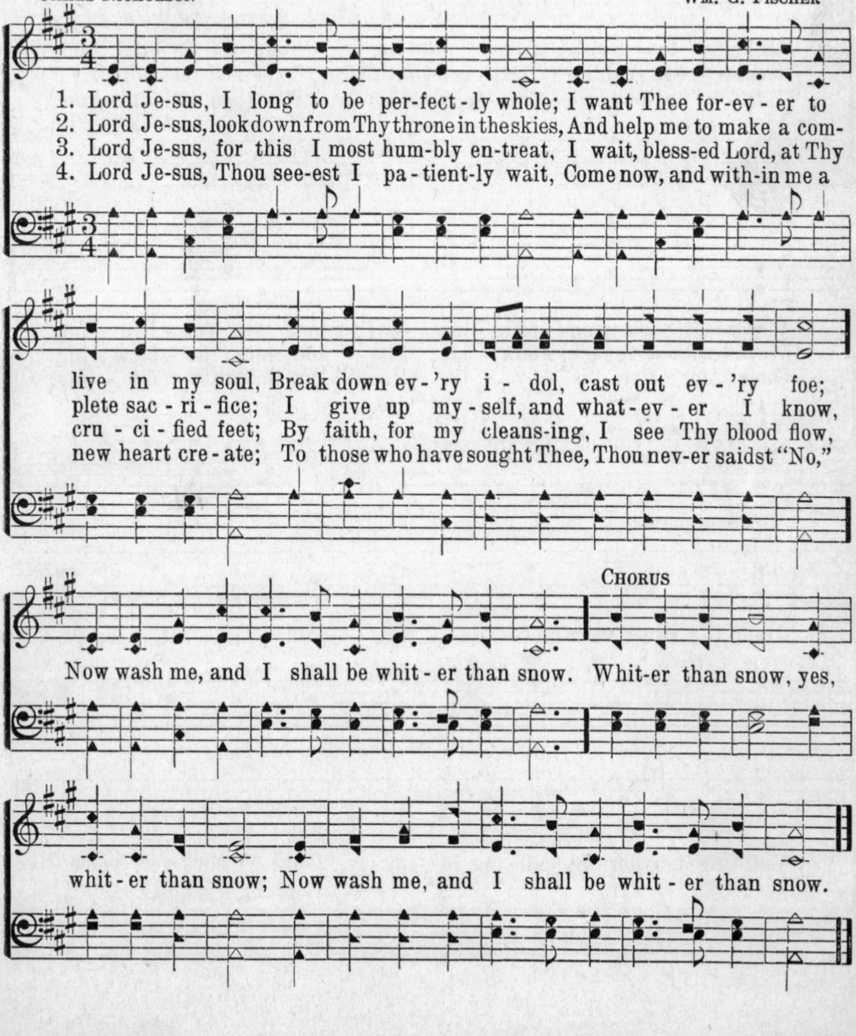
1. Lord Je-sus, I long to be per-fect - ly whole; I want Thee for-ev - er to
2. Lord Je-sus, look down from Thy throne in the skies, And help me to make a com-
3. Lord Je-sus, for this I most hum-bly en-treat, I wait, bless-ed Lord, at Thy
4. Lord Je-sus, Thou see-est I pa - tient-ly wait, Come now, and with-in me a
live in my soul, Break down ev - 'ry i - dol, cast out ev - 'ry foe;
plete sac - ri - fice; I give up my - self, and what - ev - er I know,
cru - ci - fied feet; By faith, for my cleans-ing, I see Thy blood flow,
new heart cre - ate; To those who have sought Thee, Thou nev-er saidst "No,"
Now wash me, and I shall be whit - er than snow.
CHORUS
Whit-er than snow, yes,
whit - er than snow; Now wash me, and I shall be whit - er than snow.

163 Jesus Calls Thee

Mrs. S. A. Collins — W. H. Doane

1. Je - sus, gra-cious One, call-eth now to thee, "Come, O sin - ner, come!"
2. Still He waits for thee, plead-ing pa-tient - ly, "Come, O come to Me!"
3. Wea - ry, sin-sick soul, called so gra-cious-ly, Canst thou dare re - fuse?
Calls so ten-der - ly, calls so lov - ing - ly, "Now, O sin - ner, come."
"Heav - y - la - den one, I thy grief have borne, Come and rest in Me."
Mer - cy of-fered thee, free - ly, ten - der - ly, Wilt thou still a - buse?
Words of peace and bless - ing, Christ's own love con - fess - ing;
Words with love o'er - flow - ing, Life and bliss be - stow - ing;
Come, for time is fly - ing, Haste, thy lamp is dy - ing;
Refrain
Hear the sweet voice of Je - sus, Full, full of love;
Call - ing ten - der - ly, call - ing lov - ing - ly, "Come, O sin - ner, come."

Once For All

P. P. B. P. P. Bliss

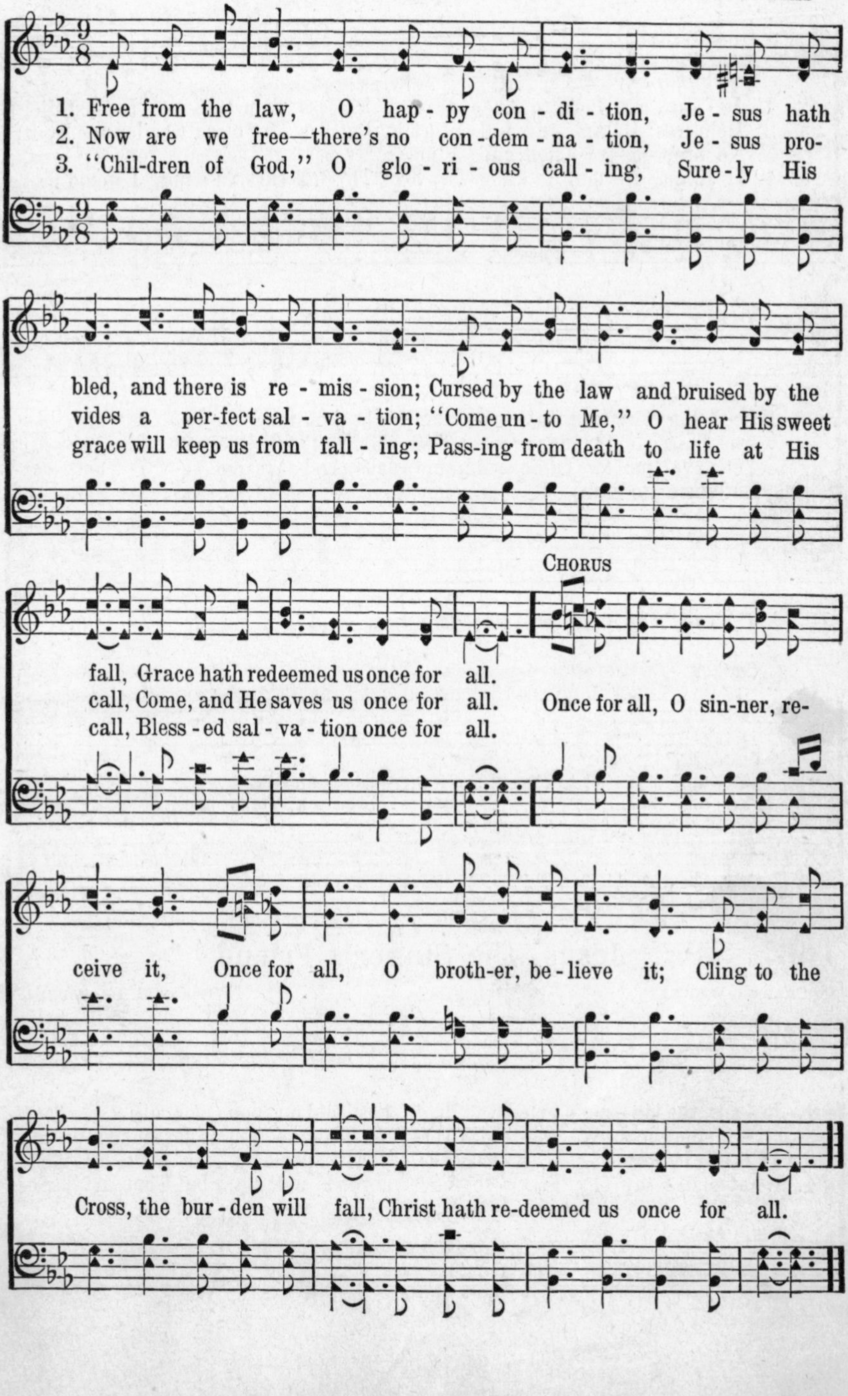
1. Free from the law, O hap - py con - di - tion, Je - sus hath
2. Now are we free—there's no con - dem - na - tion, Je - sus pro-
3. "Chil-dren of God," O glo - ri - ous call - ing, Sure - ly His
bled, and there is re - mis - sion; Cursed by the law and bruised by the
vides a per-fect sal - va - tion; "Come un - to Me," O hear His sweet
grace will keep us from fall - ing; Pass-ing from death to life at His
fall, Grace hath redeemed us once for all.
call, Come, and He saves us once for all.
call, Bless - ed sal - va - tion once for all.
CHORUS
Once for all, O sin-ner, re-
ceive it, Once for all, O broth-er, be - lieve it; Cling to the
Cross, the bur - den will fall, Christ hath re-deemed us once for all.

165 Take Me As I Am

J. H. S. — J. H. STOCKTON

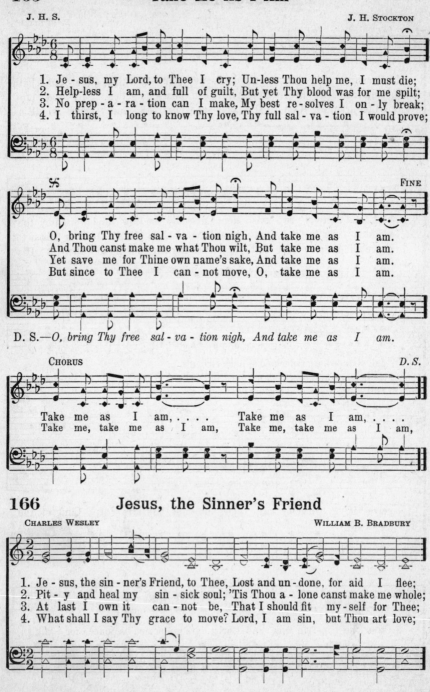

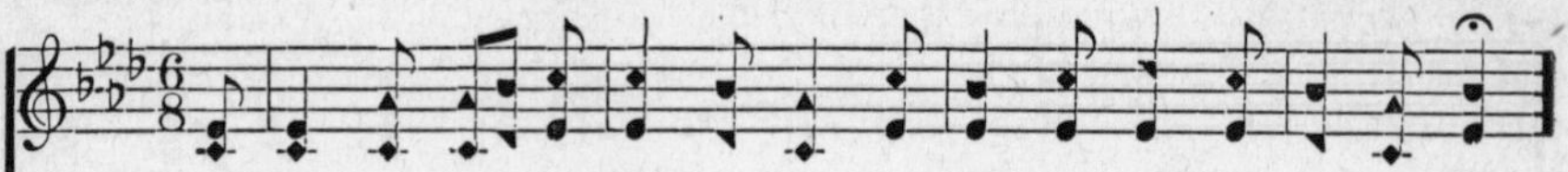

1. Je - sus, my Lord, to Thee I cry; Un-less Thou help me, I must die;
2. Help-less I am, and full of guilt, But yet Thy blood was for me spilt;
3. No prep - a - ra - tion can I make, My best re - solves I on - ly break;
4. I thirst, I long to know Thy love, Thy full sal - va - tion I would prove;

FINE

O, bring Thy free sal - va - tion nigh, And take me as I am.
And Thou canst make me what Thou wilt, But take me as I am.
Yet save me for Thine own name's sake, And take me as I am.
But since to Thee I can - not move, O, take me as I am.

D. S.—*O, bring Thy free sal - va - tion nigh, And take me as I am.*

CHORUS — *D.S.*

Take me as I am, ... Take me as I am, ...
Take me, take me as I am, Take me, take me as I am,

166 Jesus, the Sinner's Friend

CHARLES WESLEY — WILLIAM B. BRADBURY

1. Je - sus, the sin - ner's Friend, to Thee, Lost and un - done, for aid I flee;
2. Pit - y and heal my sin - sick soul; 'Tis Thou a - lone canst make me whole;
3. At last I own it can - not be, That I should fit my - self for Thee;
4. What shall I say Thy grace to move? Lord, I am sin, but Thou art love;

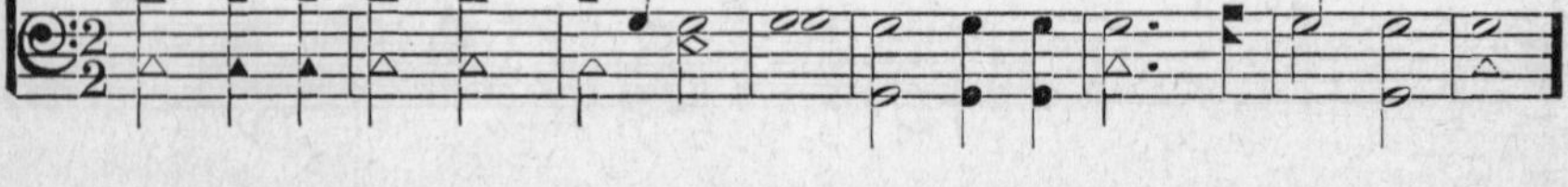

Jesus, the Sinner's Friend

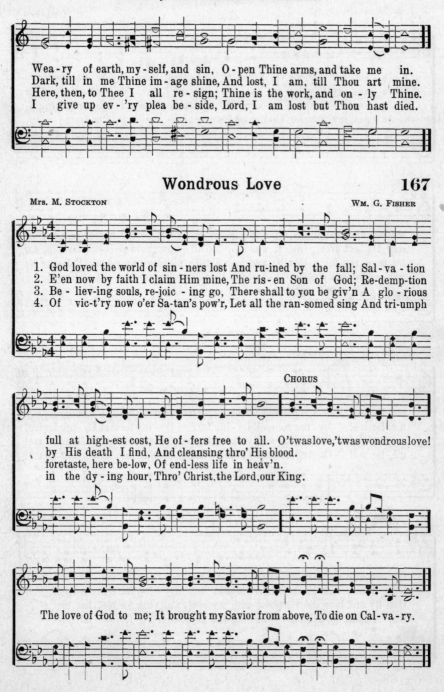

Wea - ry of earth, my - self, and sin, O - pen Thine arms, and take me in.
Dark, till in me Thine im - age shine, And lost, I am, till Thou art mine.
Here, then, to Thee I all re - sign; Thine is the work, and on - ly Thine.
I give up ev - 'ry plea be - side, Lord, I am lost but Thou hast died.

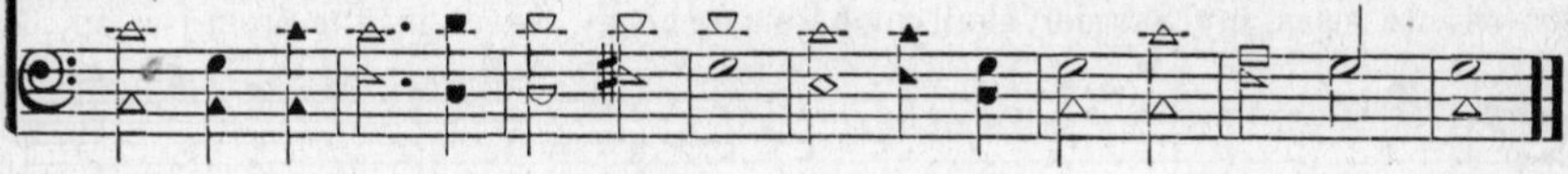

Wondrous Love 167

Mrs. M. Stockton — Wm. G. Fisher

1. God loved the world of sin - ners lost And ru-ined by the fall; Sal - va - tion
2. E'en now by faith I claim Him mine, The ris - en Son of God; Re-demp-tion
3. Be - liev-ing souls, re-joic - ing go, There shall to you be giv'n A glo - rious
4. Of vic-t'ry now o'er Sa-tan's pow'r, Let all the ran-somed sing And tri-umph

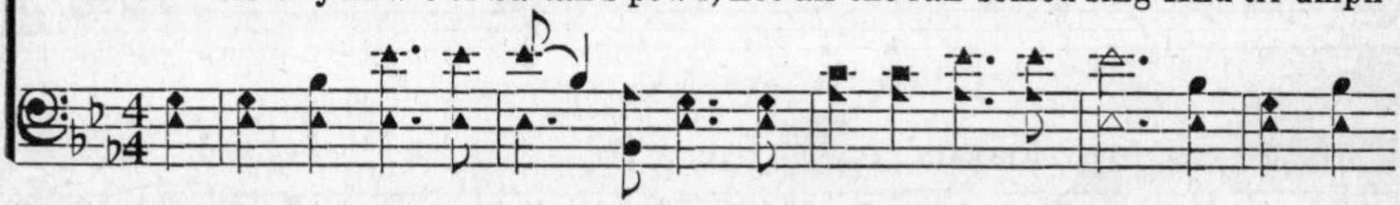

Chorus

full at high-est cost, He of - fers free to all. O'twaslove,'twaswondrouslove!
by His death I find, And cleansing thro' His blood.
foretaste, here be-low, Of end-less life in heav'n.
in the dy - ing hour, Thro' Christ, the Lord, our King.

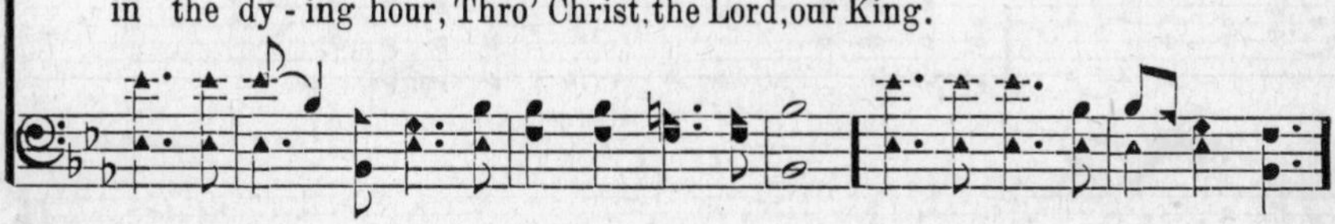

The love of God to me; It brought my Savior from above, To die on Cal - va - ry.

168 Seeking for Me

A. N. E. E. Hasty

1. Je - sus, my Sav-ior, to Beth - le-hem came, Born in a man-ger to
2. Je - sus, my Sav-ior, on Cal - va - ry's tree, Paid the great debt, and my
3. Je - sus, my Sav-ior, the same as of old, While I was wan-d'ring a-
4. Je - sus, my Sav-ior, shall come from on high—Sweet is the prom-ise as
sor-row and shame; Oh, it was won-der-ful—blest be His name! Seek-ing for
soul He set free; Oh, it was won-der-ful—how could it be? Dy - ing for
far from the fold, Gen-tly and long did He plead with my soul, Call - ing for
wea - ry years fly; Oh, I shall see Him de-scend-ing the sky, Com-ing for
Refrain
For me!........
For me!........
me, for me! Seeking for me! Seeking for me! Seeking for me! Seeking for me!
me, for me! Dy - ing for me! Dy - ing for me! Dy - ing for me! Dy - ing for me!
me, for me! Call-ing for me! Call-ing for me! Call-ing for me! Call-ing for me!
me, for me! Coming for me! Coming for me! Coming for me! Coming for me!
Oh, it was won-der-ful—blest be His name! Seek-ing for me, for me!
Oh, it was won-der-fu!—how could it be? Dy - ing for me, for me!
Gen-tly and long did He plead with my soul, Call - ing for me, for me!
Oh, I shall see Him de-scend - ing the sky, Com-ing for me, for me!

Jesus, I Come

W. T. Sleeper — Geo. C. Stebbins

1. Out of my bond-age, sor-row and night, Je-sus, I come, Je-sus, I come;
2. Out of my shame-ful fail-ure and loss, Je-sus, I come, Je-sus, I come;
3. Out of un-rest and ar-ro-gant pride, Je-sus, I come, Je-sus, I come;
4. Out of the fear and dread of the tomb, Je-sus, I come, Je-sus, I come;

In-to Thy free-dom, glad-ness and light, Je-sus, I come to Thee;
In-to the glo-rious gain of Thy cross, Je-sus, I come to Thee;
In-to Thy bless-ed will to a-bide, Je-sus, I come to Thee;
In-to the joy and light of Thy home, Je-sus, I come to Thee;

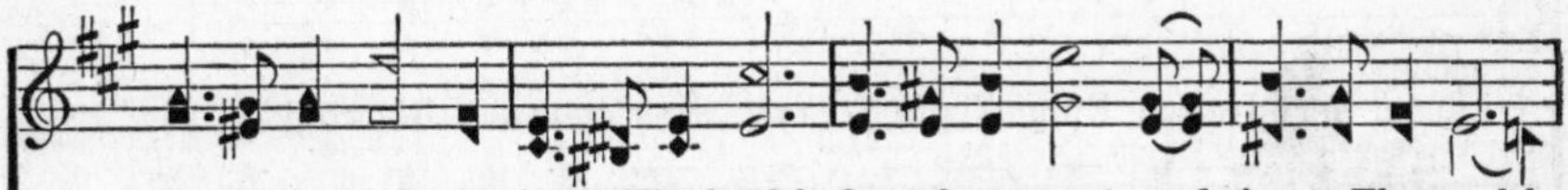

Out of my sick-ness in-to Thy health, Out of my want and in-to Thy wealth,
Out of earth's sorrows in-to Thy balm, Out of life's storms and in-to Thy calm,
Out of my-self to dwell in Thy love, Out of de-spair in-to rap-tures a-bove,
Out of the depths of ru-in un-told, In-to the peace of Thy sheltering fold,

Out of my sin and in-to Thy-self, Je-sus, I come to Thee.
Out of dis-tress to ju-bi-lant psalm, Je-sus, I come to Thee.
Up-ward for aye on wings like a dove, Je-sus, I come to Thee.
Ev-er Thy glo-rious face to be-hold, Je-sus, I come to Thee.

170 Have You Any Room For Jesus?

Arr. by W. W. D. from L. W. M. C. C. WILLIAMS

1. Have you an - y room for Je - sus, He who bore your load of sin?
2. Room for pleas-ure, room for busi - ness, But for Christ the Cru - ci - fied,
3. Have you an - y room for Je - sus, As in grace He calls a - gain?
4. Room and time now give to Je - sus, Soon will pass God's day of grace;
As He knocks and asks ad-mis - sion, Sin - ner, will you let Him in?
Not a place that He can en - ter, In the heart for which He died?
O to-day is time ac-cept - ed, To-mor - row you may call in vain.
Soon thy heart left cold and si - lent, And thy Sav-ior's pleading cease.
CHORUS
Room for Je-sus, King of glo - ry! Has - ten now His word o - bey;
Swing the heart's door wide-ly o - pen, Bid Him en - ter while you may.

171 Lord, I'm Coming Home

W. J. K. WM J. KIRKPATRICK

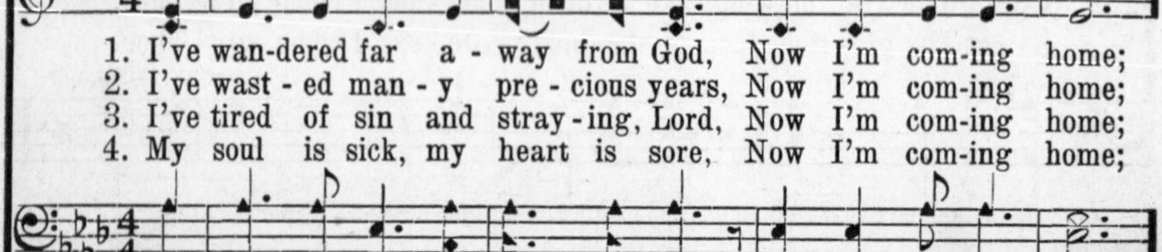
1. I've wan-dered far a - way from God, Now I'm com-ing home;
2. I've wast - ed man - y pre - cious years, Now I'm com-ing home;
3. I've tired of sin and stray - ing, Lord, Now I'm com-ing home;
4. My soul is sick, my heart is sore, Now I'm com-ing home;

Lord, I'm Coming Home

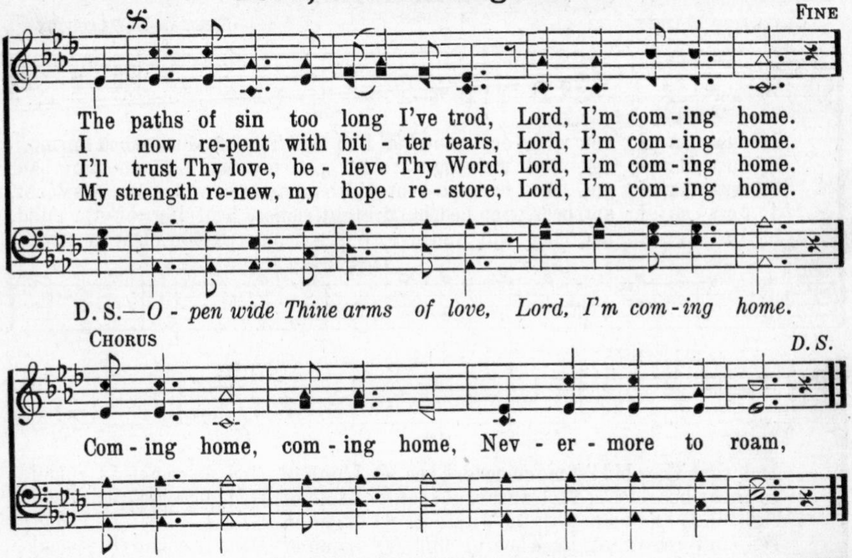
FINE
The paths of sin too long I've trod, Lord, I'm com-ing home.
I now re-pent with bit - ter tears, Lord, I'm com-ing home.
I'll trust Thy love, be - lieve Thy Word, Lord, I'm com-ing home.
My strength re-new, my hope re - store, Lord, I'm com-ing home.
D. S.—*O - pen wide Thine arms of love, Lord, I'm com-ing home.*
CHORUS
D. S.
Com-ing home, com-ing home, Nev - er - more to roam,

I Am Coming Home **172**

L. H. L. HARTSOUGH

1. I hear Thy welcome voice, That calls me, Lord, to Thee For cleansing in Thy precious blood That flowed on Cal - va - ry.
2. Tho' coming weak and vile, Thou dost my strength assure; Thou dost my vileness full - y cleanse, Till spot - less all and pure.
3. 'Tis Je - sus calls me on To per - fect faith and love, To per - fect hope, and peace, and trust, For earth and heav'n a - bove.
CHORUS
I am com-ing, Lord! Com-ing now to Thee! Wash me, cleanse me in the blood That flowed on Cal-va-ry!

173 Just As I Am

CHARLOTTE ELLIOTT — WILLIAM B. BRADBURY

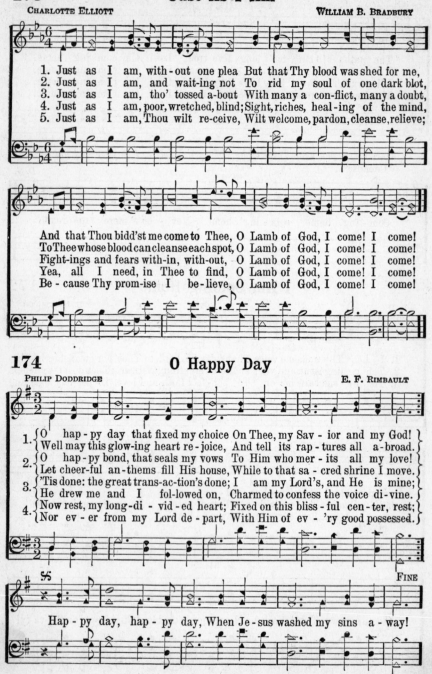

1. Just as I am, with-out one plea But that Thy blood was shed for me,
2. Just as I am, and wait-ing not To rid my soul of one dark blot,
3. Just as I am, tho' tossed a-bout With many a con-flict, many a doubt,
4. Just as I am, poor, wretched, blind; Sight, riches, heal-ing of the mind,
5. Just as I am, Thou wilt re-ceive, Wilt welcome, pardon, cleanse, relieve;

And that Thou bidd'st me come to Thee, O Lamb of God, I come! I come!
To Thee whose blood can cleanse each spot, O Lamb of God, I come! I come!
Fight-ings and fears with-in, with-out, O Lamb of God, I come! I come!
Yea, all I need, in Thee to find, O Lamb of God, I come! I come!
Be - cause Thy prom-ise I be-lieve, O Lamb of God, I come! I come!

174 O Happy Day

PHILIP DODDRIDGE — E. F. RIMBAULT

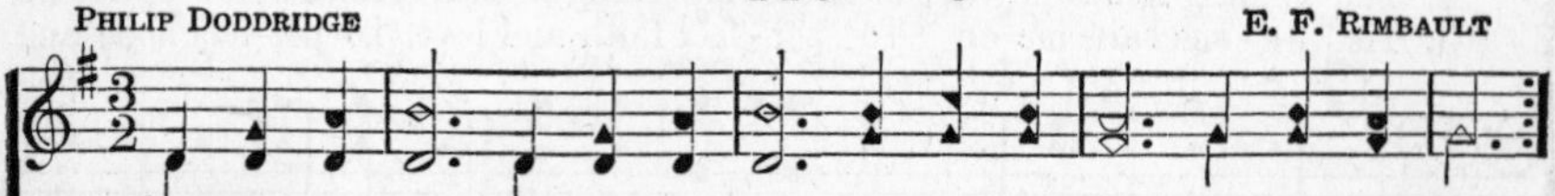

1. { O hap - py day that fixed my choice On Thee, my Sav - ior and my God!
Well may this glow-ing heart re - joice, And tell its rap - tures all a - broad. }
2. { O hap - py bond, that seals my vows To Him who mer - its all my love!
Let cheer-ful an-thems fill His house, While to that sa - cred shrine I move. }
3. { 'Tis done: the great trans-ac-tion's done; I am my Lord's, and He is mine;
He drew me and I fol-lowed on, Charmed to confess the voice di - vine. }
4. { Now rest, my long-di - vid - ed heart; Fixed on this bliss - ful cen - ter, rest;
Nor ev - er from my Lord de - part, With Him of ev - 'ry good possessed. }

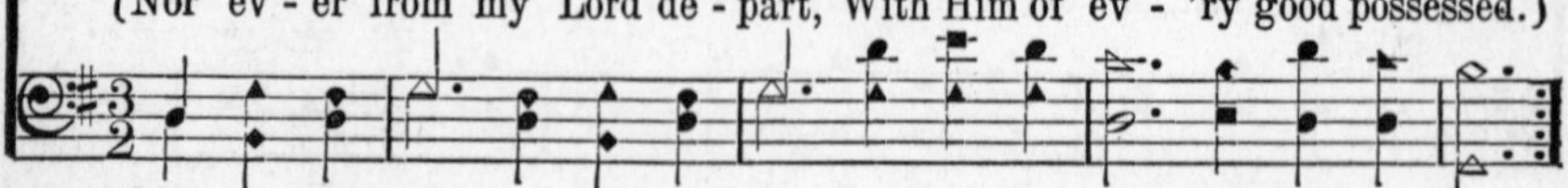

Hap - py day, hap - py day, When Je - sus washed my sins a - way!

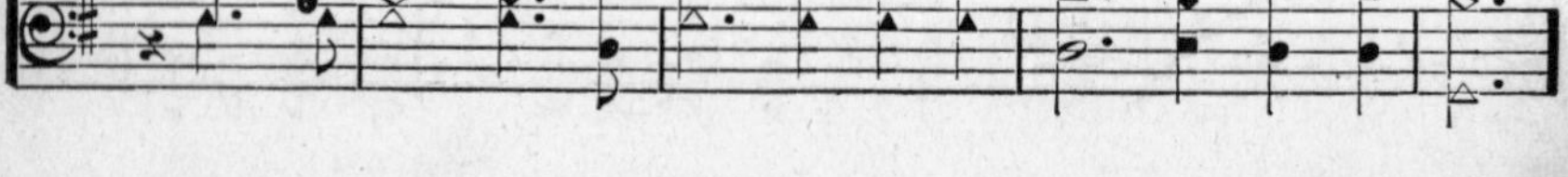

O Happy Day

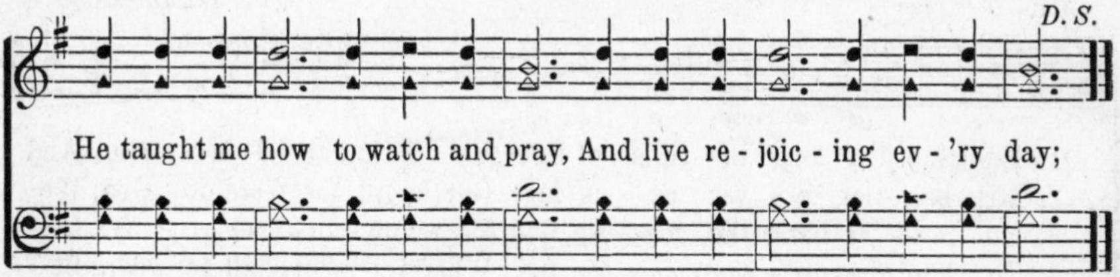
D. S.
He taught me how to watch and pray, And live re - joic - ing ev - 'ry day;

Near the Cross

FANNY J. CROSBY W. H. DOANE

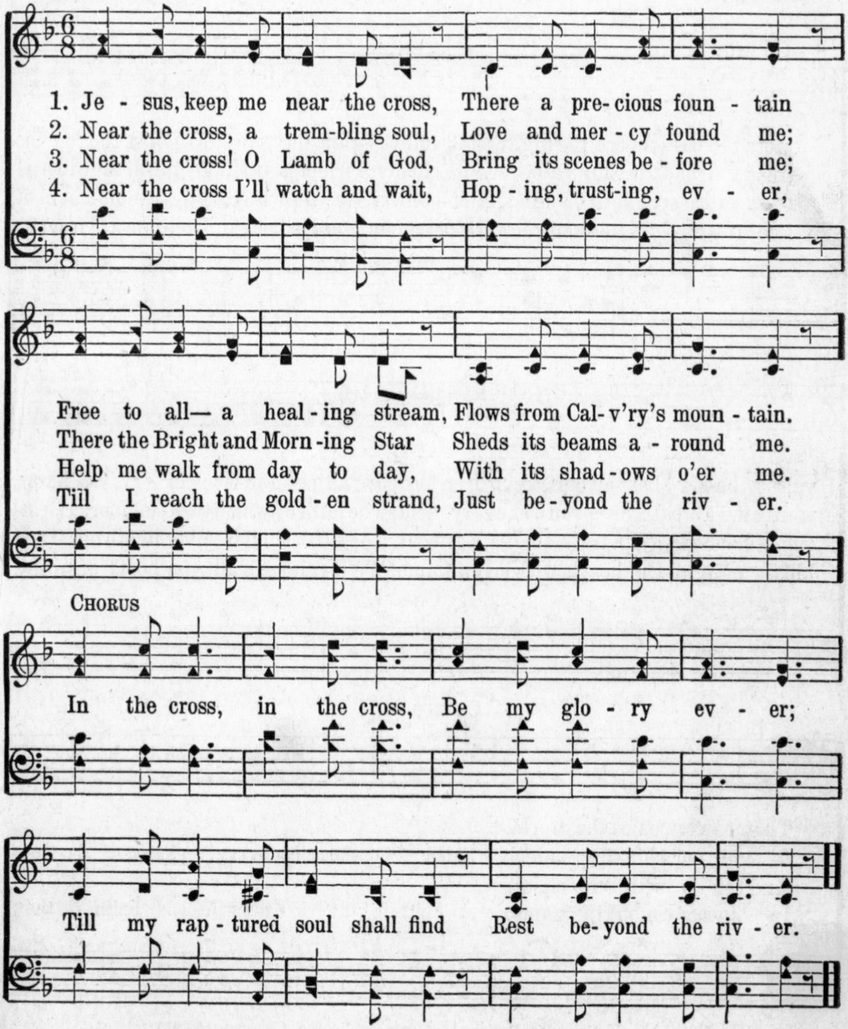
1. Je - sus, keep me near the cross, There a pre-cious foun - tain
2. Near the cross, a trem-bling soul, Love and mer - cy found me;
3. Near the cross! O Lamb of God, Bring its scenes be - fore me;
4. Near the cross I'll watch and wait, Hop - ing, trust-ing, ev - er,
Free to all— a heal - ing stream, Flows from Cal - v'ry's moun - tain.
There the Bright and Morn - ing Star Sheds its beams a - round me.
Help me walk from day to day, With its shad - ows o'er me.
Till I reach the gold - en strand, Just be - yond the riv - er.
CHORUS
In the cross, in the cross, Be my glo - ry ev - er;
Till my rap - tured soul shall find Rest be - yond the riv - er.

176 Faith Is the Victory

JOHN H. YATES — IRA D. SANKEY

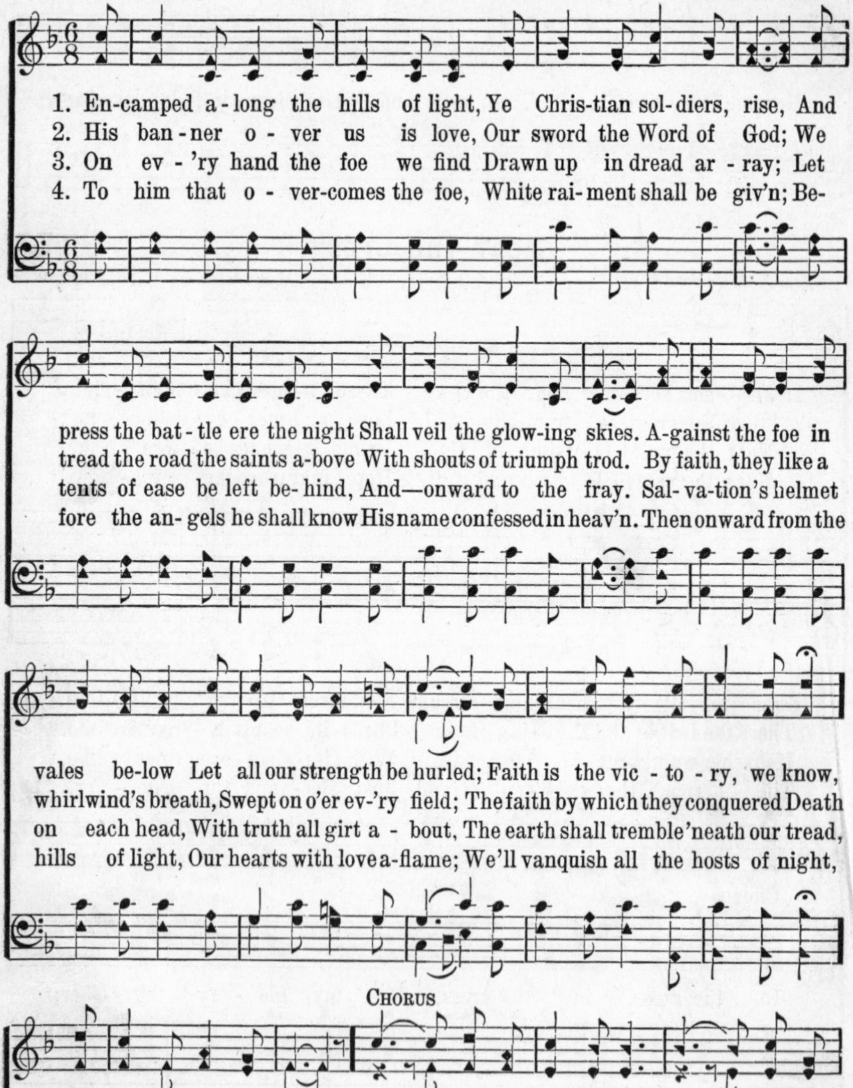
1. En-camped a-long the hills of light, Ye Chris-tian sol-diers, rise, And
2. His ban-ner o-ver us is love, Our sword the Word of God; We
3. On ev-'ry hand the foe we find Drawn up in dread ar-ray; Let
4. To him that o-ver-comes the foe, White rai-ment shall be giv'n; Be-
press the bat-tle ere the night Shall veil the glow-ing skies. A-gainst the foe in
tread the road the saints a-bove With shouts of triumph trod. By faith, they like a
tents of ease be left be-hind, And—onward to the fray. Sal-va-tion's helmet
fore the an-gels he shall know His name confessed in heav'n. Then onward from the
vales be-low Let all our strength be hurled; Faith is the vic-to-ry, we know,
whirlwind's breath, Swept on o'er ev-'ry field; The faith by which they conquered Death
on each head, With truth all girt a-bout, The earth shall tremble 'neath our tread,
hills of light, Our hearts with love a-flame; We'll vanquish all the hosts of night,
CHORUS
That o-ver-comes the world.
Is still our shin-ing shield. Faith is the vic-to-ry! Faith is the
And ech-o with our shout.
In Je-sus' conqu'ring name. Faith is the vic-to-ry! Faith is the

Faith Is the Victory

vic - to-ry! Oh, glo-ri-ous vic - to - ry, That o - ver-comes the world.
vic - to-ry!

Take Time to Be Holy 177

W. D. LONGSTAFF GEO. C. STEBBINS

1. Take time to be ho - ly, Speak oft with thy Lord; A - bide in Him
2. Take time to be ho - ly, The world rush-es on;.. Spend much time in
3. Take time to be ho - ly, Let Him be thy Guide, And run not be-
4. Take time to be ho - ly, Be calm in thy soul;. Each tho't and each

al - ways, And feed on His Word. Make friends of God's chil - dren;
se - cret With Je - sus a - lone— By look - ing to Je - sus,
fore Him, What - ev - er be - tide;.. In joy or in sor - row,
mo - tive Be - neath His con - trol;.. Thus led by His Spir - it

Help those who are weak; For - get-ting in noth-ing His bless-ing to seek.
Like Him thou shalt be;.. Thy friends in thy con-duct His likeness shall see.
Still fol - low thy Lord, And, look-ing to Je - sus, Still trust in His Word.
To foun-tains of love, Thou soon shalt be fit - ted For serv-ice a - bove.

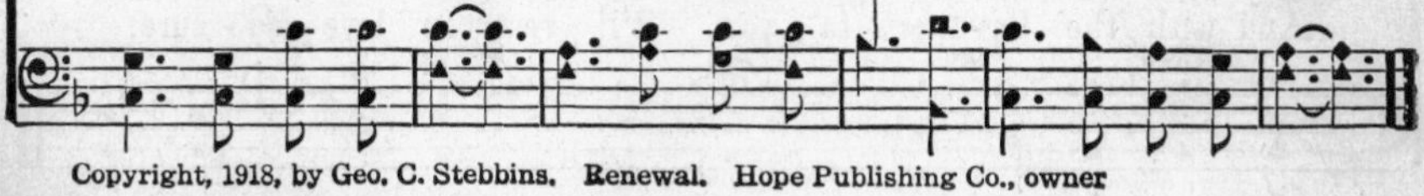

178 Shine in My Heart, Lord Jesus

F. P. GRIFFITH

A. C. KOLB

Devotional
1. Shine in my heart, Lord Je - sus, And lead me in - to light,
2. Shine in my heart, Lord Je - sus, I need Thee ev - 'ry day,
3. In - crease my faith, Lord Je - sus, May Thy dear pre - cious blood,
4. Come, Ho - ly Spir - it, fill me, Come show me all my need;
5. And when the king of ter - rors Shall stand a - cross my way,
Dis - pel each cloud and shad - ow And chase a - way my night;
To help me keep Thy stat - utes To walk the nar - row way;
Of sin com - plete - ly cleanse me And make me pure and good;
With heav'n's re - fresh - ing man - na My hun - gry spir - it feed;
Oh, help me to go for - ward, Re - gard - less of his sway;
Shine on my soul, O Je - sus, And warm me with Thy love,
Oh, leave me not, my Sav - ior, Or else I faint, I fall;
In - crease my love O Je - sus, And bind my heart to Thee,
And though the way is rug - ged, And though my path is drear,
Thy rod and staff to help me, My safe - ty will in - sure,
Oh, help me when I need Thee, Thy faith - ful - ness to prove.
Come in Thy might and help me When Thou dost hear me call.
So when my days are num - bered Thy smile of love I'll see.
Thy pres - ence will sus - tain me, Give com - fort, hope, and cheer.
And with the Fa - ther's fa - vor I'll rest in love se - cure.

Thou Didst Teach the Thronging People 179

HENRY S. NINDE — COLLEGE. 8. 5. 8. 5. — F. K. MARCH

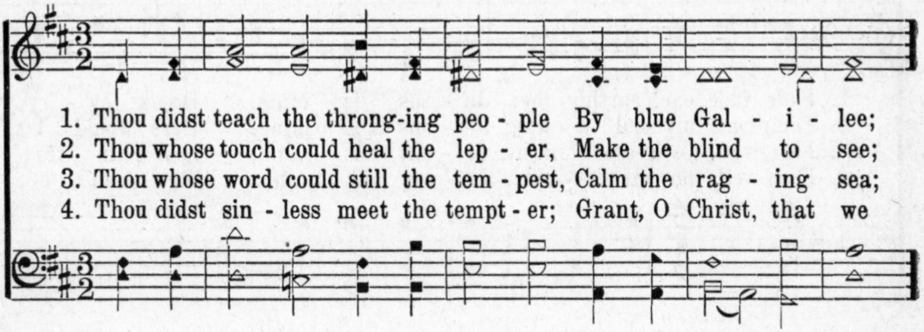

1. Thou didst teach the throng-ing peo - ple By blue Gal - i - lee;
2. Thou whose touch could heal the lep - er, Make the blind to see;
3. Thou whose word could still the tem - pest, Calm the rag - ing sea;
4. Thou didst sin - less meet the tempt - er; Grant, O Christ, that we

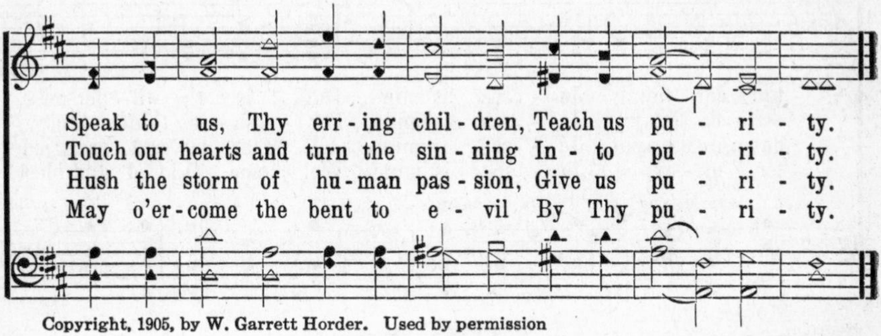

Speak to us, Thy err - ing chil - dren, Teach us pu - ri - ty.
Touch our hearts and turn the sin - ning In - to pu - ri - ty.
Hush the storm of hu - man pas - sion, Give us pu - ri - ty.
May o'er - come the bent to e - vil By Thy pu - ri - ty.

Fast to Thine Arm 180

G. W. L. — G. W. LYON

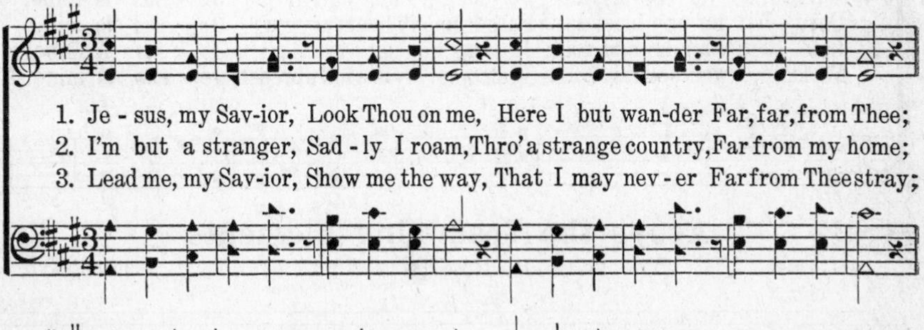

1. Je - sus, my Sav-ior, Look Thou on me, Here I but wan-der Far, far, from Thee;
2. I'm but a stranger, Sad - ly I roam, Thro' a strange country, Far from my home;
3. Lead me, my Sav-ior, Show me the way, That I may nev - er Far from Thee stray;

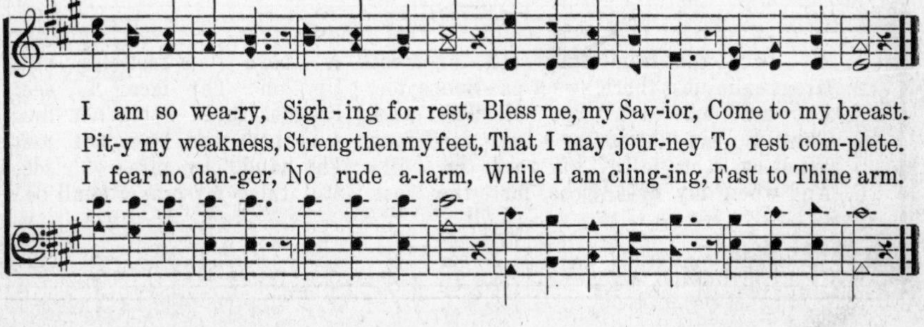

I am so wea-ry, Sigh - ing for rest, Bless me, my Sav-ior, Come to my breast.
Pit-y my weakness, Strengthen my feet, That I may jour-ney To rest com-plete.
I fear no dan-ger, No rude a-larm, While I am cling-ing, Fast to Thine arm.

181 Fade, Fade, Each Earthly Joy

JANE C. BONAR — THEODORE E. PERKINS

1. Fade, fade, each earthly joy; Je - sus is mine. Break ev - 'ry
2. Tempt not my soul a - way; Je - sus is mine. Here would I
3. Fare-well, ye dreams of night; Je - sus is mine. Lost in this
4. Fare-well, mor-tal - i - ty; Je - sus is mine. Wel - come, e-

ten - der tie; Je - sus is mine. Dark is the wil - der-ness,
ev - er stay; Je - sus is mine. Per - ish - ing things of clay,
dawn-ing bright, Je - sus is mine. All that my soul has tried
ter - ni - ty; Je - sus is mine. Wel - come, O loved and blest,

Earth has no resting-place, Je - sus a - lone can bless; Je - sus is mine.
Born but for one brief day, Pass from my heart a - way; Je - sus is mine.
Left but a dis-mal void; Je - sus has sat - is - fied; Je - sus is mine.
Welcome, sweet scenes of rest, Welcome, my Savior's breast; Je - sus is mine.

182 Above the Trembling Elements

MRS. PRICE — DUNDEE. C. M. — GUIL. FRANC

Slowly

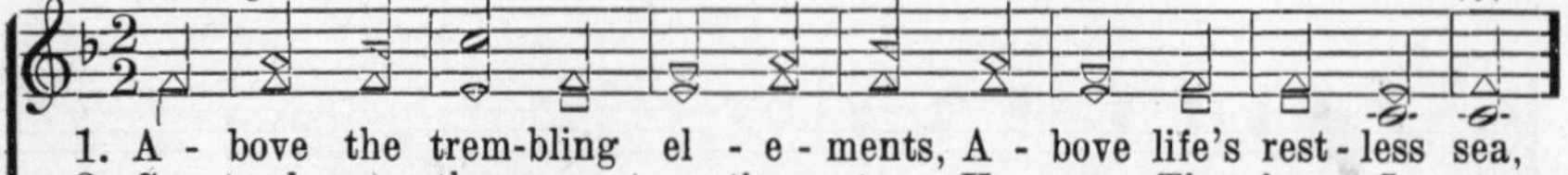

1. A - bove the trem-bling el - e - ments, A - bove life's rest - less sea,
2. Great calm-ness there, sweet pa - tience too, Up - on Thy face I see:
3. I am not wea - ry of Thy work, From earth I would not flee;
4. That I may bless my ten - der friends, And those who love not me;
5. What-ev - er falls, of good or ill, Thy hand, Thy care I see,
6. And when my eyes close for the last, Still this my prayer shall be,—

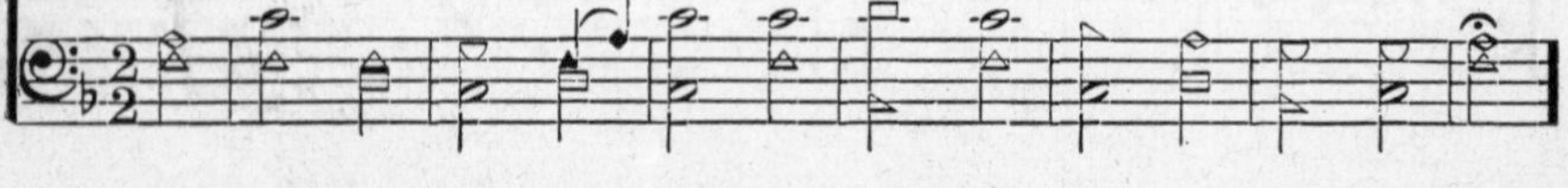

Above the Trembling Elements

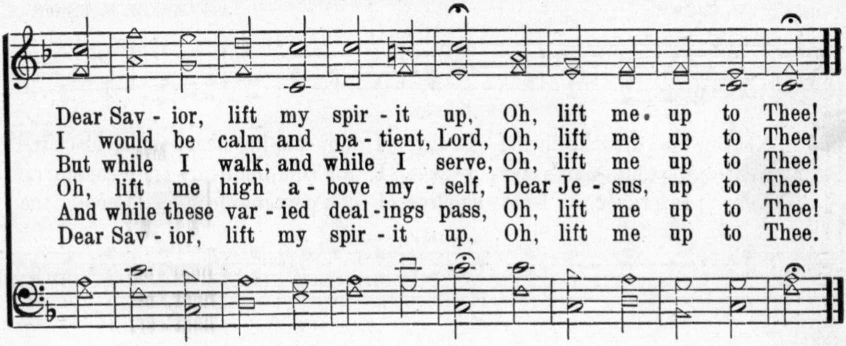
Dear Sav - ior, lift my spir - it up, Oh, lift me up to Thee!
I would be calm and pa - tient, Lord, Oh, lift me up to Thee!
But while I walk, and while I serve, Oh, lift me up to Thee!
Oh, lift me high a - bove my - self, Dear Je - sus, up to Thee!
And while these var - ied deal - ings pass, Oh, lift me up to Thee!
Dear Sav - ior, lift my spir - it up, Oh, lift me up to Thee.

Savior, More Than Life 183

FANNY J. CROSBY W. H. DOANE

1. Sav - ior, more than life to me, I am cling-ing, cling-ing close to Thee;
2. Thro' this chang-ing world be-low, Lead me gen - tly, gen - tly as I go;
3. Let me love Thee more and more, Till this fleet-ing, fleet-ing life is o'er;
FINE
Let Thy pre-cious blood ap-plied, Keep me ev - er, ev - er near Thy side.
Trusting Thee, I can-not stray, I can nev - er, nev - er lose my way.
Till my soul is lost in love, In a bright-er, bright-er world a - bove.
D. S.—May Thy ten - der love to me Bind me clo - ser, clo - ser, Lord, to Thee.
REFRAIN
Ev - 'ry day, ev - 'ry hour, Let me feel Thy cleans-ing pow'r;
Ev - 'ry day and hour, ev - 'ry day and hour,
D. S.

Nearer the Cross

FANNY J. CROSBY — MRS. J. F. KNAPP

1. "Near-er the cross!" my heart can say, I am com-ing near-er; Near-er the
2. Near-er the Chris-tian's mer-cy-seat, I am com-ing near-er; Feasting my
3. Near-er in prayer my hope as-pires, I am com-ing near-er; Deep-er the
cross from day to day, I am com-ing near-er; Near-er the cross where
soul on man-na sweet, I am com-ing near-er; Strong-er in faith, more
love my soul de-sires, I am com-ing near-er; Near-er the end of
Je-sus died, Near-er the foun-tain's crim-son tide, Near-er my Sav-ior's
clear I see Je-sus, who gave Him-self for me; Near-er to Him I
toil and care, Near-er the joy I long to share, Near-er the crown I
wound-ed side, I am com-ing near-er, I am com-ing near-er.
still would be, Still I'm com-ing near-er, Still I'm com-ing near-er.
soon shall wear, I am com-ing near-er, I am com-ing near-er.

I Want to Love Him More

F. L. SNYDER HOWARD E. SMITH

1. There is a sto - ry ev - er new, I'll tell it o'er and o'er,
2. The Prince of life, yet as a babe, He came in days of yore,
3. The sto - ry ev - er sweet - er grows, How on the cross He bore
4. Oh, how He suf - fered on the tree, No love like that be - fore;
How Je - sus gave His life for me; I want to love Him more.
To bring good-will and peace to men; I want to love Him more.
My sins, and by His stripes I'm healed; I want to love Him more.
I know and feel I love Him, yet I want to love Him more.
REFRAIN
I want to love Him more, I want to love Him more;
love Him more,
love Him more;
He did so ver - y much for me, I want to love Him more.
love Him more.

186 Nearer, Still Nearer

C. H. M. Mrs. C. H. Morris

1. Nearer, still nearer, close to Thy heart, Draw me, my Sav-ior, so precious Thou
2. Nearer, still nearer, noth-ing I bring, Naught as an of-f'ring to Je-sus my
3. Nearer, still nearer, Lord, to be Thine, Sin, with its fol-lies, I glad-ly re-
4. Nearer, still nearer, while life shall last, Till safe in glo-ry my an-chor is

art; Fold me, O fold me close to Thy breast, Shel-ter me safe in that
King; On-ly my sin-ful, now contrite heart, Grant me the cleansing Thy
sign; All of its pleasures, pomp and its pride, Give me but Je-sus, my
cast; Thro' endless a-ges, ev-er to be, Near-er, my Sav-ior, still

"Ha-ven of Rest," Shel-ter me safe in that "Ha-ven of Rest."
blood doth im-part, Grant me the cleansing Thy blood doth im-part.
Lord cru-ci-fied, Give me but Je-sus, my Lord cru-ci-fied.
near-er to Thee, Near-er, my Sav-ior, still near-er to Thee.

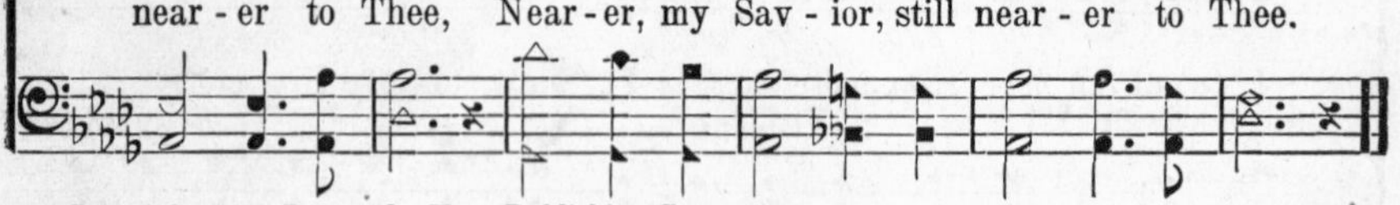

Copyright, 1926, Renewal. Hope Publishing Co., owner

187 My Prayer

P. P. B. P. P. Bliss

1. More ho-li-ness give me, More striv-ing with-in; More pa-tience in
2. More grat-i-tude give me, More trust in the Lord; More pride in His
3. More pu-ri-ty give me, More strength to o'er-come; More freedom from

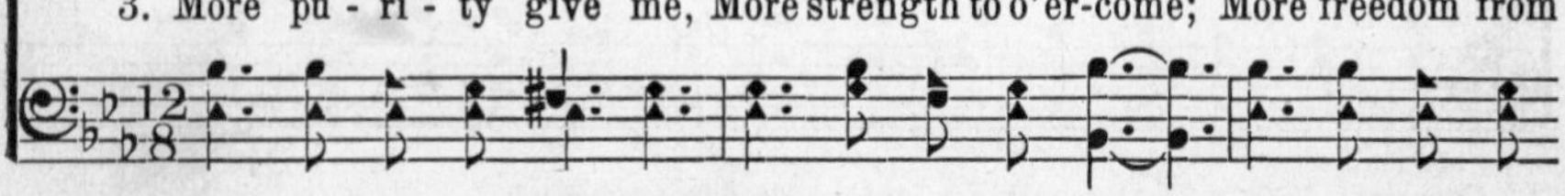

My Prayer

suf - f'ring, More sor - row for sin; More faith in my Sav - ior,
glo - ry, More hope in His word; More tears for His sor - rows,
earth-stains, More long-ings for home; More fit for the king - dom,

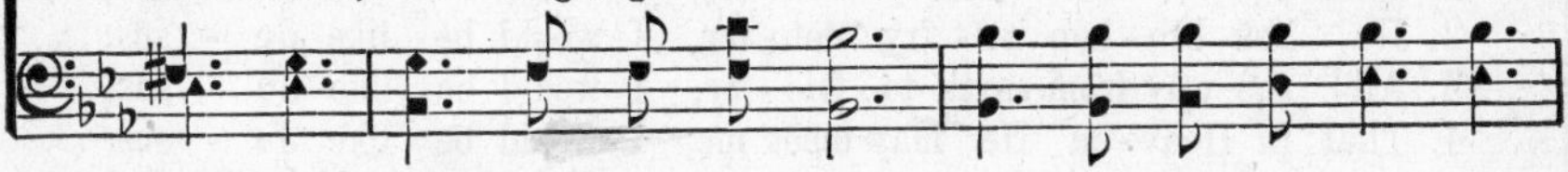

More sense of His care; More joy in His serv-ice, More pur-pose in prayer.
More pain at His grief; More meekness in tri - al, More praise for re - lief.
More used would I be; More blessed and ho - ly, More, Sav-ior, like Thee.

I'll Live For Him 188

R. E. HUDSON C. R. DUNBAR

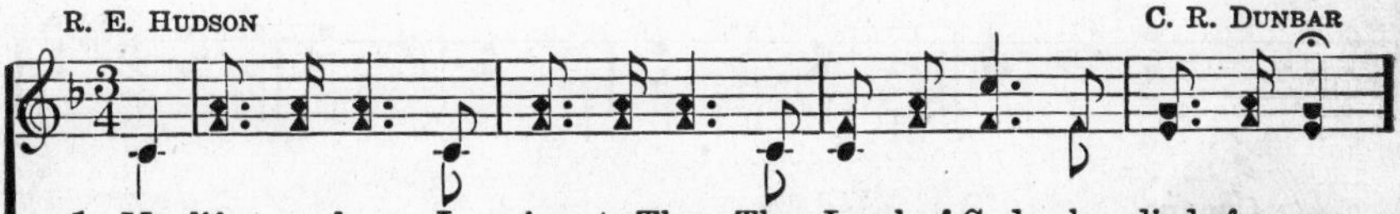

1. My life, my love I give to Thee, Thou Lamb of God who died for me;
2. I now be-lieve Thou dost re-ceive, For Thou hast died that I might live;
3. O Thou who died on Cal - va - ry, To save my soul and make me free,

CHO.–*I'll live for Him who died for me, How hap-py then my life shall be!*

D. C. CHORUS

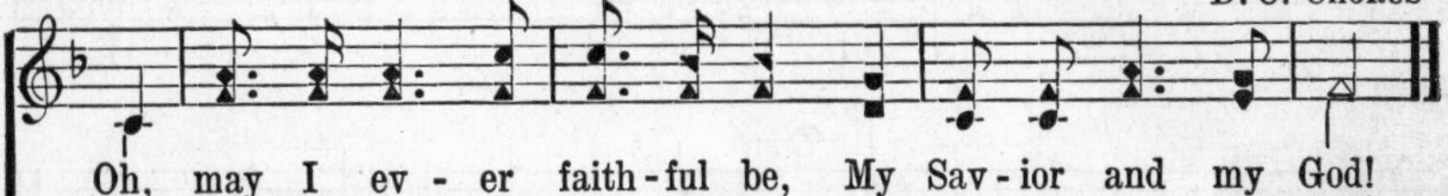

Oh, may I ev - er faith - ful be, My Sav - ior and my God!
And now henceforth I'll trust in Thee, My Sav - ior and my God!
I'll con - se - crate my life to Thee, My Sav - ior and my God!

I'll live for Him who died for me, My Sav - ior and my God!

189 I Would Be Like Jesus

James Rowe B. D. Ackley

1. Earth-ly pleas-ures vain-ly call me; I would be like Je - sus;
2. He has bro-ken ev-'ry fet-ter, I would be like Je - sus;
3. All the way from earth to Glo-ry, I would be like Je - sus;
4. That in Heav-en He may meet me, I would be like Je - sus;
would be like Je-sus;
Noth-ing world-ly shall en-thrall me; I would be like Je - sus.
That my soul may serve Him bet-ter, I would be like Je - sus.
Tell-ing o'er and o'er the sto-ry, I would be like Je - sus.
That His words "Well done" may greet me, I would be like Je - sus.
would be like Je-sus.
Chorus.
Be like Je-sus, this my song, In the home and in the throng;
Be like Je-sus, all day long! I would be like Je-sus. A-men.

Blessed Assurance

FANNY J. CROSBY

MRS. J. F. KNAPP

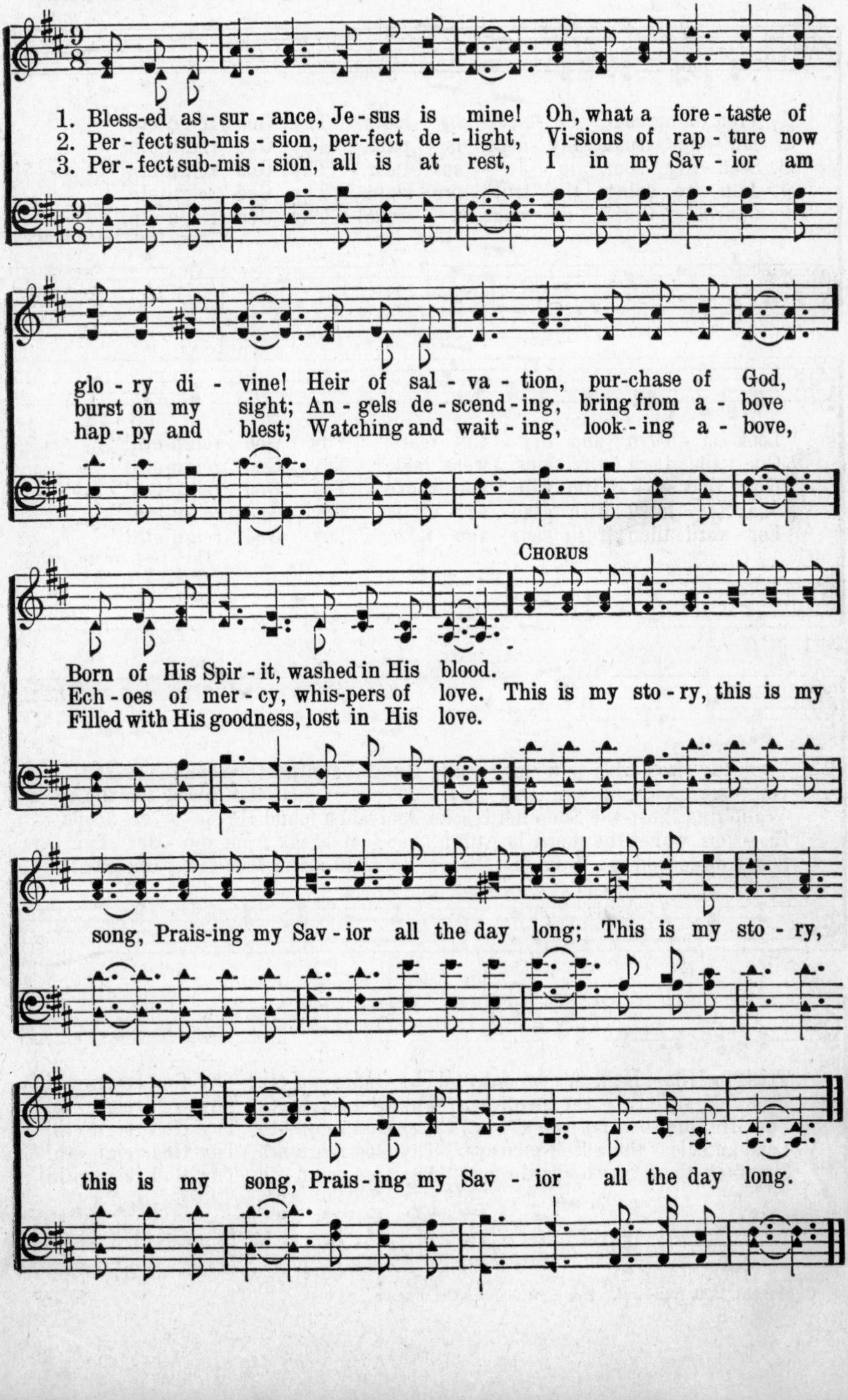
1. Bless-ed as-sur - ance, Je - sus is mine! Oh, what a fore - taste of glo - ry di - vine! Heir of sal - va - tion, pur-chase of God, Born of His Spir - it, washed in His blood.
2. Per - fect sub-mis - sion, per-fect de - light, Vi-sions of rap - ture now burst on my sight; An - gels de - scend - ing, bring from a - bove Ech - oes of mer - cy, whis-pers of love.
3. Per - fect sub-mis - sion, all is at rest, I in my Sav - ior am hap - py and blest; Watching and wait - ing, look - ing a - bove, Filled with His goodness, lost in His love.
CHORUS
This is my sto - ry, this is my song, Prais-ing my Sav - ior all the day long; This is my sto - ry, this is my song, Prais - ing my Sav - ior all the day long.

191 Thy God Reigneth!

F. S. Shepherd, arr. | James McGranahan

1. Trem-bling soul, be - set by fears, "Thy God reign-eth!"
2. Sin - ful soul, thy debt is paid, "Thy God reign-eth!"
3. Seek - ing soul, to Je - sus turn, "Thy God reign-eth!"
4. Join, ye saints, the truth pro - claim, "Thy God reign-eth!"
5. Church of Christ, a - wake, a - wake! "Thy God reign-eth!"

"Thy God reign-eth!"

Look a - bove and dry thy tears: "Thy God reign-eth!"
On the Lord thy sins were laid, "Thy God reign-eth!"
None that seek Him will He spurn, "Thy God reign-eth!"
Shout it forth with glad ac - claim, "Thy God reign-eth!"
For - ward, then, fresh cour - age take: "Thy God reign-eth!"

"Thy God reign - eth!"

Tho' thy foes with pow'r as - sail, Naught against thee shall pre - vail;
On the cross of Cal - va - ry Je - sus shed His blood for thee,
Wand'ring sheep the Shep-herd seeks, And when found He ev - er keeps,
Zi - on, wake! the morn is nigh, See, it break from yon - der sky;
Soon, de - scend-ing from His throne, He shall claim thee for His own;

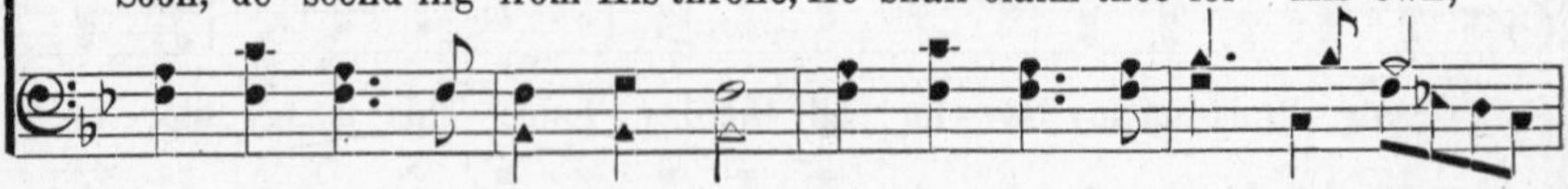

Trust in Him—He'll nev-er fail: "Thy God reign-eth, Thy God reign-eth!"
From all sin to set thee free: "Thy God reign-eth, Thy God reign-eth!"
For "He slum-bers not, nor sleeps:" "Thy God reign-eth, Thy God reign-eth!"
Loud and clear the watch-men cry: "Thy God reign-eth, Thy God reign-eth!"
Sin shall then be o-ver-thrown: "Thy God reign-eth, Thy God reign-eth!"

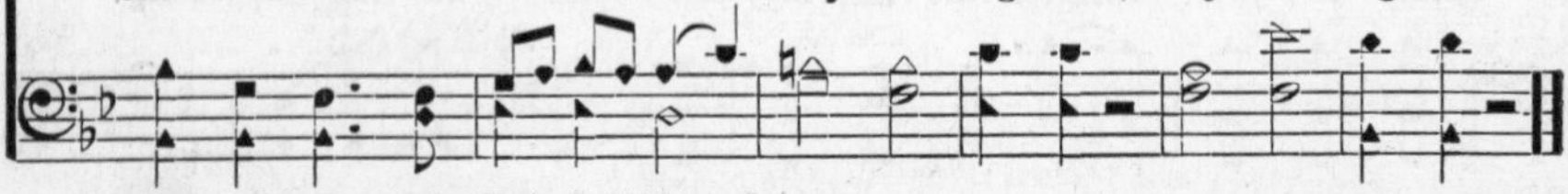

Moment By Moment

D. W. WHITTLE — MAY WHITTLE MOODY

1, Dy - ing with Je - sus, by death reckoned mine; Liv - ing with Je - sus, a
2. Nev - er a tri - al that He is not there, Nev - er a bur - den that
3. Nev - er a heart-ache, and nev - er a groan, Nev - er a tear-drop and
4. Nev - er a weak-ness that He doth not feel, Nev - er a sick-ness that
new life di-vine; Look-ing to Je - sus till glo - ry doth shine, Mo - ment by
He doth not bear, Nev - er a sor - row that He doth not share, Mo - ment by
nev - er a moan; Nev - er a dan - ger but there on the throne, Mo - ment by
He can-not heal; Mo - ment by moment, in woe or in weal, Je - sus, my
CHORUS
mo - ment, O Lord, I am Thine.
mo - ment, I'm un - der His care; Moment by mo - ment I'm kept in His love;
mo - ment He thinks of His own.
Sav - ior, a-bides with me still.
Mo - ment by mo - ment I've life from a - bove; Look - ing to Je - sus till
glo - ry doth shine; Mo - ment by mo - ment, O Lord, I am Thine.

193 Jesus, I Am Resting

JEAN SOPHIE PIGOTT — J. MOUNTAIN

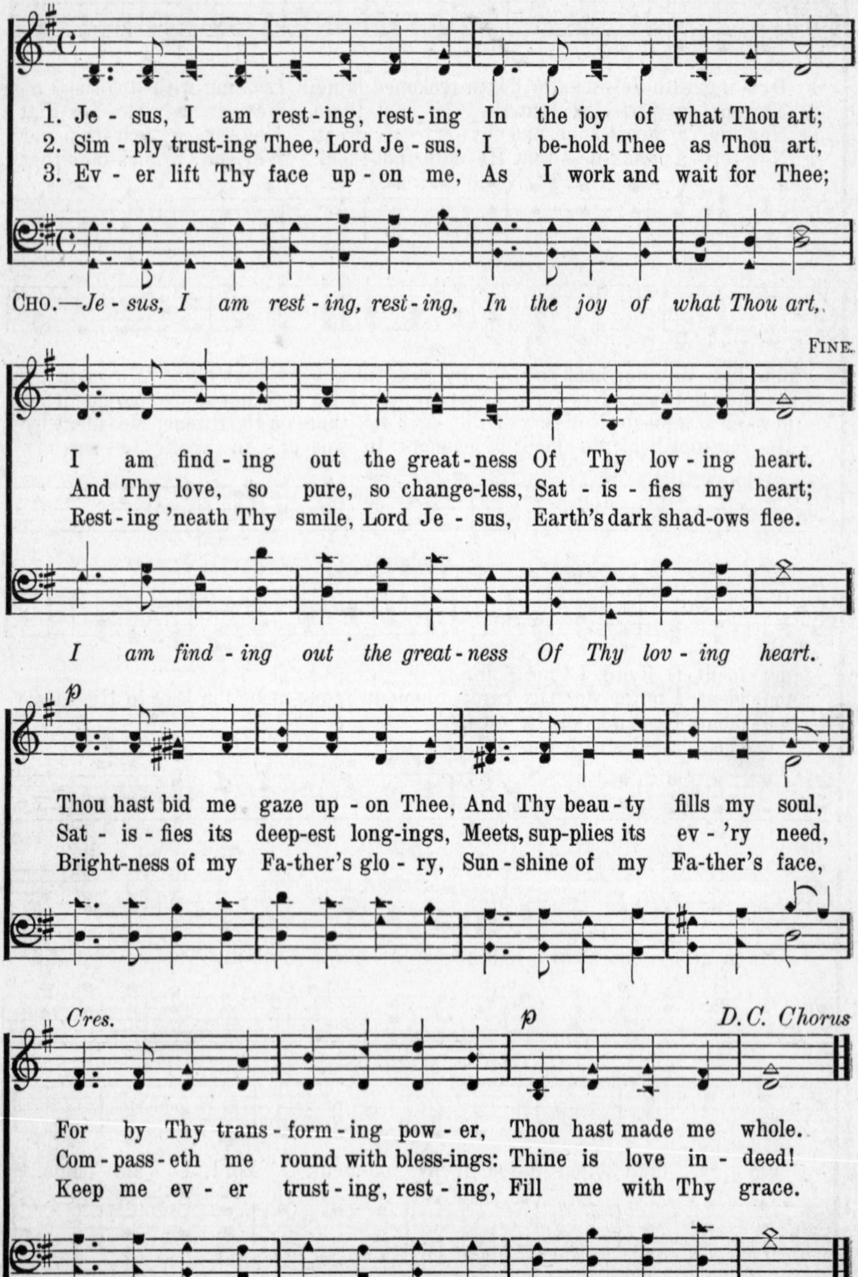
1. Je - sus, I am rest - ing, rest - ing In the joy of what Thou art;
2. Sim - ply trust-ing Thee, Lord Je - sus, I be-hold Thee as Thou art,
3. Ev - er lift Thy face up - on me, As I work and wait for Thee;
CHO.—Je - sus, I am rest - ing, rest - ing, In the joy of what Thou art,
FINE.
I am find - ing out the great - ness Of Thy lov - ing heart.
And Thy love, so pure, so change-less, Sat - is - fies my heart;
Rest - ing 'neath Thy smile, Lord Je - sus, Earth's dark shad-ows flee.
I am find - ing out the great - ness Of Thy lov - ing heart.
p
Thou hast bid me gaze up - on Thee, And Thy beau - ty fills my soul,
Sat - is - fies its deep-est long-ings, Meets, sup-plies its ev - 'ry need,
Bright-ness of my Fa-ther's glo - ry, Sun - shine of my Fa-ther's face,
Cres.
p
D.C. Chorus
For by Thy trans - form - ing pow - er, Thou hast made me whole.
Com - pass - eth me round with bless-ings: Thine is love in - deed!
Keep me ev - er trust - ing, rest - ing, Fill me with Thy grace.

I Know Whom I Have Believed

EL NATHAN | JAMES MCGRANAHAN

Moderato
1. I know not why God's won-drous grace To me He hath made known,
2. I know not how this sav - ing faith To me He did im - part,
3. I know not how the Spir - it moves, Con-vinc-ing men of sin,
4. I know not what of good or ill May be re-served for me,
5. I know not when my Lord may come, At night or noon-day fair,
Nor why un - wor - thy—Christ in love Re-deemed me for His own.
Nor how be - liev - ing in His Word Wrought peace within my heart.
Re - veal - ing Je - sus thro' the Word, Cre - at - ing faith in Him.
Of wea - ry ways or gold - en days, Be - fore His face I see.
Nor if I walk the vale with Him, Or "meet Him in the air."
CHORUS
But "I know whom I have be - liev - ed, and am per-suad-ed that He is
a - ble To keep that which I've committed Un - to Him a-gainst that day."

195 He Hideth My Soul

FANNY J. CROSBY

WM. J. KIRKPATRICK

Allegretto
1. A won-der-ful Sav-ior is Je-sus my Lord, A won-der-ful
2. A won-der-ful Sav-ior is Je-sus my Lord, He tak-eth my
3. With num-ber-less bless-ings each mo-ment He crowns, And filled with His
4. When clothed in His brightness, transport-ed I rise To meet Him in
Sav-ior to me, He hid-eth my soul in the cleft of the rock, Where
bur-den a-way, He hold-eth me up, and I shall not be moved, He
full-ness di-vine, I sing in my rap-ture, oh, glo-ry to God For
clouds of the sky, His per-fect sal-va-tion, His won-der-ful love, I'll
CHORUS
riv-ers of pleas-ure I see.
giv-eth me strength as my day. He hid-eth my soul in the cleft of the rock
such a Re-deem-er as mine!
shout with the mil-lions on high.
That shadows a dry, thirst-y land; He hid-eth my life in the depths of His love,
And cov-ers me there with His hand, And cov-ers me there with His hand.

Beulah Land

EDGAR PAGE — JNO. R. SWENEY

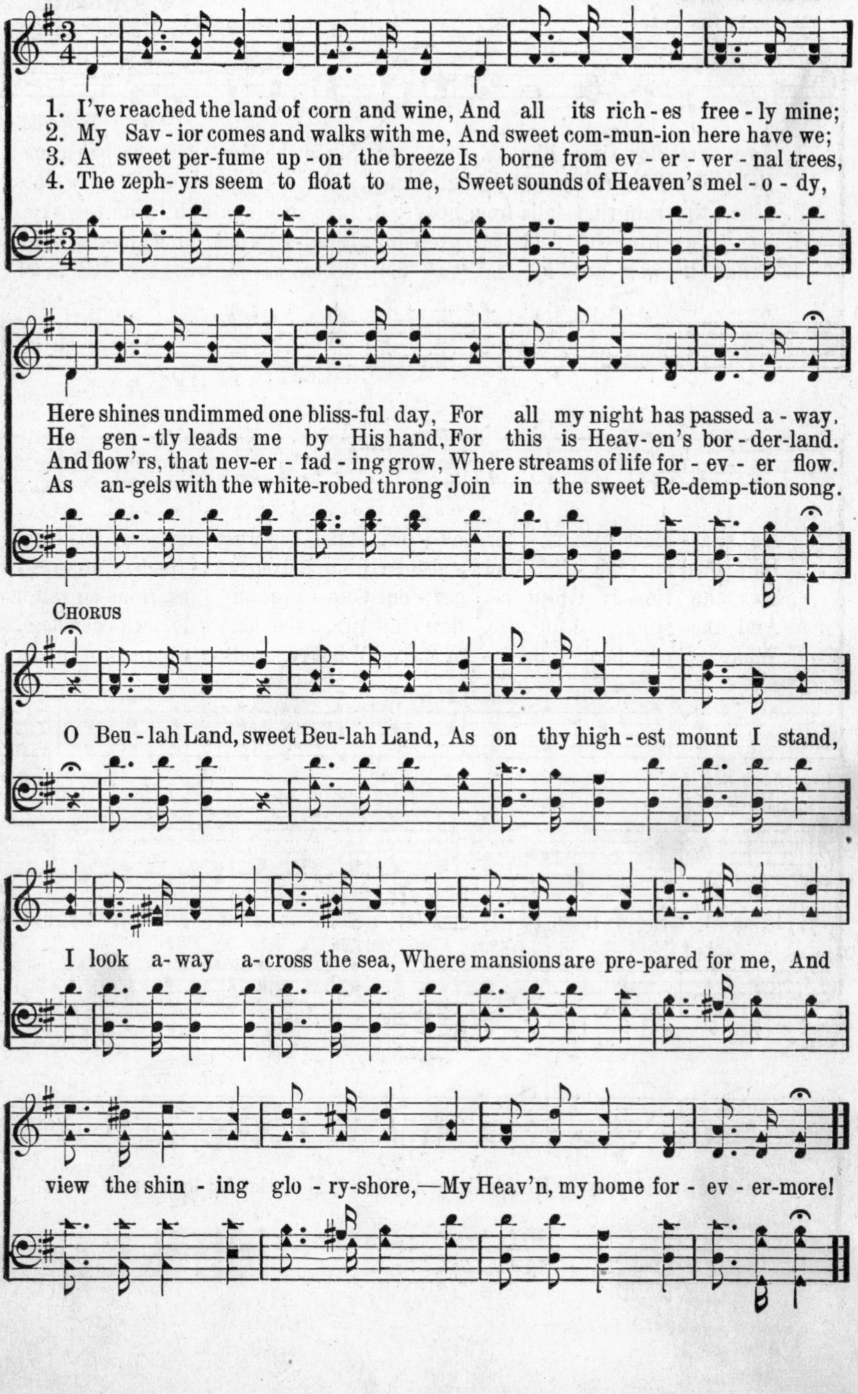
1. I've reached the land of corn and wine, And all its rich - es free - ly mine;
2. My Sav - ior comes and walks with me, And sweet com-mun-ion here have we;
3. A sweet per-fume up - on the breeze Is borne from ev - er - ver - nal trees,
4. The zeph- yrs seem to float to me, Sweet sounds of Heaven's mel - o - dy,
Here shines undimmed one bliss-ful day, For all my night has passed a - way.
He gen - tly leads me by His hand, For this is Heav - en's bor - der-land.
And flow'rs, that nev-er - fad - ing grow, Where streams of life for - ev - er flow.
As an-gels with the white-robed throng Join in the sweet Re-demp-tion song.
CHORUS
O Beu - lah Land, sweet Beu-lah Land, As on thy high - est mount I stand,
I look a- way a- cross the sea, Where mansions are pre-pared for me, And
view the shin - ing glo - ry-shore,—My Heav'n, my home for - ev - er-more!

197 Blessed Quietness

Manie Payne Ferguson

W. S. Marshall
Adapted by James M. Kirk

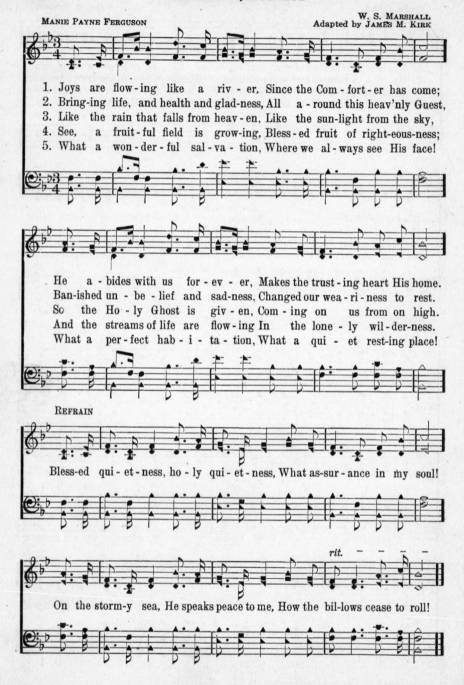

1. Joys are flow-ing like a riv-er, Since the Com-fort-er has come;
2. Bring-ing life, and health and glad-ness, All a-round this heav'nly Guest,
3. Like the rain that falls from heav-en, Like the sun-light from the sky,
4. See, a fruit-ful field is grow-ing, Bless-ed fruit of right-eous-ness;
5. What a won-der-ful sal-va-tion, Where we al-ways see His face!

He a-bides with us for-ev-er, Makes the trust-ing heart His home.
Ban-ished un-be-lief and sad-ness, Changed our wea-ri-ness to rest.
So the Ho-ly Ghost is giv-en, Com-ing on us from on high.
And the streams of life are flow-ing In the lone-ly wil-der-ness.
What a per-fect hab-i-ta-tion, What a qui-et rest-ing place!

Refrain

Bless-ed qui-et-ness, ho-ly qui-et-ness, What as-sur-ance in my soul!

rit.

On the storm-y sea, He speaks peace to me, How the bil-lows cease to roll!

Victory Through Grace

Sallie Martin — Jno. R. Sweney

1. Con-quer-ing now and still to con-quer, Rid-eth a King in His might,
2. Con-quer-ing now and still to con-quer, Who is this won-der - ful King?
3. Con-quer-ing now and still to con-quer, Je - sus, Thou Ru-ler of all,
Lead-ing the host of all the faith-ful In - to the midst of the fight;
Whence are the ar-mies which He lead-eth, While of His glo - ry they sing?
Thrones and their scepters all shall per-ish, Crowns and their splendor shall fall,
See them with cour-age ad - vanc-ing, Clad in their bril-liant ar - ray,
He is our Lord and Re - deem - or, Sav - ior and Mon - arch di - vine;
Yet shall the ar - mies Thou lead - est, Faith-ful and true to the last,
FINE.
Shout-ing the name of their Lead-er, Hear them ex - ult - ing - ly say:
They are the stars that for - ev - er Bright in His King-dom will shine.
Find in Thy man-sions e - ter - nal Rest, when their warfare is past.
D.S.—Yet to the true and the faith - ful Vic - t'ry is prom-ised thro' grace.
CHORUS
D. S.
Not to the strong is the bat - tle, Not to the swift is the race,

199

My Anchor Holds

W. C. MARTIN, arr. D. B. TOWNER

1. Tho' the an - gry sur - ges roll On my tem - pest-driv - en soul,
2. Might-y tides a - bout me sweep, Per - ils lurk with - in the deep,
3. I can feel the an - chor fast As I meet each sud - den blast,
4. Troub-les al - most 'whelm the soul; Griefs like bil - lows o'er me roll;
I am peace - ful, for I know, Wild - ly though the winds may blow,
An - gry clouds o'er-shade the sky, And the tem - pest ris - es high;
And the ca - ble, though un - seen, Bears the heav - y strain be - tween;
Tempters seek to lure a - stray; Storms ob - scure the light of day:
I've an an - chor safe and sure, That can ev - er-more en - dure.
Still I stand the tem-pest's shock, For my an - chor grips the Rock.
Thro' the storm I safe - ly ride, Till the turn - ing of the tide.
But in Christ I can be bold, I've an an - chor that shall hold.
CHORUS
And it holds, my an - chor holds; Blow your wild - est, then, O
And it holds,....... my an - chor holds; Blow your wild - - - est,
gale, On my bark so small and frail: By His grace I shall not
then, O gale,

My Anchor Holds

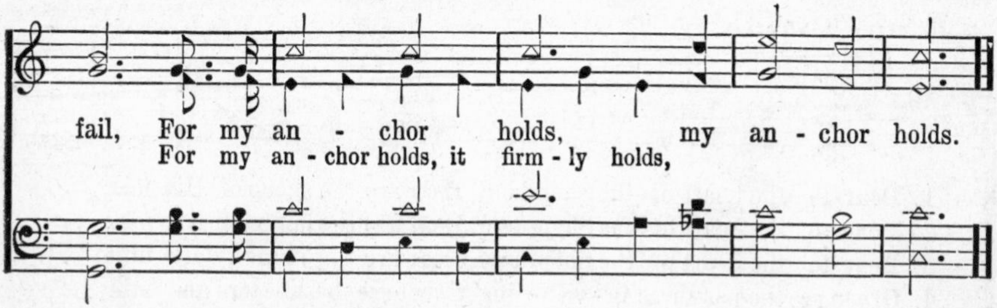
fail, For my an - chor holds, my an - chor holds.
For my an - chor holds, it firm - ly holds,

Have Thine Own Way, Lord 200

A. A. P. Geo. C. Stebbins

Slowly

1. Have Thine own way, Lord! Have Thine own way!.. Thou art the
2. Have Thine own way, Lord! Have Thine own way!.. Search me and
3. Have Thine own way, Lord! Have Thine own way!.. Wound-ed and
4. Have Thine own way, Lord! Have Thine own way!.. Hold o'er my

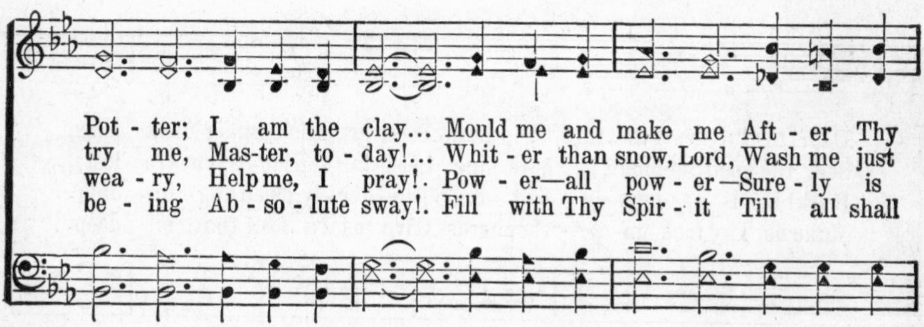
Pot - ter; I am the clay... Mould me and make me Aft - er Thy
try me, Mas-ter, to - day!... Whit - er than snow, Lord, Wash me just
wea - ry, Help me, I pray!. Pow - er—all pow - er—Sure - ly is
be - ing Ab - so - lute sway!. Fill with Thy Spir - it Till all shall

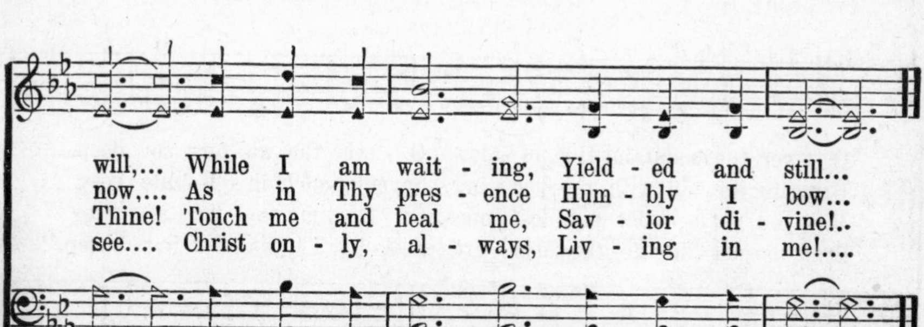
will,... While I am wait - ing, Yield - ed and still...
now,... As in Thy pres - ence Hum - bly I bow...
Thine! Touch me and heal me, Sav - ior di - vine!..
see.... Christ on - ly, al - ways, Liv - ing in me!....

201 Dear to the Heart of the Shepherd

Mrs. Mary B. Wingate　　　　Wm. J. Kirkpatrick

Duet

1. Dear to the heart of the Shep-herd, Dear are the sheep of His fold;...
2. Dear to the heart of the Shep-herd, Dear are the lambs of His fold;...
3. Dear to the heart of the Shep-herd, Dear are the "nine-ty and nine;".
4. Green are the pas-tures in-vit - ing, Sweet are the wa-ters and "still;"..
Dear is the love that He gives them, Dear-er than sil-ver or gold...
Some from the pastures are stray - ing, Hun-gry and help-less and cold...
Dear are the sheep that have wandered Out in the des-ert to pine...
Lord, we will an-swer Thee glad - ly, "Yes, bless-ed Mas-ter, we will!...
Dear to the heart of the Shep-herd, Dear are His "oth-er" lost sheep;
See, the good Shepherd is seek - ing, Seek-ing the lambs that are lost;..
Hark! He is ear-nest - ly call - ing, Ten - der - ly plead-ing to - day;..
Make us Thy true un-der - shepherds, Give us a love that is deep;.
O - ver the mountains He fol - lows, O - ver the wa-ters so deep..
Bringing them in with re - joic - ing, Saved at such in - fi - nite cost...
"Will you not seek for my lost ones, Off from my shel-ter a - stray?"
Send us out in - to the des - ert, Seek-ing Thy wan-der-ing sheep."

Dear to the Heart of the Shepherd

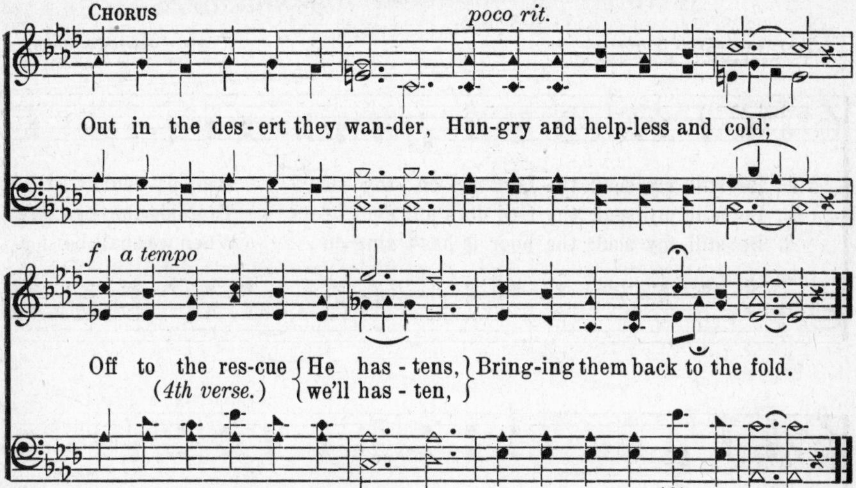
CHORUS
poco rit.
Out in the des-ert they wan-der, Hun-gry and help-less and cold;
f a tempo
Off to the res-cue {He has-tens, (4th verse.) we'll has-ten,} Bring-ing them back to the fold.

Thou Thinkest, Lord, of Me 202

E. D. MUND E. S. LORENZ

1. A - mid the tri - als which I meet, A - mid the thorns that pierce my feet,
2. The cares of life come thronging fast, Up - on my soul their shad-ow cast;
3. Let shad-ows come, let shad-ows go, Let life be bright or dark with woe,
FINE
One tho't re-mains su - preme-ly sweet, Thou think-est, Lord, of me!
Their gloom re-minds my heart at last, Thou think-est, Lord, of me!
I am con-tent, for this I know, Thou think-est, Lord, of me!
D.S.–What need I fear when Thou art near, And think-est, Lord, of me?
CHORUS
D.S.
Thou think-est, Lord, of me, (of me,) Thou thinkest, Lord, of me; (of me;)

203 Be Still, My Soul

FINLANDIA. 10. 10. 10. 10. 10. 10.

KATHARINA VON SCHLEGEL
Tr. by JANE L. BORTHWICK

JEAN SIBELIUS
Arr. for "The Hymnal"

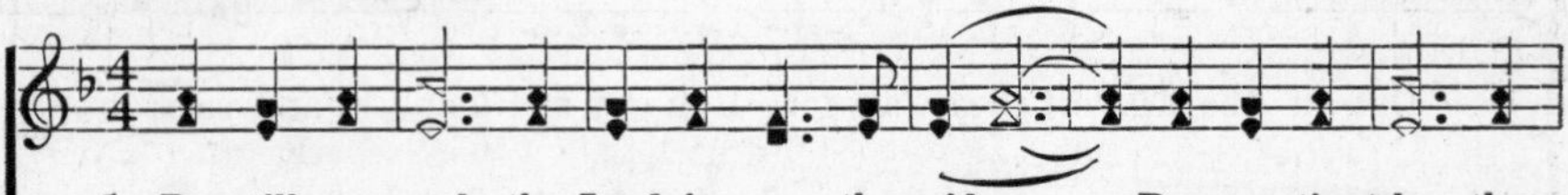

1. Be still, my soul: the Lord is on thy side; Bear pa-tient-ly the
2. Be still, my soul: thy God doth un-der-take To guide the fu-ture
3. Be still, my soul: the hour is has-t'ning on When we shall be for-

cross of grief or pain; Leave to thy God to or-der and pro-vide;
as He has the past. Thy hope, thy con-fi-dence let noth-ing shake;
ev-er with the Lord, When dis-ap-point-ment, grief, and fear are gone,

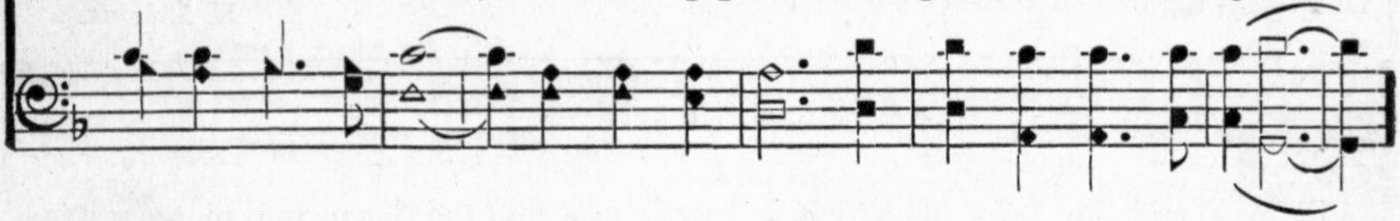

In ev-'ry change He faith-ful will re-main. Be still, my soul: thy
All now mys-te-rious shall be bright at last. Be still, my soul: the
Sor-row for-got, life's pur-est joys re-stored. Be still, my soul: when

best, thy heav'n-ly Friend Thro' thorn-y ways leads to a joy-ful end.
waves and winds still know His voice who ruled them while He dwelt be-low.
change and tears are past, All safe and bless-ed we shall meet at last.

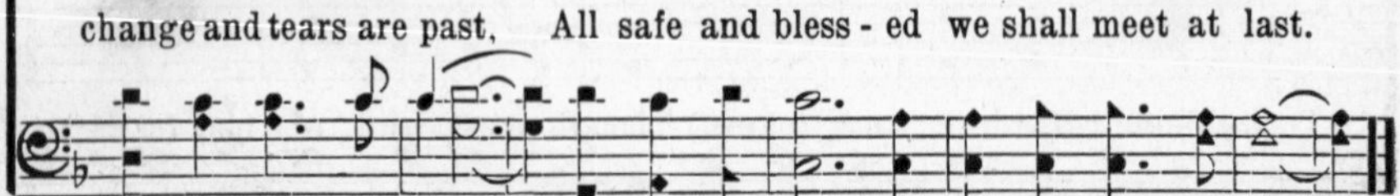

O Rock of Ages

H. L. HASTINGS — HUBERT P. MAIN

1. My soul at last a rest hath found, A rest that will not fail;
2. I'll hide me in this ref - uge strong, From ev - 'ry storm - y blast;
3. Ye com-fort-less and temp-est - tost, By sins and woes op - prest,
4. Ye thirst - y, from this smit-ten Rock Life's crys-tal wa - ters spring;
A sure and cer - tain anch'rage ground In Christ with - in the vail.
And sit and sing un - til the waves Of wrath are o - ver - past.
Ye tempt - ed, troub - led, ru - ined, lost, Come find in Christ your rest.
There hide from ev - 'ry storm - y shock, And rest, and drink, and sing.
CHORUS
O Rock of A-ges cleft for me, In Thee my soul se-cure-ly hide;
O Rock
In Thee
My tow'r of strength, I fly to Thee, And safe - ly there a - bide.

Copyright, 1915, by Hubert P. Main, Renewal. Hope Publishing Co., owner

205 "Thou Remainest"

D. W. WHITTLE (El Nathan) — JAMES MCGRANAHAN

Moderato, with expression

1. "Thou re-main-est," blest Re-deem-er, Lord of peace and Lord of strife;
2. Sat-is-fy-ing ev-'ry long-ing Of my sin-ful soul for grace;
3. One by one my loved may leave me, Voic-es sweet no more be heard;
4. When from earth Thou, Lord, shalt call me, Calm I'll lay my bur-den down;

Je-sus, Sav-ior, Lord for-ev-er, "Thou re-main-est," Christ my life.
From my weak-ness nev-er turn-ing, "Thou re-main-est," Christ my peace.
But of God naught can be-reave me, "Thou re-main-est," Christ my Lord.
For I know, what-e'er be-fall me, "Thou re-main-est," Christ my crown.

CHORUS

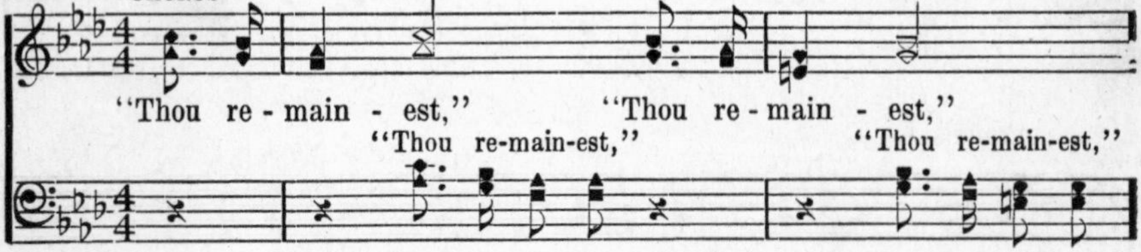

"Thou re-main-est," "Thou re-main-est,"
"Thou re-main-est," "Thou re-main-est,"

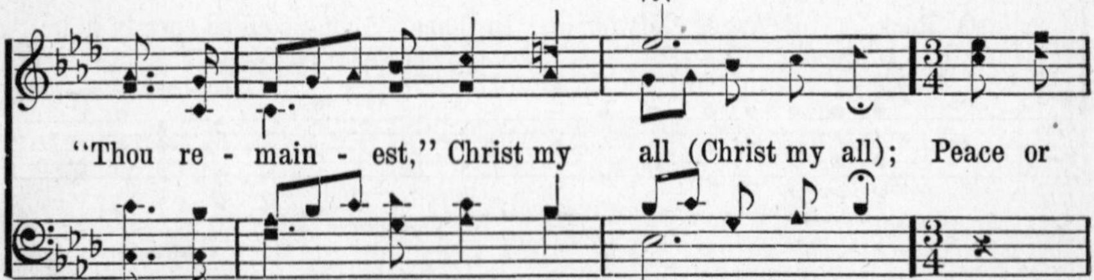

"Thou re-main-est," Christ my all (Christ my all); Peace or

con-flict, joy or sor-row, "Thou re-main-est," Christ my all.

Copyright, 1912, Renewal. Hope Publishing Co., owner

Under His Wings

William O. Cushing — Ira D. Sankey

1. Un - der His wings I am safe - ly a - bid - ing; Tho' the night deep - ens and tem - pests are wild, Still I can trust Him; I know He will keep me; He has re - deemed me, and I am His child.
2. Un - der His wings, what a ref - uge in sor - row! How the heart yearn - ing - ly turns to His rest! Oft - en when earth has no balm for my heal - ing, There I find com - fort, and there I am blest.
3. Un - der His wings, O what pre - cious en - joy - ment! There will I hide till life's tri - als are o'er; Shel - tered, pro - tect - ed, no e - vil can harm me; Rest - ing in Je - sus I'm safe ev - er - more.
Chorus
Un - der His wings, un - der His wings, Who from His love can sev - er?
Un - der His wings my soul shall a - bide, Safe - ly a - bide for - ev - er.

Copyright, 1924, by G. V. Sankey. Renewal. Hope Publishing Company, owner

207 If, On a Quiet Sea

AUGUSTUS M. TOPLADY
Alt. by others

SELVIN. S. M.

Arr. by LOWELL MASON

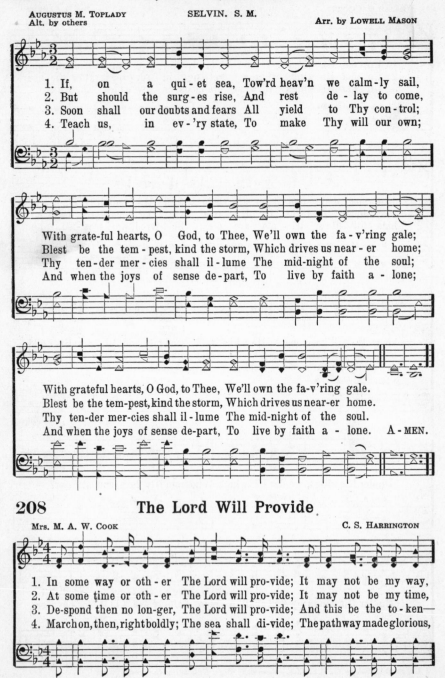

1. If, on a qui-et sea, Tow'rd heav'n we calm-ly sail,
2. But should the surg-es rise, And rest de-lay to come,
3. Soon shall our doubts and fears All yield to Thy con-trol;
4. Teach us, in ev-'ry state, To make Thy will our own;

With grate-ful hearts, O God, to Thee, We'll own the fa-v'ring gale;
Blest be the tem-pest, kind the storm, Which drives us near-er home;
Thy ten-der mer-cies shall il-lume The mid-night of the soul;
And when the joys of sense de-part, To live by faith a-lone;

With grateful hearts, O God, to Thee, We'll own the fa-v'ring gale.
Blest be the tem-pest, kind the storm, Which drives us near-er home.
Thy ten-der mer-cies shall il-lume The mid-night of the soul.
And when the joys of sense de-part, To live by faith a-lone. A-MEN.

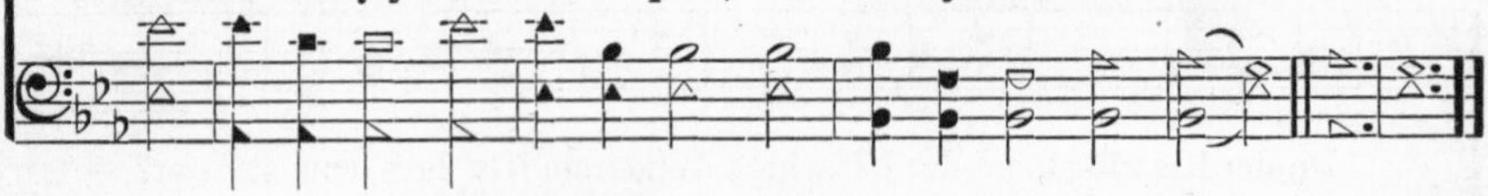

208 The Lord Will Provide

MRS. M. A. W. COOK

C. S. HARRINGTON

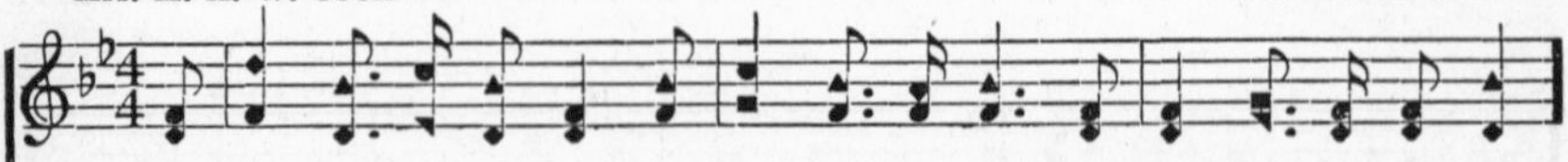

1. In some way or oth-er The Lord will pro-vide; It may not be my way,
2. At some time or oth-er The Lord will pro-vide; It may not be my time,
3. De-spond then no lon-ger, The Lord will pro-vide; And this be the to-ken—
4. March on, then, right boldly; The sea shall di-vide; The pathway made glorious,

The Lord Will Provide

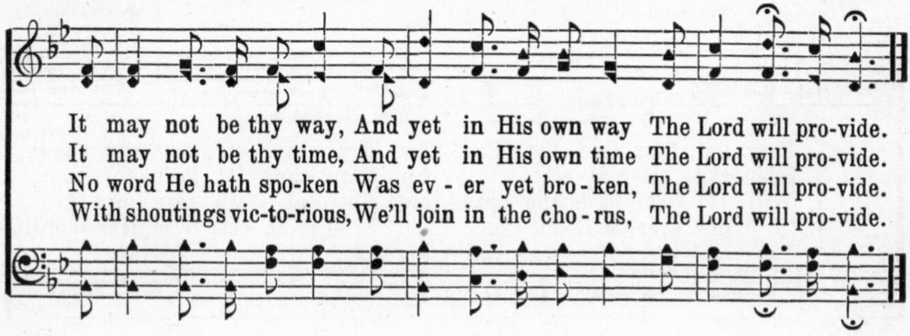
It may not be thy way, And yet in His own way The Lord will pro-vide.
It may not be thy time, And yet in His own time The Lord will pro-vide.
No word He hath spo-ken Was ev - er yet bro - ken, The Lord will pro-vide.
With shoutings vic-to-rious, We'll join in the cho - rus, The Lord will pro-vide.

Hold Thou My Hand 209

FANNY J. CROSBY 11s. 10s. HUBERT P. MAIN

Moderato

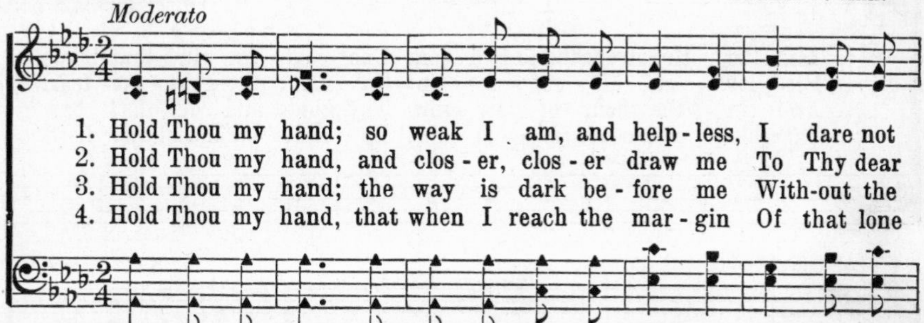
1. Hold Thou my hand; so weak I am, and help - less, I dare not
2. Hold Thou my hand, and clos - er, clos - er draw me To Thy dear
3. Hold Thou my hand; the way is dark be - fore me With-out the
4. Hold Thou my hand, that when I reach the mar - gin Of that lone

take one step with-out Thy aid; Hold Thou my hand; for then, O
self—my hope, my joy, my all; Hold Thou my hand, lest hap - ly
sun - light of Thy face di - vine; But when by faith I catch its
riv - er Thou didst cross for me, A heav'n-ly light may flash a-

lov-ing Sav - ior, No dread of ill shall make my soul a - fraid.
I should wan-der, And, miss-ing Thee, my trem-bling feet shall fall.
ra-diant glo - ry, What heights of joy, what rap-t'rous songs are mine!
long its wa - ters, And ev - 'ry wave like crys - tal bright shall be.

210 Trust Him

CHARLOTTE G. HOMER — CHAS. H. GABRIEL

1. Fear not, for God the Fa - ther Thy se - cret sor - row knows,
2. His eye is al - ways watch - ing, His ear is keen to hear;
3. Will He who feeds the spar - row Not al - so care for thee,
4. "I nev - er will for - sake thee!" Blest prom - ise from His Word!
And to thy strength He tem - pers The cold - est wind that blows.
His love is all - suf - fi - cient To calm the grav - est fear.
And in the hour of sor - row Thy guide and com - fort be?
Take heart, and cease re - pin - ing; Be - lieve on Christ the Lord.
REFRAIN
Then trust Him in shine and shade; Trust Him, be not a - fraid:
He's walk - ing close be - side thee; His hand will safe - ly guide thee;
His wings se - cure - ly hide thee; Then trust! Be not a - fraid.
rit.

Trust and Obey

J. H. SAMMIS — D. B. TOWNER

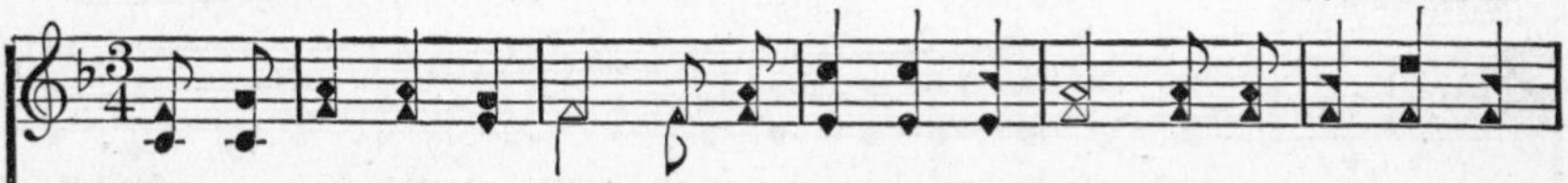

1. When we walk with the Lord In the Light of His Word What a glo - ry He
2. Not a shad-ow can rise, Not a cloud in the skies, But His smile quickly
3. Not a bur - den we bear, Not a sor - row we share, But our toil He doth
4. But we nev - er can prove The de-lights of His love Un - til all on the
5. Then in fel - low-ship sweet We will sit at His feet, Or we'll walk by His

sheds on our way! While we do His good-will, He a-bides with us still,
drives it a - way; Not a doubt or a fear, Not a sigh nor a tear,
rich - ly re - pay; Not a grief nor a loss, Not a frown or a cross,
al - tar we lay; For the fa - vor He shows, And the joy He be-stows,
side in the way; What He says we will do, Where He sends we will go,—

CHORUS.

And with all who will trust and o - bey.
Can a - bide while we trust and o - bey.
But is blest if we trust and o - bey. Trust and o - bey, for there's no oth-er
Are for them who will trust and o - bey.
Nev - er fear, on - ly trust and o - bey.

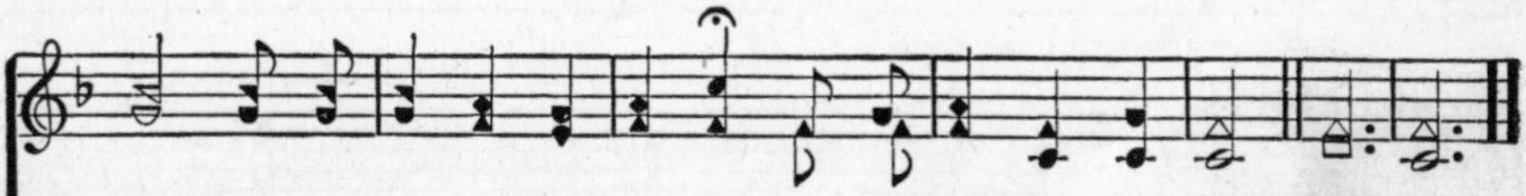

way To be hap - py in Je - sus, But to trust and o - bey. A - MEN.

212 When the Roll is Called Up Yonder

J. M. B. — J. M. BLACK

1. When the trumpet of the Lord shall sound, and time shall be no more, And the
2. On that bright and cloudless morning when the dead in Christ shall rise, And the
3. Let us la - bor for the Mas - ter from the dawn till set - ting sun, Let us
morning breaks, e-ter-nal, bright and fair; When the saved of earth shall gather
glo - ry of His res - ur-rec-tion share; When His cho-sen ones shall gather
talk of all His wondrous love and care; Then when all of life is o - ver,
o - ver on the oth-er shore, And the roll is called up yon-der, I'll be there.
to their home beyond the skies, And the roll is called up yon-der, I'll be there.
and our work on earth is done, And the roll is called up yon-der, I'll be there.
CHORUS.
When the roll . . . . . . is called up yon - - - - der, When the
When the roll is called up yon - der, I'll be there,
roll . . . . is called up yon - - der, When the roll . . . . is called up
When the roll is called up yon-der, I'll be there, When the roll is called up

When the Roll is Called Up Yonder

yon - der, When the roll is called up yon - der, I'll be there.

Leaning On the Everlasting Arms 213

E. A. HOFFMAN

A. J. SHOWALTER

1. What a fel-low-ship, what a joy di-vine, Leaning on the ev-er-last-ing arms;
2. Oh, how sweet to walk in this pilgrim way, Leaning on the ev-er-last-ing arms;
3. What have I to dread, what have I to fear, Leaning on the ev-er-last-ing arms?
What a bless-ed-ness, what a peace is mine, Leaning on the ev-er-last-ing arms.
Oh, how bright the path grows from day to day, Leaning on the ev-er-last-ing arms.
I have bless-ed peace with my Lord so near, Leaning on the ev-er-last-ing arms.
REFRAIN
Lean - ing, lean - ing, Safe and se-cure from all a-larms;
Lean-ing on Je - sus, lean-ing on Je - sus,
Lean - ing, lean - ing, Lean-ing on the ev-er-last-ing arms.
Lean-ing on Je - sus, lean-ing on Je - sus,

214 O God of Love, O King of Peace

HENRY W. BAKER — HESPERUS — HENRY W. BAKER

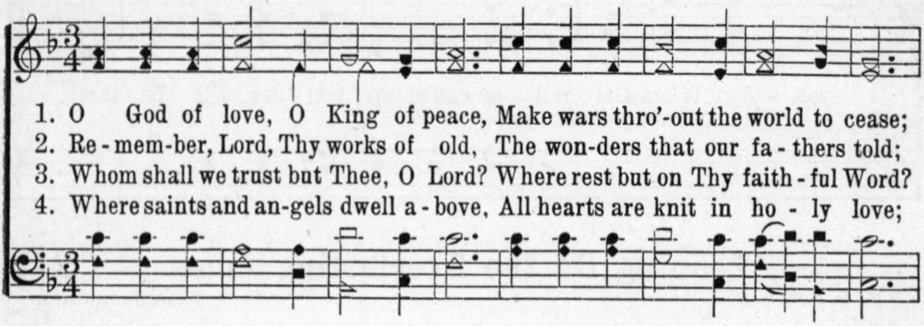
1. O God of love, O King of peace, Make wars thro'-out the world to cease;
2. Re-mem-ber, Lord, Thy works of old, The won-ders that our fa-thers told;
3. Whom shall we trust but Thee, O Lord? Where rest but on Thy faith-ful Word?
4. Where saints and an-gels dwell a-bove, All hearts are knit in ho-ly love;

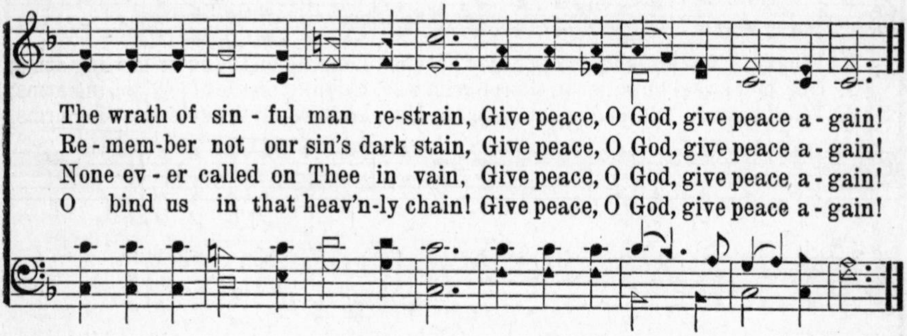
The wrath of sin-ful man re-strain, Give peace, O God, give peace a-gain!
Re-mem-ber not our sin's dark stain, Give peace, O God, give peace a-gain!
None ev-er called on Thee in vain, Give peace, O God, give peace a-gain!
O bind us in that heav'n-ly chain! Give peace, O God, give peace a-gain!

215 Close to Thee

FANNY J. CROSBY — SILAS J. VAIL

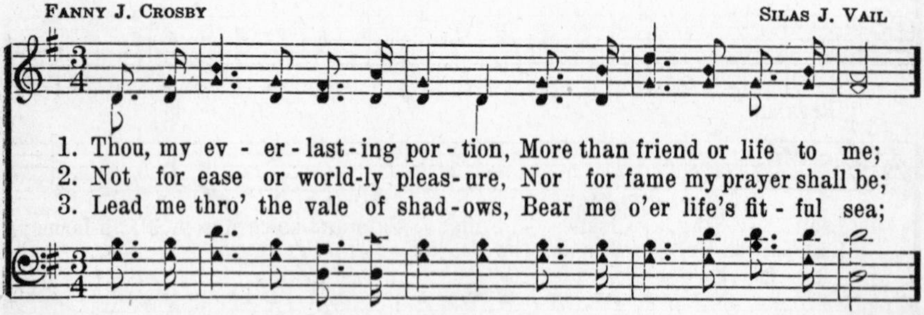
1. Thou, my ev-er-last-ing por-tion, More than friend or life to me;
2. Not for ease or world-ly pleas-ure, Nor for fame my prayer shall be;
3. Lead me thro' the vale of shad-ows, Bear me o'er life's fit-ful sea;

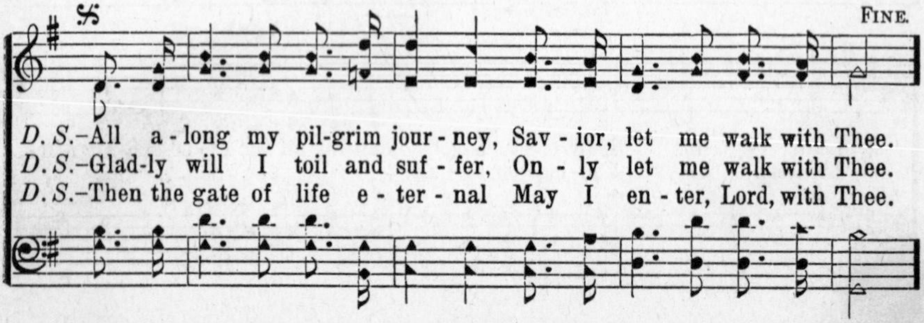
FINE.
D. S.–All a-long my pil-grim jour-ney, Sav-ior, let me walk with Thee.
D. S.–Glad-ly will I toil and suf-fer, On-ly let me walk with Thee.
D. S.–Then the gate of life e-ter-nal May I en-ter, Lord, with Thee.

Close to Thee

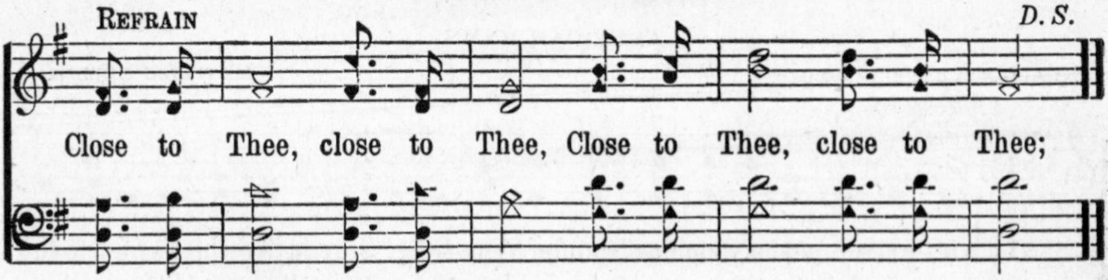
Refrain
D. S.
Close to Thee, close to Thee, Close to Thee, close to Thee;

'Tis So Sweet to Trust in Jesus 216

Louisa M. R. Stead Wm. J. Kirkpatrick

1. 'Tis so sweet to trust in Je - sus, Just to take Him at His Word;
2. O how sweet to trust in Je - sus, Just to trust His cleans-ing blood;
3. Yes, 'tis sweet to trust in Je - sus, Just from sin and self to cease;
4. I'm so glad I learned to trust Thee, Pre - cious Je - sus, Sav - ior, Friend;
Just to rest up - on His prom-ise; Just to know, "Thus saith the Lord."
Just in sim - ple faith to plunge me 'Neath the heal - ing, cleans-ing flood!
Just from Je - sus sim - ply tak - ing Life and rest, and joy and peace.
And I know that Thou art with me, Wilt be with me to the end.
Chorus
Je - sus, Je - sus, how I trust Him! How I've proved Him o'er and o'er!
p
Je - sus, Je - sus, pre - cious Je - sus! O for grace to trust Him more!

Angel of Peace

AMERICAN HYMN

OLIVER WENDELL HOLMES — MATTHIAS KELLER

Maestoso
1. An - gel of peace, thou hast wandered too long! Spread thy white wings to the
2. Joy - ous we meet, on this al - tar of thine, Min-gling the gifts we have
3. An - gels of Beth - le-hem, an-swer the strain! Hark! a new birth-song is
sunshine of love! Come while our voic-es are blend-ed in song, Fly to our
gathered for thee, Sweet with the o - dors of myr-tle and pine, Breeze of the
fill - ing the sky! Loud as the storm-wind that tumbles the main Bid the full
ark like the storm-beaten dove,—Fly to our ark on the wings of the dove;
prai-rie and breath of the sea,— Mead-ow and mountain and for - est and sea;
breath of the or - gan re - ply,— Let the loud tem - pest of voic - es re - ply;
Speed o'er the far-sound-ing bil - lows of song, Crowned with thine ol - ive-leaf
Sweet is the fra-grance of myr-tle and pine, Sweet - er the in-cense we
Roll its long surge like the earth-shaking main! Swell the vast song till it

Angel of Peace

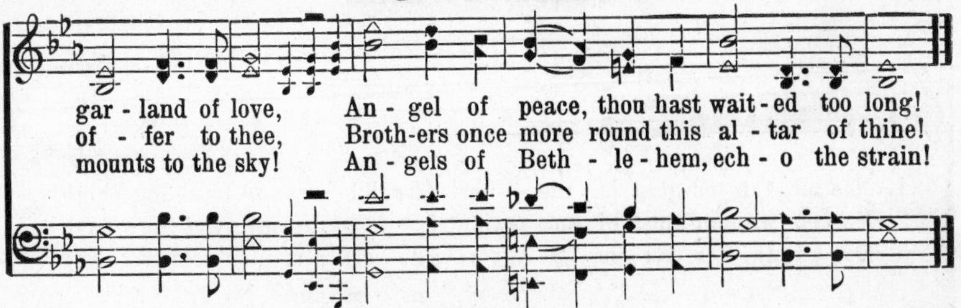
gar - land of love, An - gel of peace, thou hast wait - ed too long!
of - fer to thee, Broth-ers once more round this al - tar of thine!
mounts to the sky! An - gels of Beth - le - hem, ech - o the strain!

His Yoke is Easy 218

R. E. Hudson

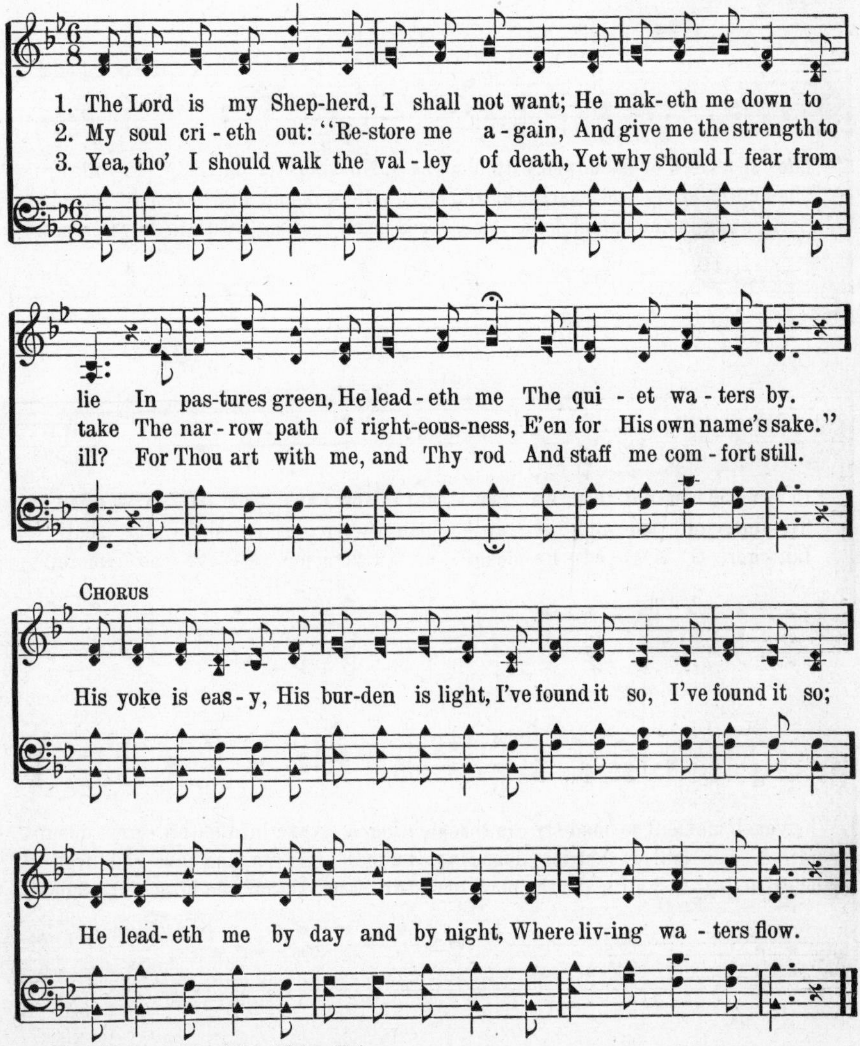
1. The Lord is my Shep-herd, I shall not want; He mak-eth me down to lie In pas-tures green, He lead - eth me The qui - et wa - ters by.
2. My soul cri - eth out: "Re-store me a - gain, And give me the strength to take The nar - row path of right-eous-ness, E'en for His own name's sake."
3. Yea, tho' I should walk the val - ley of death, Yet why should I fear from ill? For Thou art with me, and Thy rod And staff me com - fort still.
Chorus
His yoke is eas - y, His bur-den is light, I've found it so, I've found it so;
He lead-eth me by day and by night, Where liv-ing wa - ters flow.

Used by permission of Mrs. Walter Heiss

219 **Peace! Be Still!**

MARY A. BAKER — H. R. PALMER

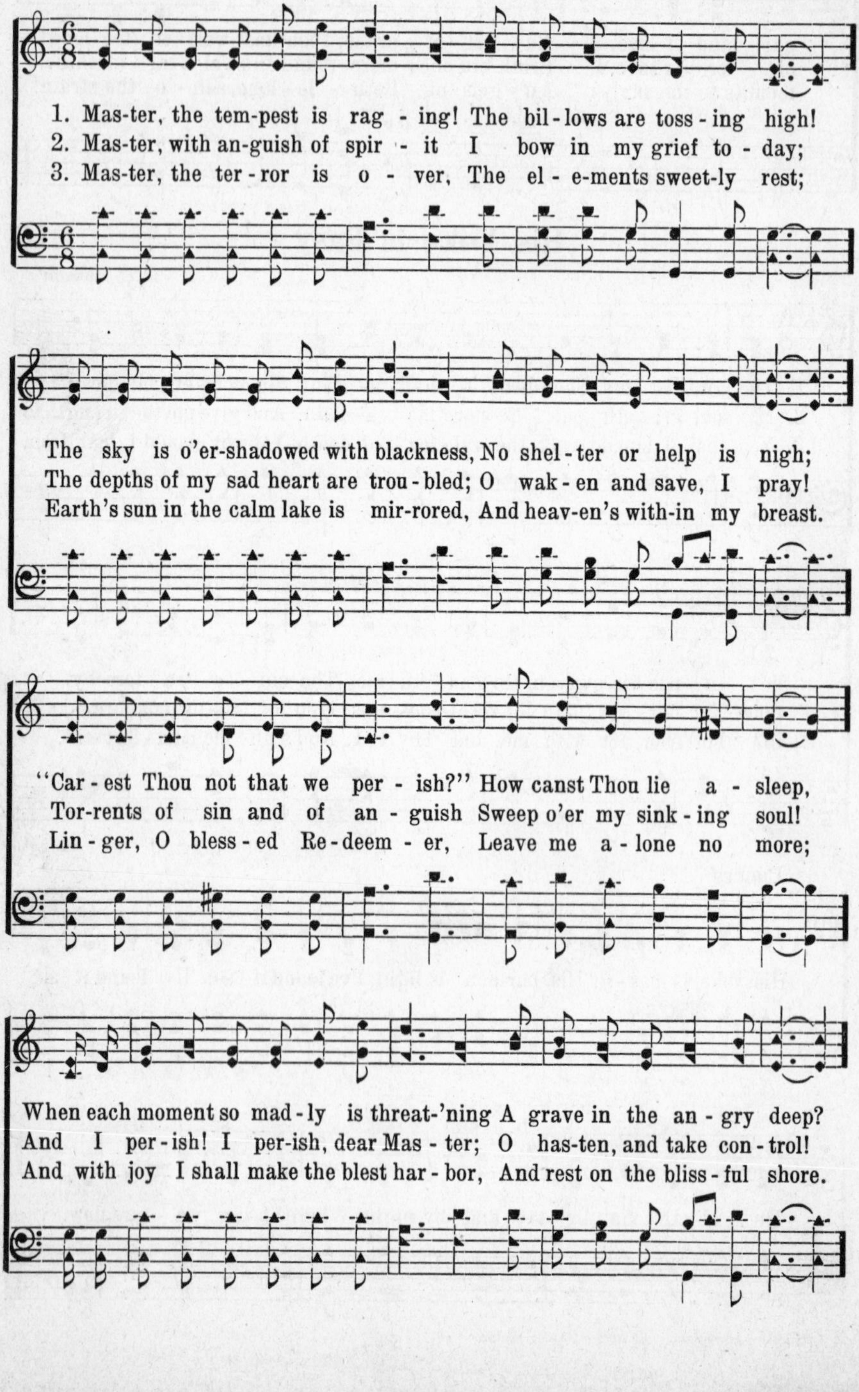
1. Mas-ter, the tem-pest is rag - ing! The bil-lows are toss-ing high!
2. Mas-ter, with an-guish of spir - it I bow in my grief to - day;
3. Mas-ter, the ter-ror is o - ver, The el - e-ments sweet-ly rest;
The sky is o'er-shadowed with blackness, No shel-ter or help is nigh;
The depths of my sad heart are trou-bled; O wak-en and save, I pray!
Earth's sun in the calm lake is mir-rored, And heav-en's with-in my breast.
"Car-est Thou not that we per - ish?" How canst Thou lie a - sleep,
Tor-rents of sin and of an - guish Sweep o'er my sink - ing soul!
Lin - ger, O bless - ed Re - deem - er, Leave me a - lone no more;
When each moment so mad - ly is threat-'ning A grave in the an - gry deep?
And I per - ish! I per-ish, dear Mas - ter; O has-ten, and take con - trol!
And with joy I shall make the blest har - bor, And rest on the bliss - ful shore.

Peace! Be Still!

220 We Have An Anchor

PRISCILLA J. OWENS — WM. J. KIRKPATRICK

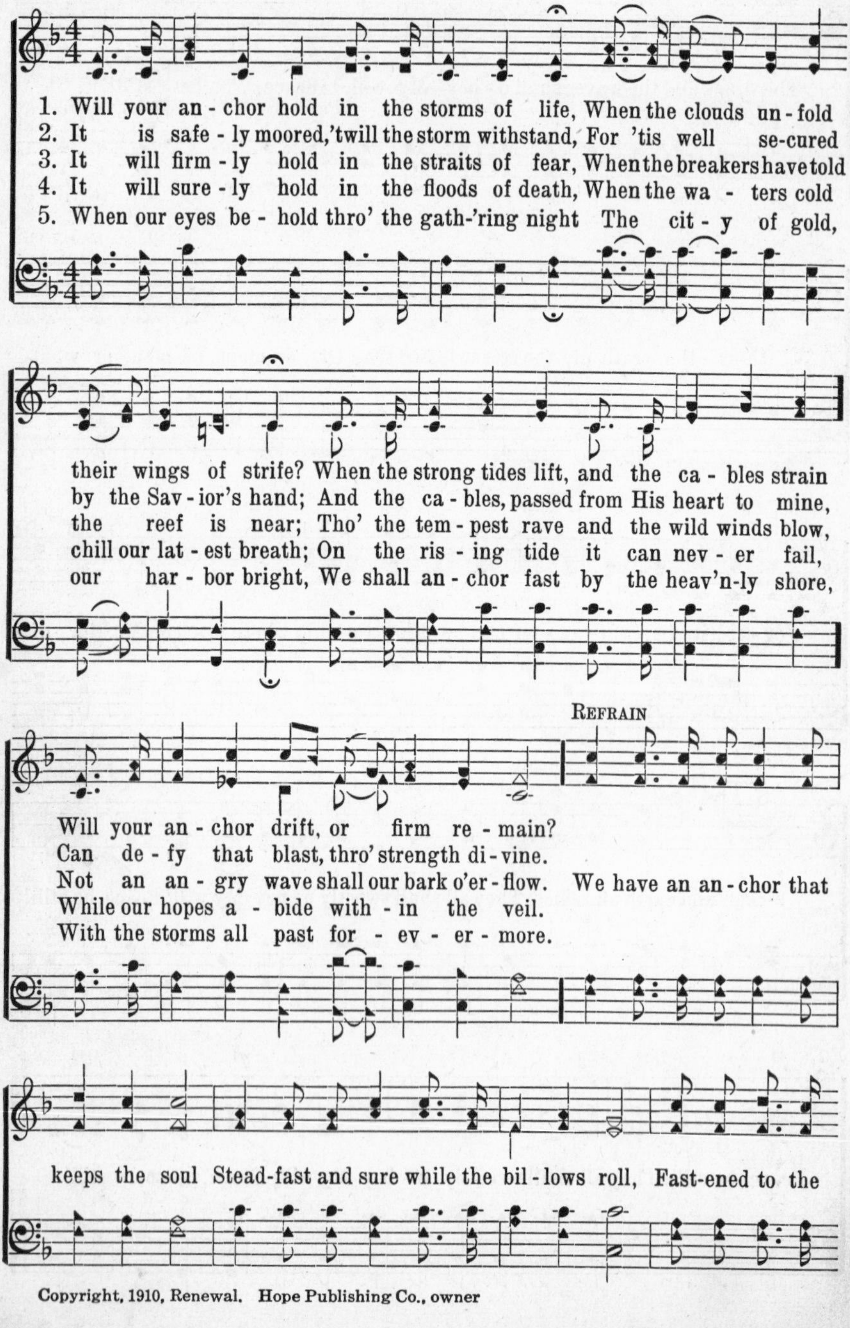
1. Will your an - chor hold in the storms of life, When the clouds un - fold
2. It is safe - ly moored,'twill the storm withstand, For 'tis well se-cured
3. It will firm - ly hold in the straits of fear, When the breakers have told
4. It will sure - ly hold in the floods of death, When the wa - ters cold
5. When our eyes be - hold thro' the gath-'ring night The cit - y of gold,
their wings of strife? When the strong tides lift, and the ca - bles strain
by the Sav - ior's hand; And the ca - bles, passed from His heart to mine,
the reef is near; Tho' the tem - pest rave and the wild winds blow,
chill our lat - est breath; On the ris - ing tide it can nev - er fail,
our har - bor bright, We shall an - chor fast by the heav'n-ly shore,
Will your an - chor drift, or firm re - main?
Can de - fy that blast, thro' strength di - vine.
Not an an - gry wave shall our bark o'er - flow.
While our hopes a - bide with - in the veil.
With the storms all past for - ev - er - more.
REFRAIN
We have an an - chor that
keeps the soul Stead-fast and sure while the bil - lows roll, Fast-ened to the

We Have An Anchor

Rock which can-not move, Grounded firm and deep in the Sav-ior's love.

Hide Me

221

FANNY J. CROSBY

W. H. DOANE

1. Hide me, O my Sav-ior, hide me In Thy ho-ly place;
2. Hide me, when the storm is rag-ing O'er life's troub-led sea;
3. Hide me, when my heart is break-ing With its weight of woe;
Rest-ing there be-neath Thy glo-ry, O let me see Thy face.
Like a dove on o-cean's bil-lows, O let me fly to Thee.
When in tears I seek the com-fort Thou canst a-lone be-stow.
REFRAIN
Hide me, hide me, O bless-ed Sav-ior, hide me;
Hide me, hide me, safe-ly hide me,
O Sav-ior, keep me Safe-ly, O Lord, with Thee.
O my Sav-ior, keep Thou me,

Hide Thou Me

FANNY J. CROSBY — ROBERT LOWRY

1. In Thy cleft, O Rock of A - ges, Hide Thou me; When the
2. From the snare of sin - ful pleas - ure, Hide Thou me; Thou, my
3. In the lone - ly night of sor - row, Hide Thou me; Till in
fit - ful tem - pest rag - es, Hide Thou me; Where no
soul's e - ter - nal treas - ure, Hide Thou me; When the
glo - ry dawns the mor - row, Hide Thou me; In the
mor - tal arm can sev - er From my heart Thy love for-
world its pow'r is wield - ing, And my heart is al - most
sight of Jor - dan's bil - low, Let Thy bos - om be my
ev - er, Hide me, O Thou Rock of A - ges, Safe in Thee.
yield-ing, Hide me, O Thou Rock of A - ges, Safe in Thee.
pil - low; Hide me, O Thou Rock of A - ges, Safe in Thee.

In Heavenly Love Abiding 223

ANNA L. WARING MENDELSSOHN-BARTHOLDY

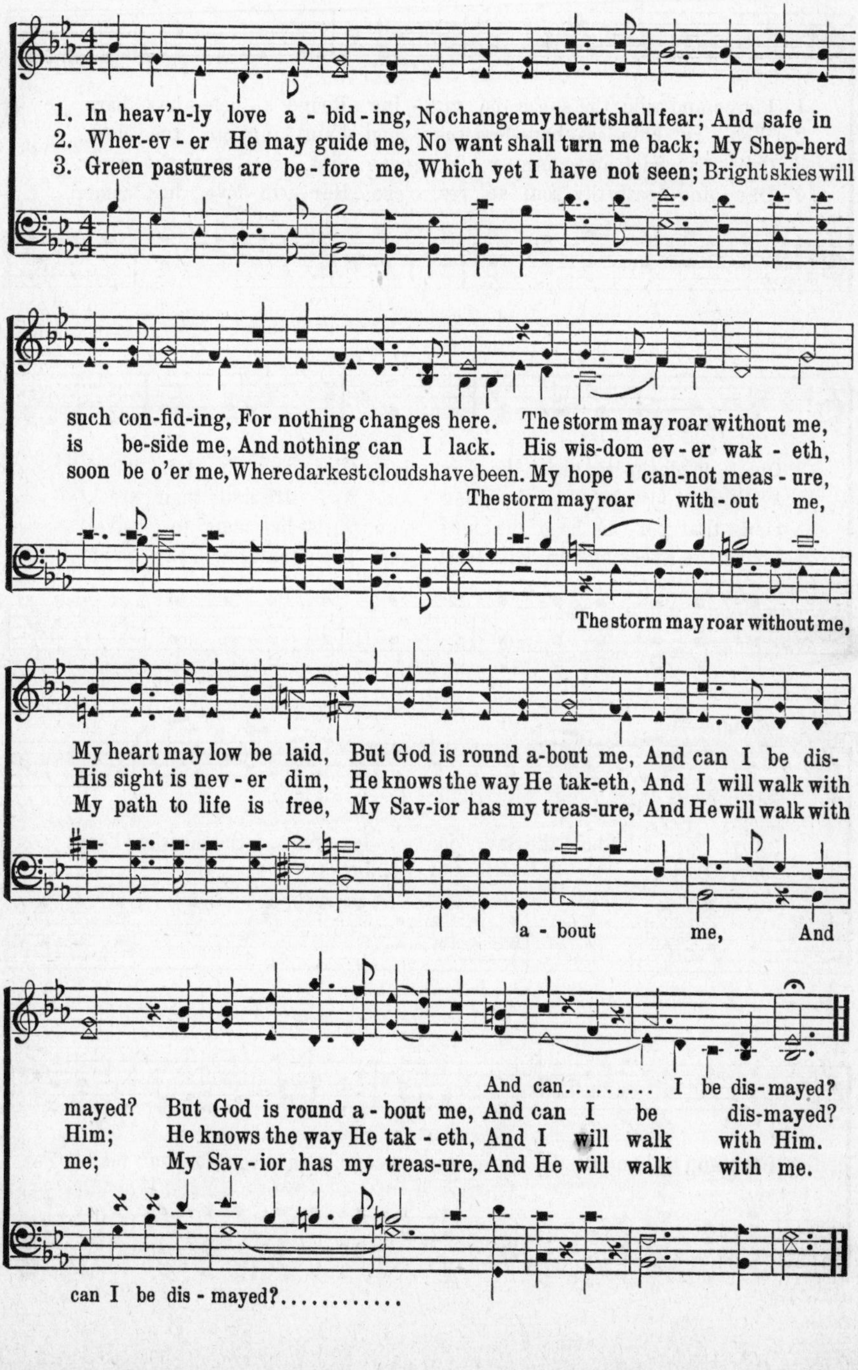
1. In heav'n-ly love a - bid - ing, No change my heart shall fear; And safe in
2. Wher-ev - er He may guide me, No want shall turn me back; My Shep-herd
3. Green pastures are be - fore me, Which yet I have not seen; Bright skies will
such con-fid-ing, For nothing changes here. The storm may roar without me,
is be-side me, And nothing can I lack. His wis-dom ev - er wak - eth,
soon be o'er me, Where darkest clouds have been. My hope I can-not meas - ure,
The storm may roar with - out me,
The storm may roar without me,
My heart may low be laid, But God is round a-bout me, And can I be dis-
His sight is nev - er dim, He knows the way He tak-eth, And I will walk with
My path to life is free, My Sav-ior has my treas-ure, And He will walk with
a - bout me, And
And can......... I be dis-mayed?
mayed? But God is round a - bout me, And can I be dis-mayed?
Him; He knows the way He tak - eth, And I will walk with Him.
me; My Sav - ior has my treas-ure, And He will walk with me.
can I be dis - mayed?............

224 I'll Stand By Until the Morning

W. W. D. JAMES McGRANAHAN

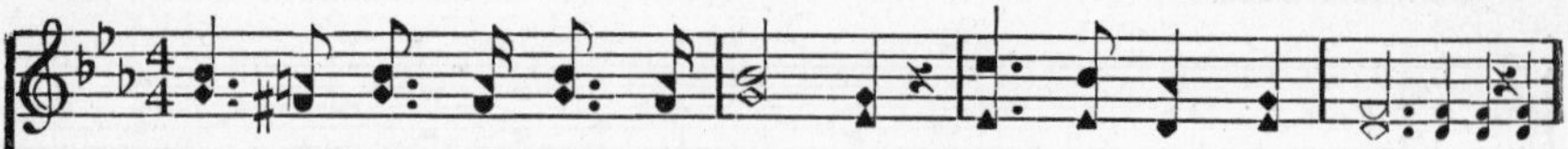

1. Fierce and wild the storm is rag - ing Round a help - less bark,
2. Wea - ry, help-less, hope-less sea - men Faint - ing on the deck,
3. On a wild and storm - y o - cean, Sink - ing 'neath the wave,
4. Dar - ing death thy soul to res - cue, He in love has come,

On to doom 'tis swift - ly driv - ing, O'er the wa - ters dark!
With what joy they hail their Sav - ior, As He hails their wreck!
Souls that per - ish heed the mes - sage, Christ has come to save!
Leave the wreck and in Him trust - ing, Thou shalt reach thy home!

CHORUS

Joy, ... be-hold the Sav - ior, Joy, ... the message hear,
Joy, O joy, be - hold the Sav-ior, Joy, O joy, the mes-sage hear,

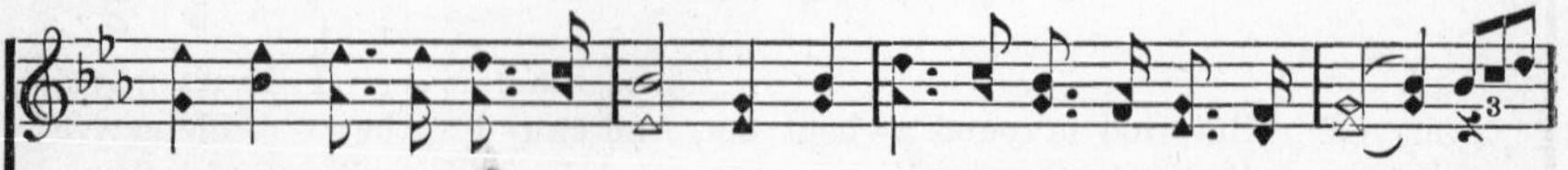

"I'll stand by un - til the morn-ing, I've come to save you, do not fear," Yes,

I'll Stand By Until the Morning

I'll stand by un-til the morn-ing, I've come to save you, do not fear (do not fear).

Guide Me, O Thou Great Jehovah
225

THOMAS HASTINGS

Welsh

1. Guide me, O Thou great Je - ho - vah, Pil - grim thro' this
2. O - pen now the crys - tal foun - tain, Whence the heal - ing
3. When I tread the verge of Jor - dan, Bid my anx - ious
bar - ren land: I am weak, but Thou art might-y; Hold me with Thy
streams do flow; Let the fier - y, cloud-y pil - lar, Lead me all the
fears sub - side; Bear me thro' the swell-ing cur-rent; Land me safe on
pow'r-ful hand: Bread of heav - en, Bread of heav - en, Feed me
jour - ney thro': Strong De - liv - 'rer, Strong De - liv - 'rer, Be Thou
Ca - naan's side: Songs of prais - es, Songs of prais - es I will
till I want no more, Feed me till I want no more.
still my strength and shield, Be Thou still my strength and shield.
ev - er sing to Thee. I will ev - er sing to Thee.
1. want no more,

226

In His Keeping

Mrs. C. H. M. — Mrs. C. H. Morris

1. When the ear-ly morning breaking, Slumber from my eye-lids shaking, Comes the bless-ed tho't with wak-ing, I am in His keep-ing. Day ad-vanc-es, la-bor bring-ing, Care, her mantle 'round me flinging, Yet midst all my soul keeps singing, I am in His care.
2. Some-times dark clouds hang o'er me, Not one step I see be-fore me, Still, my Sav-ior, I a-dore Thee, I am in His keep-ing. I can trust His hand to guide me, 'Neath His wings He'll safely hide me, And no harm can e'er be-tide me,
3. Gen-tle e-ven-tide is near-ing, Light from heaven dis-ap-pear-ing, Still the bless-ed tho't so cheer-ing, I am in His keep-ing. Now night's curtains gather 'round me, Yet its dan-gers have not found me, For His angel guards surround me,
CHORUS
I am in my Father's keeping, I am in His ten-der care; Wheth-er wak-ing, wheth-er sleep-ing, I am in His care.
rit.

Jesus Leads

JOHN R. CLEMENTS

JNO. R. SWENEY

Andante

1. Like a shep-herd, ten-der, true, Je-sus leads,... Je-sus leads,...
2. All a-long life's rug-ged road Je-sus leads,... Je-sus leads,...
3. Thro' the sun-lit ways of life Je-sus leads,... Je-sus leads,...
Je-sus leads, Je-sus leads,
Dai-ly finds us pas-tures new, Je-sus leads,... Je-sus leads;
Till we reach yon blest a-bode, Je-sus leads,... Je-sus leads;
Thro' the warrings and the strife Je-sus leads,... Je-sus leads;
Je-sus leads, Je-sus leads;
If thick mists are o'er the way, Or the flock 'mid danger feeds,
All the way, be-fore, He's trod, And He now the flock precedes,
When we reach the Jordan's tide, Where life's bound'ry-line re-cedes,
If thick mists are o'er the way, Or the flock 'mid danger feeds,
rit.
He will watch them lest they stray, Je-sus leads,... Je-sus leads.
Safe in-to the fold of God, Je-sus leads,... Je-sus leads.
He will spread the waves a-side, Je-sus leads,... Je-sus leads.
Je-sus leads,

I Must Tell Jesus

E. A. H. E. A. Hoffman

1. I must tell Je - sus all of my tri - als; I can - not bear these
2. I must tell Je - sus all of my troub - les; He is a kind, com -
3. Tempted and tried I need a great Sav - ior, One who can help my
4. O how the world to e - vil al - lures me! O how my heart is
bur - dens a - lone; In my dis - tress He kind - ly will help me;
pas - sion - ate Friend; If I but ask Him, He will de - liv - er,
bur - dens to bear; I must tell Je - sus, I must tell Je - sus;
tempt - ed to sin! I must tell Je - sus, and He will help me
He ev - er loves and cares for His own.
Make of my troub - les quick - ly an end.
He all my cares and sor - rows will share.
O - ver the world the vic - t'ry to win.
CHORUS
I must tell Je - sus!
I must tell Je - sus! I can - not bear my bur - dens a - lone; I must tell
Je - sus! I must tell Je - sus! Je - sus can help me, Je - sus a - lone.

I Heard the Voice of Jesus Say

HORATIUS BONAR — Old English Air

1. I heard the voice of Je - sus say, "Come un - to Me and rest;
2. I heard the voice of Je - sus say, "Be - hold, I free - ly give
3. I heard the voice of Je - sus say, "I am this dark world's Light;
Lay down, thou wea-ry one, lay down Thy head up - on My breast!"
The liv - ing wa - ter; thirst - y one, Stoop down, and drink, and live!"
Look un - to Me, thy morn shall rise, And all thy day be bright!"
rit.
I came to Je - sus as I was, Wea-ry, and worn, and sad;
I came to Je - sus, and I drank Of that life - giv - ing stream;
I looked to Je - sus, and I found In Him my Star, my Sun;
rit.
I found in Him a rest - ing - place, And He has made me glad.
My thirst was quenched, my soul re - vived, And now I live in Him.
And in that light of life I'll walk, Till all my jour-ney's done.

230 **Safe in the Arms of Jesus**

FANNY J. CROSBY — W. H. DOANE

1. Safe in the arms of Je - sus, Safe on His gen-tle breast, There by His
2. Safe in the arms of Je - sus, Safe from cor-rod-ing care, Safe from the
3. Je-sus, my heart's dear ref - uge, Je - sus has died for me; Firm on the
love o'er-shad - ed, Sweet-ly my soul shall rest. Hark! 'tis the voice of
world's temp-ta - tions, Sin can-not harm me there. Free from the blight of
Rock of A - ges, Ev - er my trust shall be. Here let me wait with
an - gels, Borne in a song to me,.. O - ver the fields of glo - ry,
sor - row, Free from my doubts and fears; On - ly a few more tri - als,
pa - tience, Wait till the night is o'er; Wait till I see the morn - ing
CHORUS
O - ver the jas - per sea.......
On - ly a few more tears!..... Safe in the arms of Je - sus, Safe on His
Break on the gold - en shore.....
gen - tle breast, There by His love o'er - shad - ed, Sweetly my soul shall rest.

God, the All-Merciful

HENRY F. CHORLEY

ALEXIS F. LWOFF

1. God, the All - pow - er - ful! King, who or - dain - est
2. God, the All - mer - ci - ful! earth hath for - sak - en
3. God, the All - right - eous One! man hath de - fied Thee;
4. So shall Thy chil - dren in thank - ful de - vo - tion
Great winds Thy clar - ions, the light - nings Thy sword;
Thy way of bless - ed - ness, slight - ed Thy Word;
Yet to e - ter - ni - ty stand - eth Thy Word;
Laud Him who saved them from per - il ab - horred,
Show forth Thy pit - y on high where Thou reign - est;
Bid not Thy wrath in its ter - rors a - wak - en;
False - hood and wrong shall not tar - ry be - side Thee;
Sing - ing in cho - rus from o - cean to o - cean,
Give to us peace in our time, O Lord.
Give to us peace in our time, O Lord.
Give to us peace in our time, O Lord.
"Peace to the na - tions, and praise to the Lord."

232 Lord, as I Walk with Thee

STELLA KAUFFMAN — LELAND BYLER

1. Lord, as I walk with Thee from day to day, Teach me to
2. When in my path the cross-road lies a - head, Help me to
3. As in the eve - ning, when I tru - ly say, "I in the
4. Lord, show the road that leads un - to Thy throne; With Thee to

learn to love Thy bless - ed way; When I would wan - der,
choose the path that I should tread; Tho' broad and wide the
paths of God have walked to - day," So, I would say in
lead I can - not be a - lone; And as I walk through

lead my err - ing feet, Hold Thou my hand till jour - neys are com - plete.
road that leads from Thee, Teach me to choose the path that is for me.
that last day to God, "Lord, in Thy way I have for - ev - er trod."
glad - ness and thro' tears, Keep Thou my feet thro' - out the pass - ing years.

Copyright, 1938, in *Life Songs No. 2*. Mennonite Publishing House, owner

233 Jesus, Savior, Pilot Me

EDWARD HOPPER — J. E. GOULD

FINE.

1. Je - sus, Sav - ior, pi - lot me, O - ver life's tem - pes - tuous sea;
2. As a moth - er stills her child, Thou canst hush the o - cean wild;
3. When at last I near the shore, And the fear - ful break - ers roar

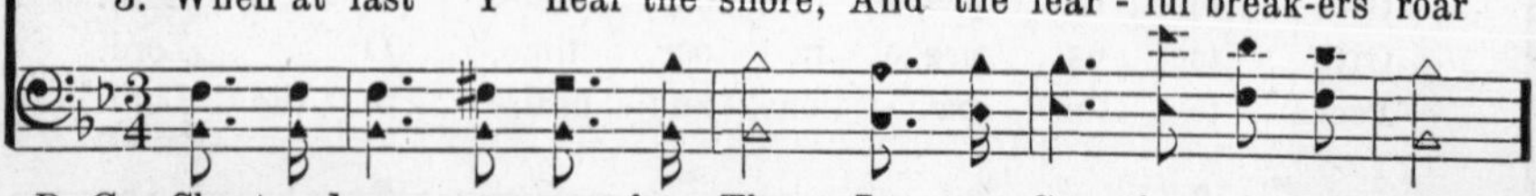

D. C.—Chart and com - pass came from Thee; Je - sus, Sav - ior, pi - lot me.
D. C.—Won - drous Sov'reign of the sea, Je - sus, Sav - ior, pi - lot me.
D. C.—May I hear Thee say to me, "Fear not, I will pi - lot thee!"

Jesus, Savior, Pilot Me

D. C.
Un-known waves be-fore me roll, Hid - ing rocks and treach'rous shoal;
Bois-t'rous waves o-bey Thy will When Thou say'st to them, "Be still!"
'Twixt me and the peace-ful rest, Then while lean-ing on Thy breast,

Precious Promise

234

Nathaniel Niles

P. P. Bliss

1. Pre-cious prom-ise God hath giv - en To the wea - ry pass - er - by,
2. When temp-ta-tions al - most win thee, And thy trust - ed watch-ers fly,
3. When thy se - cret hopes have per-ished In the grave of years gone by,
4. When the shades of life are fall - ing, And the hour has come to die,
On the way from earth to heav - en, "I will guide thee with mine eye."
Let this prom - ise ring with - in thee, "I will guide thee with mine eye."
Let this prom - ise still be cher-ished, "I will guide thee with mine eye."
Hear the trust - y Pi - lot call - ing, "I will guide thee with mine eye."
Chorus
I will guide thee, I will guide thee, I will guide thee with mine eye;
On the way from earth to heav - en, I will guide thee with mine eye.

Lead Me, Savior

F. M. D. FRANK M. DAVIS

1. Sav - ior, lead me, lest I stray, Gen - tly lead me all the way;
2. Thou the ref-uge of my soul When life's storm-y bil-lows roll;
3. Sav - ior, lead me, then at last, When the storm of life is past,
1. Sav - ior, lead me, lest I stray, Gen - tly lead me all the way;
I am safe when by Thy side, I would in Thy love a-bide.
I am safe when Thou art nigh, All my hopes on Thee re-ly.
To the land of end-less day, Where all tears are wiped away.
I am safe when by Thy side, I would in Thy love a-bide.
CHORUS
Lead me, lead me, Sav - ior, lead me, lest I stray;......
lest I stray;
Gen-tly down the stream of time, Lead me, Sav-ior, all the way.
stream of time, all the way.

Lead Me Gently Home, Father

236

W. L. T. | W. L. THOMPSON

Use as Solo or Duet
1. Lead me gen-tly home, Fa-ther, Lead me gen-tly home, When life's toils are
2. Lead me gen-tly home, Fa-ther, Lead me gen-tly home, In life's dark-est
end - ed, And part-ing days have come. Sin no more shall tempt me;
hours, Fa-ther, When life's troubles come; Keep my feet from wan-d'ring,
rit. p
Ne'er from Thee I'll roam, If thou'lt on-ly lead me, Fa-ther, Lead me gently home.
Lest from Thee I roam, Lest I fall up-on the way-side, Lead me gently home.
CHORUS
Lead me gen - tly home, Fa-ther, Lead me gen - tly;
Lead me gen - tly home, Fa - ther, Lead me gen - tly home, Fa - ther;
Lest I fall up - on the way - side, Lead me gen - tly home.
gen - tly home.

237 What God Hath Promised

ANNIE JOHNSON FLINT WILLIAM M. RUNYAN

1. God hath not prom-ised skies al-ways blue, Flow-er-strewn path-ways
2. God hath not prom-ised we shall not know Toil and temp-ta-tion,
3. God hath not prom-ised smooth roads and wide, Swift, eas-y trav-el,
all our lives through; God hath not prom-ised sun with-out rain,
trou-ble and woe; He hath not told us we shall not bear
need-ing no guide; Nev-er a moun-tain rock-y and steep,
Joy with-out sor-row, peace with-out pain.
Man-y a bur-den, man-y a care.
Nev-er a riv-er tur-bid and deep.
CHORUS
But God hath prom-ised
strength for the day, Rest for the la-bor, light for the way, Grace for the
tri-als, help from a-bove, Un-fail-ing sym-pa-thy, un-dy-ing love.

Follow On

W. O. Cushing — Robert Lowry

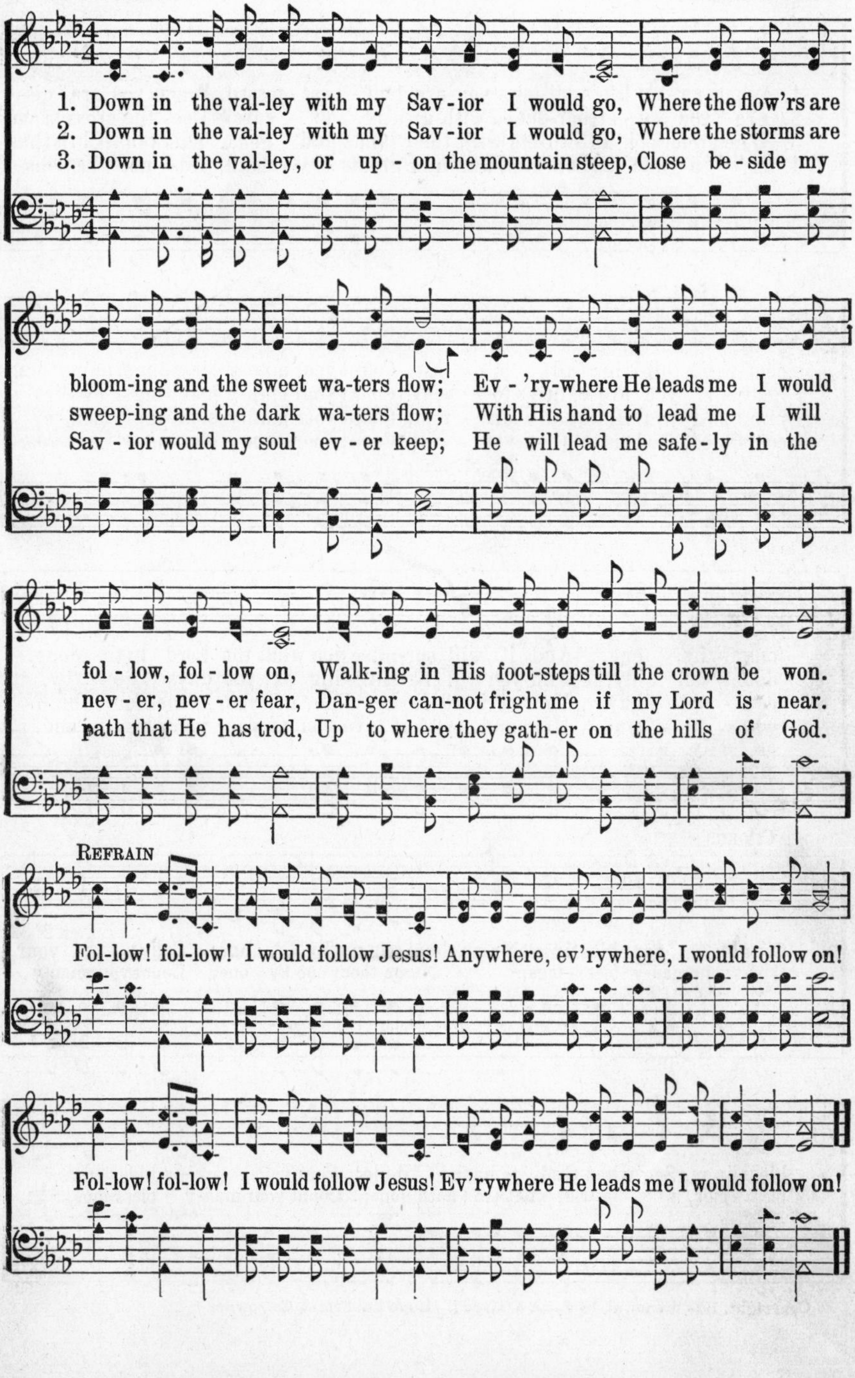
1. Down in the val-ley with my Sav-ior I would go, Where the flow'rs are bloom-ing and the sweet wa-ters flow; Ev-'ry-where He leads me I would fol-low, fol-low on, Walk-ing in His foot-steps till the crown be won.
2. Down in the val-ley with my Sav-ior I would go, Where the storms are sweep-ing and the dark wa-ters flow; With His hand to lead me I will nev-er, nev-er fear, Dan-ger can-not fright me if my Lord is near.
3. Down in the val-ley, or up-on the mountain steep, Close be-side my Sav-ior would my soul ev-er keep; He will lead me safe-ly in the path that He has trod, Up to where they gath-er on the hills of God.
Refrain
Fol-low! fol-low! I would follow Jesus! Anywhere, ev'rywhere, I would follow on!
Fol-low! fol-low! I would follow Jesus! Ev'rywhere He leads me I would follow on!

Count Your Blessings

Johnson Oatman, Jr. — E. O. Excell

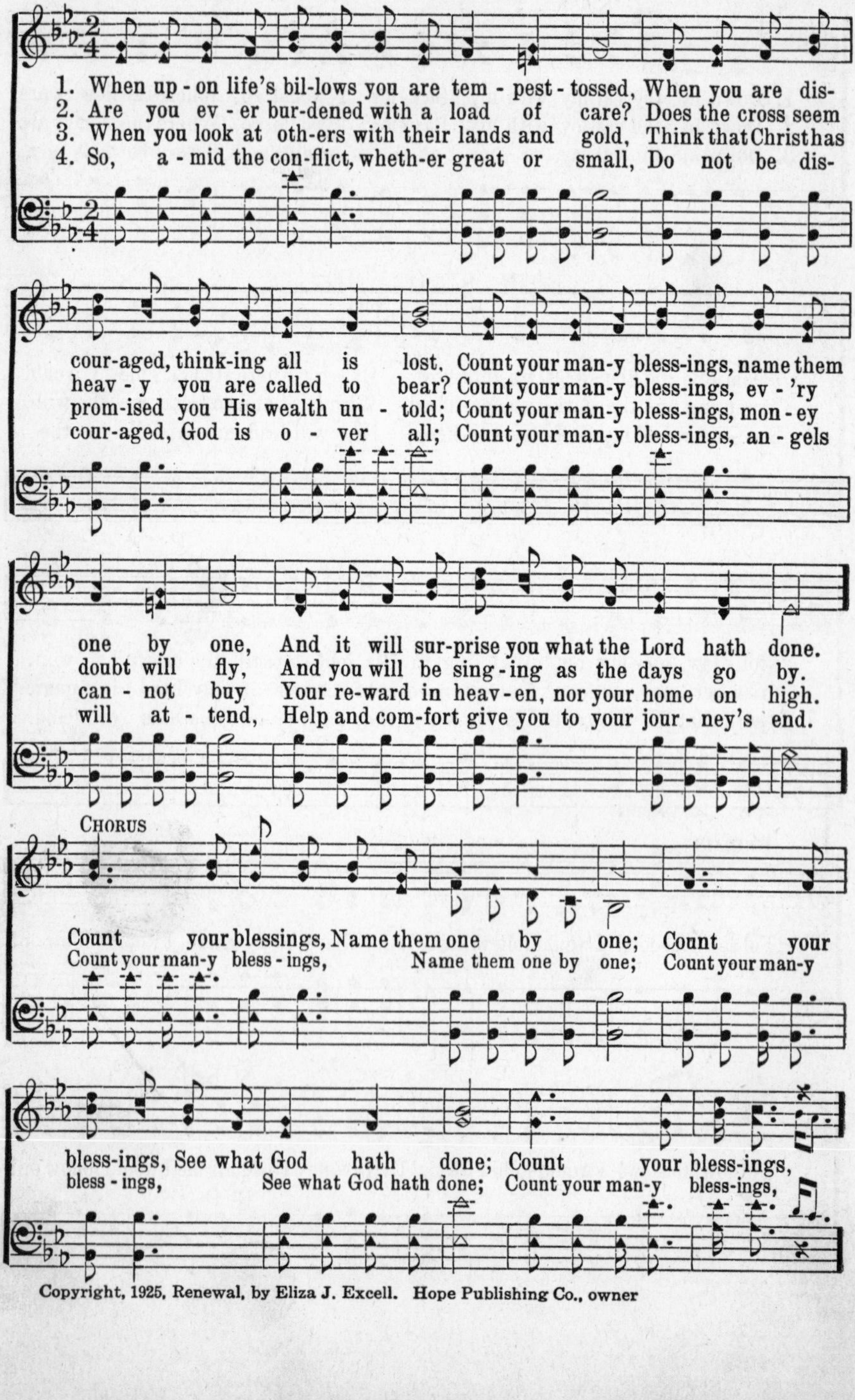
1. When up - on life's bil-lows you are tem - pest - tossed, When you are dis-cour-aged, think-ing all is lost, Count your man-y bless-ings, name them one by one, And it will sur-prise you what the Lord hath done.
2. Are you ev - er bur-dened with a load of care? Does the cross seem heav - y you are called to bear? Count your man-y bless-ings, ev - 'ry doubt will fly, And you will be sing-ing as the days go by.
3. When you look at oth-ers with their lands and gold, Think that Christ has prom-ised you His wealth un - told; Count your man-y bless-ings, mon - ey can - not buy Your re-ward in heav-en, nor your home on high.
4. So, a - mid the con-flict, wheth-er great or small, Do not be dis-cour-aged, God is o - ver all; Count your man-y bless-ings, an - gels will at - tend, Help and com-fort give you to your jour - ney's end.
Chorus
Count your blessings, Name them one by one; Count your bless-ings, See what God hath done; Count your bless-ings,
Count your man-y bless - ings, Name them one by one; Count your man-y bless - ings, See what God hath done; Count your man-y bless-ings,

Count Your Blessings

rit.
a tempo
Name them one by one; Count your man-y bless-ings, See what God hath done.

Jesus, Still Lead On 240

SEELENBRÄUTIGAM. 5. 5. 8. 8. 5. 5.

NICOLAUS L. ZINZENDORF
Tr. by JANE L. BORTHWICK

ADAM DRESE
Harmonized by SAMUEL S. WESLEY

1. Je - sus, still lead on, Till our rest be won, And, al-though the
2. If the way be drear, If the foe be near, Let not faith - less
3. Je - sus, still lead on, Till our rest be won; Heav'n-ly Lead - er,

way be cheer - less, We will fol - low, calm and fear - less;
fears o'er - take us, Let not faith and hope for - sake us;
still di - rect us, Still sup - port, con - sole, pro - tect us,

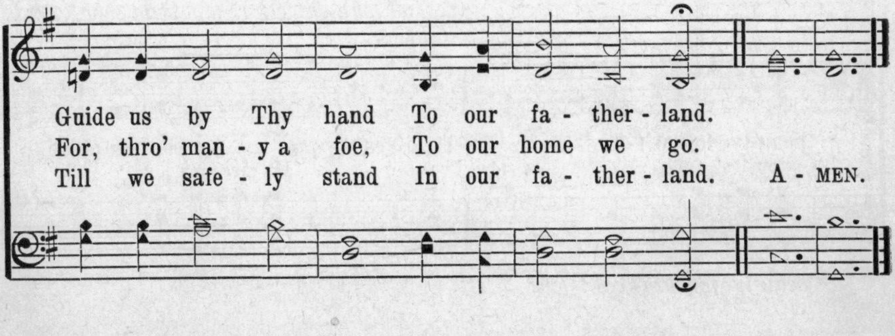
Guide us by Thy hand To our fa - ther - land.
For, thro' man - y a foe, To our home we go.
Till we safe - ly stand In our fa - ther - land. A - MEN.

Beauty for Ashes

J. G. C. J. G. CRABBE

1. I sing the love of God, my Fa - ther, Whose Spir-it a-bides with-in;
2. I sing the love of Christ my Sav - ior, Who suf-fered up - on the tree;
3. I sing the beau-ty of the Gos - pel That scatters, not thorns, but flow'rs;
Who chang-es all my grief to glad - ness, And par-dons me all my
That, in the se - cret of His pres - ence, My bond-age might free-dom
That bids me scat-ter smiles and sun-beams Wher-ev - er are lone - ly
sin. Tho' clouds may low - er dark and drear - y, Yet He has
be. He comes "to bind the bro - ken-heart - ed;" He comes the
hours. The "gar - ment of His praise" it of - fers For "heav - i-
prom-ised to be near; He gives me sun-shine for my shad - ow, And
faint-ing soul to cheer; He gives me "oil of joy" for mourn-ing, And
ness of spir - it," drear; It gives me sun-shine for my shad - ow, And
D. S.—gives me sun-shine for my shad - ow, And
FINE
CHORUS
"beau-ty for ash - es," here. He gives me joy . . . . in place of
He gives me joy
"beau-ty for ash - es," here.

Beauty for Ashes

D. S.
sor - row; He gives me love . . . . that casts out fear; He
in place of care; He gives me love that casts out fear;

Onward, Upward, Homeward! 242

ALBERT MIDLANE IRA D. SANKEY

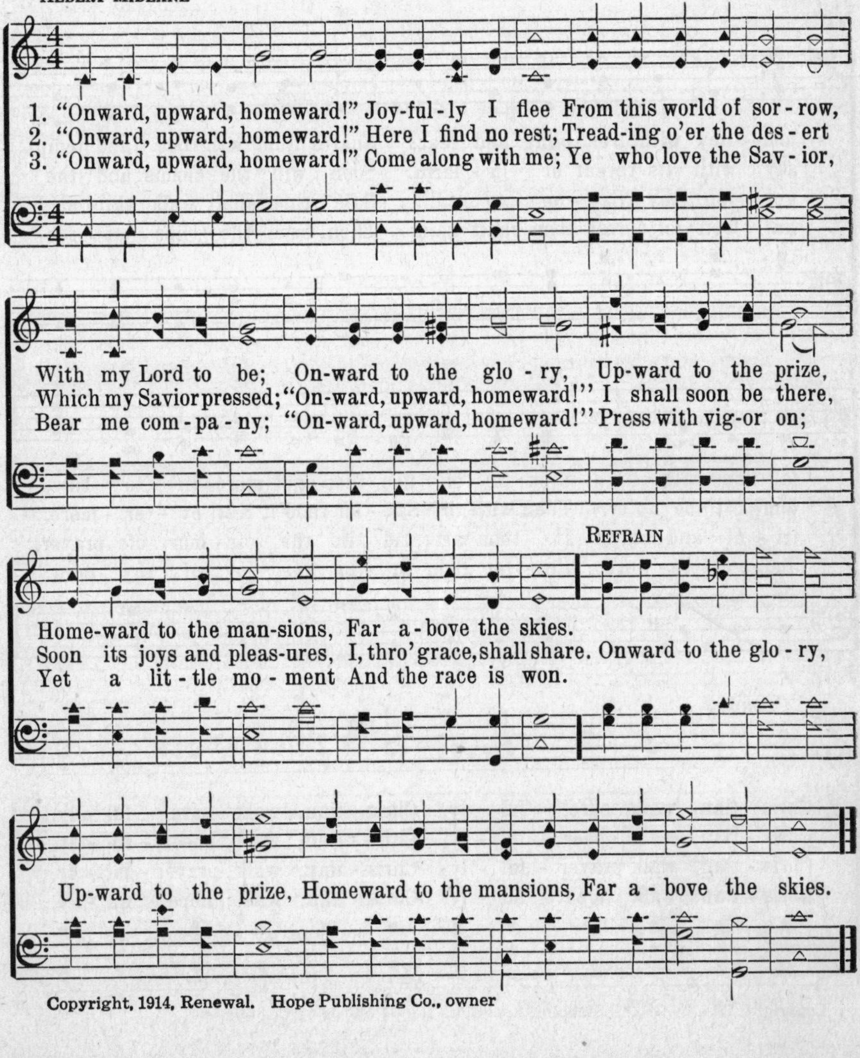
1. "Onward, upward, homeward!" Joy-ful-ly I flee From this world of sor-row,
2. "Onward, upward, homeward!" Here I find no rest; Tread-ing o'er the des-ert
3. "Onward, upward, homeward!" Come along with me; Ye who love the Sav-ior,
With my Lord to be; On-ward to the glo-ry, Up-ward to the prize,
Which my Savior pressed; "On-ward, upward, homeward!" I shall soon be there,
Bear me com-pa-ny; "On-ward, upward, homeward!" Press with vig-or on;
REFRAIN
Home-ward to the man-sions, Far a-bove the skies.
Soon its joys and pleas-ures, I, thro' grace, shall share. Onward to the glo-ry,
Yet a lit-tle mo-ment And the race is won.
Up-ward to the prize, Homeward to the mansions, Far a-bove the skies.

243 **Christian, Walk Carefully**

Words arranged

GEO. C. STEBBINS

1. Chris-tian, walk care - ful - ly, dan - ger is near; On in thy
2. Chris-tian, walk cheer - ful - ly thro' the fierce storm; Dark tho' the
3. Chris-tian, walk prayer-ful - ly, oft wilt thou fall If thou for-
4. Chris-tian, walk hope - ful - ly, sor - row and pain Cease when the
jour - ney with trem-bling and fear. Snares from with - out and temp-
sky with its threat of a - larm. Soon will the clouds and the
get on thy Sav - ior to call; Safe thou shalt walk thro' each
ha - ven of rest thou shalt gain; Then from the lips of the
ta - tions with - in Seek to en - tice thee once more in - to sin.
tem-pest be o'er, Then with thy Sav - ior thou'lt rest ev - er - more.
tri - al and care, If thou art clad in the ar - mor of prayer.
Judge thy re - ward: "En - ter thou in - to the joy of thy Lord."
CHORUS
Chris - tian, walk care - ful - ly, Chris - tian, walk care - ful - ly,
Chris - tian, walk cheer - ful - ly, Chris - tian, walk cheer - ful - ly,
Chris - tian, walk prayer - ful - ly, Chris - tian, walk prayer - ful - ly,
Chris - tian, walk hope - ful - ly, Chris - tian, walk hope - ful - ly,

Christian, Walk Carefully

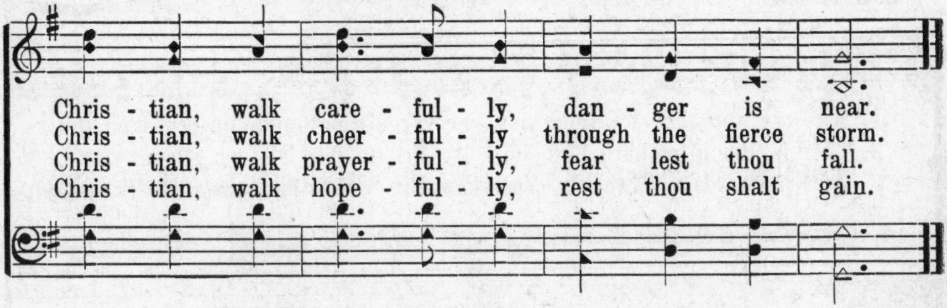
Chris - tian, walk care - ful - ly, dan - ger is near.
Chris - tian, walk cheer - ful - ly through the fierce storm.
Chris - tian, walk prayer - ful - ly, fear lest thou fall.
Chris - tian, walk hope - ful - ly, rest thou shalt gain.

Follow the Path of Jesus 244

BOUND BROOK. 7s. 6s. D. From "Hymns and Tunes"

1. Fol - low the path of Je - sus, Walk where His foot - steps lead,
2. Cling to the hand of Je - sus, All through the day and night,
3. Take up the cross of Je - sus, Shar - ing the shame He bore;

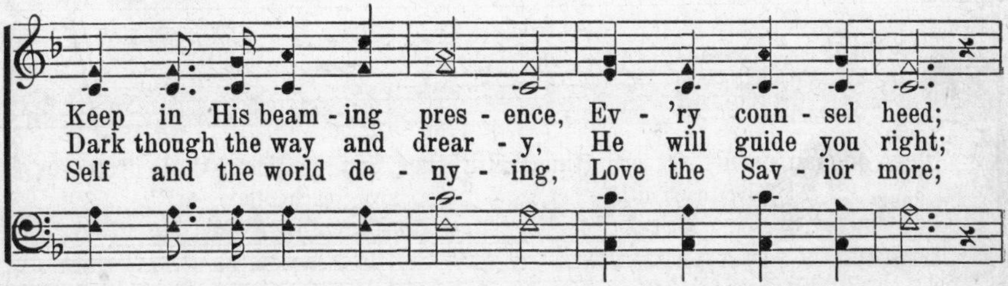
Keep in His beam - ing pres - ence, Ev - 'ry coun - sel heed;
Dark though the way and drear - y, He will guide you right;
Self and the world de - ny - ing, Love the Sav - ior more;

Watch, while the hours are fly - ing, Read - y some good to do;
Live for the good of oth - ers, Help - less, op-pressed and wrong;
Tell all the world of Je - sus, Think of their gloom and loss,

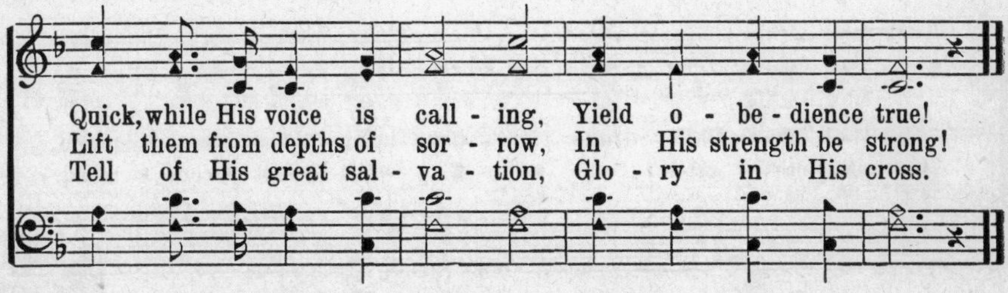
Quick, while His voice is call - ing, Yield o - be - dience true!
Lift them from depths of sor - row, In His strength be strong!
Tell of His great sal - va - tion, Glo - ry in His cross.

245 Angry Words! O Let Them Never

D. K. P. H. R. Palmer

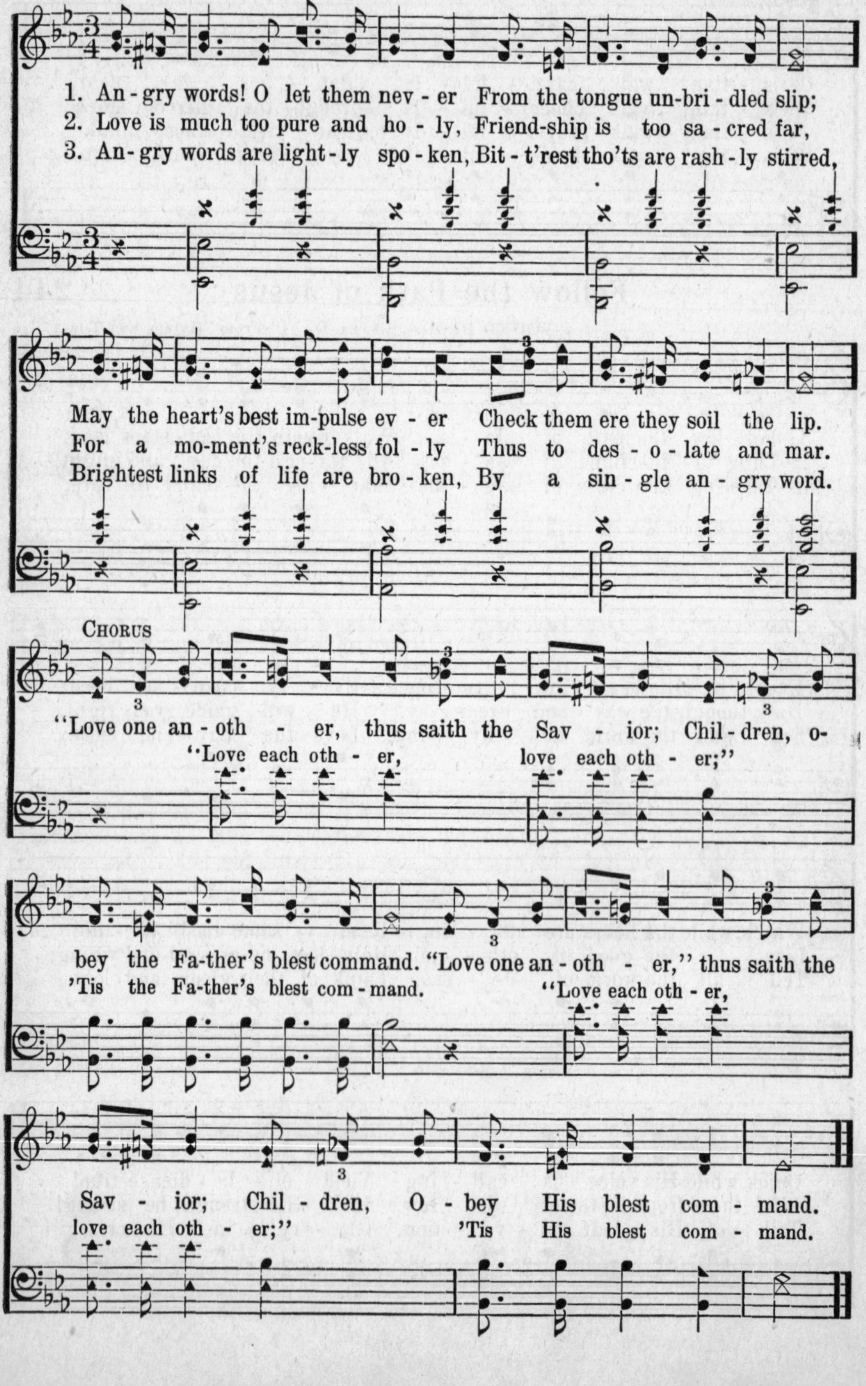
1. An-gry words! O let them nev-er From the tongue un-bri-dled slip;
2. Love is much too pure and ho-ly, Friend-ship is too sa-cred far,
3. An-gry words are light-ly spo-ken, Bit-t'rest tho'ts are rash-ly stirred,
May the heart's best im-pulse ev-er Check them ere they soil the lip.
For a mo-ment's reck-less fol-ly Thus to des-o-late and mar.
Brightest links of life are bro-ken, By a sin-gle an-gry word.
CHORUS
"Love one an-oth-er, thus saith the Sav-ior; Chil-dren, o-
"Love each oth-er, love each oth-er;"
bey the Fa-ther's blest command. "Love one an-oth-er," thus saith the
'Tis the Fa-ther's blest com-mand. "Love each oth-er,
Sav-ior; Chil-dren, O-bey His blest com-mand.
love each oth-er;" 'Tis His blest com-mand.

My Soul, Be On Thy Guard

George Heath — LABAN. S. M. — Lowell Mason

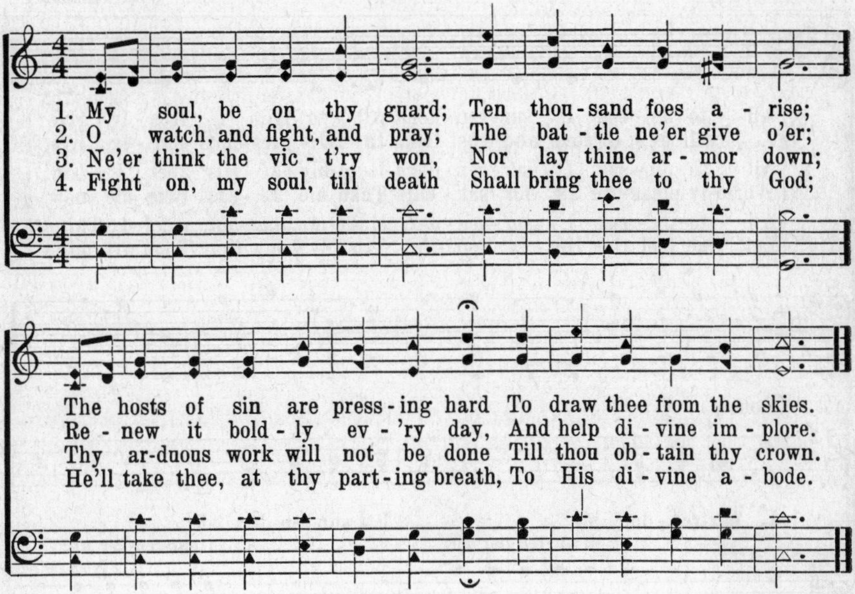
1. My soul, be on thy guard; Ten thou-sand foes a - rise;
2. O watch, and fight, and pray; The bat - tle ne'er give o'er;
3. Ne'er think the vic - t'ry won, Nor lay thine ar - mor down;
4. Fight on, my soul, till death Shall bring thee to thy God;
The hosts of sin are press - ing hard To draw thee from the skies.
Re - new it bold - ly ev - 'ry day, And help di - vine im - plore.
Thy ar-duous work will not be done Till thou ob - tain thy crown.
He'll take thee, at thy part - ing breath, To His di - vine a - bode.

I Do Not Ask, O Lord

SUBMISSION, No. 2. 10. 4. 10. 4.

Adelaide Ann Procter — Albert L. Peace

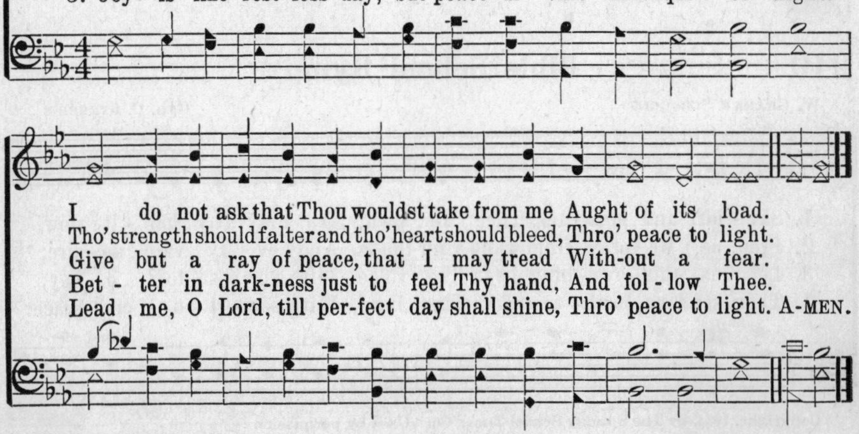
1. I do not ask, O Lord, that life may be A pleas - ant road;
2. For one thing on - ly, Lord, dear Lord, I plead: Lead me a - right,
3. I do not ask, O Lord, that Thou shouldst shed Full ra - diance here;
4. I do not ask my cross to un - der - stand, My way to see;
5. Joy is like rest-less day; but peace di - vine Like qui - et night.
I do not ask that Thou wouldst take from me Aught of its load.
Tho' strength should falter and tho' heart should bleed, Thro' peace to light.
Give but a ray of peace, that I may tread With-out a fear.
Bet - ter in dark-ness just to feel Thy hand, And fol - low Thee.
Lead me, O Lord, till per-fect day shall shine, Thro' peace to light. A-MEN.

248 I Surrender All

J. W. Van De Venter — W. S. Weeden

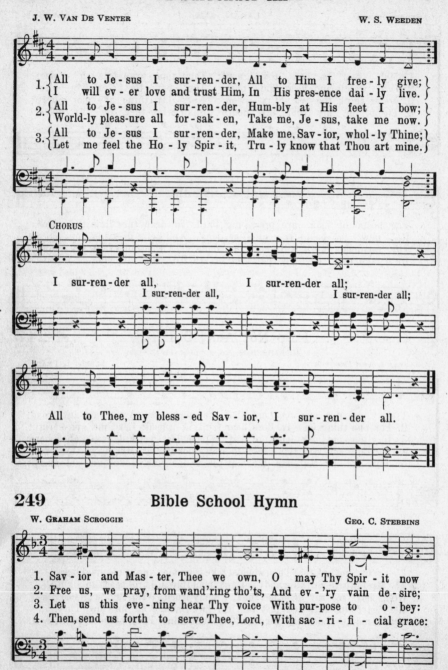

1. All to Jesus I surrender, All to Him I freely give;
I will ever love and trust Him, In His presence daily live.

2. All to Jesus I surrender, Humbly at His feet I bow;
Worldly pleasure all forsaken, Take me, Jesus, take me now.

3. All to Jesus I surrender, Make me, Savior, wholly Thine;
Let me feel the Holy Spirit, Truly know that Thou art mine.

CHORUS

I surrender all, (I surrender all,) I surrender all; (I surrender all;)

All to Thee, my blessed Savior, I surrender all.

249 Bible School Hymn

W. Graham Scroggie — Geo. C. Stebbins

1. Savior and Master, Thee we own, O may Thy Spirit now
2. Free us, we pray, from wand'ring tho'ts, And ev-'ry vain desire;
3. Let us this evening hear Thy voice With purpose to obey:
4. Then, send us forth to serve Thee, Lord, With sacrificial grace:

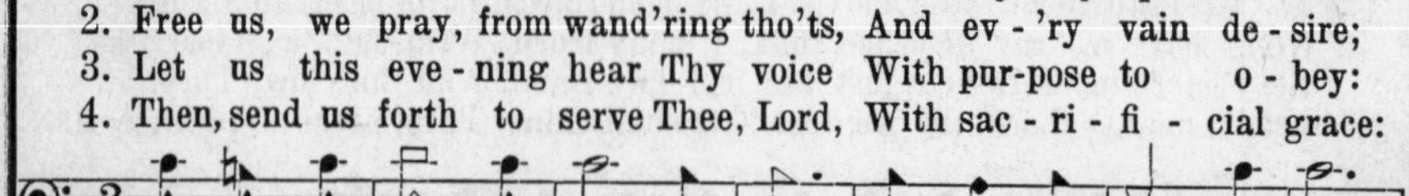

Bible School Hymn

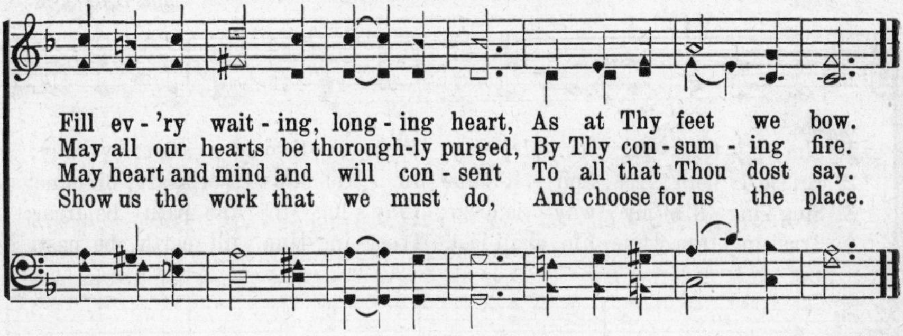
Fill ev - 'ry wait - ing, long - ing heart, As at Thy feet we bow.
May all our hearts be thorough-ly purged, By Thy con - sum - ing fire.
May heart and mind and will con - sent To all that Thou dost say.
Show us the work that we must do, And choose for us the place.

All For Jesus 250

MARY D. JAMES — Arranged

1. All for Je - sus, all for Je - sus! All my be-ing's ransomed pow'rs:
2. Let my hands perform His bid - ding, Let my feet run in His ways;
3. Since my eyes were fixed on Je - sus, I've lost sight of all be - side;
4. Oh, what won-der! how a - maz - ing! Je - sus, glo-rious King of kings,

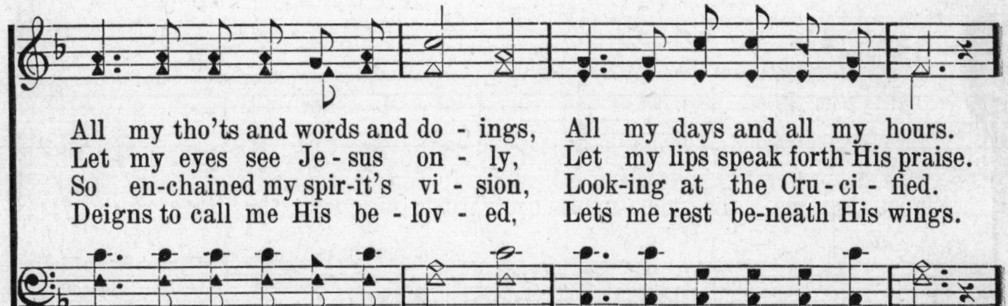
All my tho'ts and words and do - ings, All my days and all my hours.
Let my eyes see Je - sus on - ly, Let my lips speak forth His praise.
So en-chained my spir-it's vi - sion, Look-ing at the Cru - ci - fied.
Deigns to call me His be - lov - ed, Lets me rest be-neath His wings.

1
2
All for Je-sus! all for Je - sus! All my days and all my hours; hours.
All for Je-sus! all for Je - sus! Let my lips speak forth His praise; praise.
All for Je-sus! all for Je - sus! Look-ing at the Cru - ci - fied; fied.
All for Je-sus! all for Je - sus! Rest-ing now beneath His wings; wings.

251 Trusting Jesus

E. PAGE — IRA D. SANKEY

1. Sim - ply trust - ing ev - 'ry day, Trust - ing through a storm - y way;
2. Bright-ly doth His Spir - it shine In - to this poor heart of mine;
3. Sing - ing if my way is clear; Pray - ing if the path be drear;
4. Trust-ing Him while life shall last, Trust - ing Him till earth be past;
E - ven when my faith is small, Trust-ing Je - sus, that is all.
While He leads I can - not fall; Trust-ing Je - sus, that is all.
If in dan - ger, for Him call; Trust-ing Je - sus, that is all.
Till with - in the jas - per wall: Trust-ing Je - sus, that is all.
CHORUS
Trust - ing as the mo - ments fly, Trust - ing as the days go by;
Trust - ing Him what - e'er be - fall, Trust - ing Je - sus, that is all.

Jesus, I My Cross Have Taken

HENRY F. LYTE — From MOZART

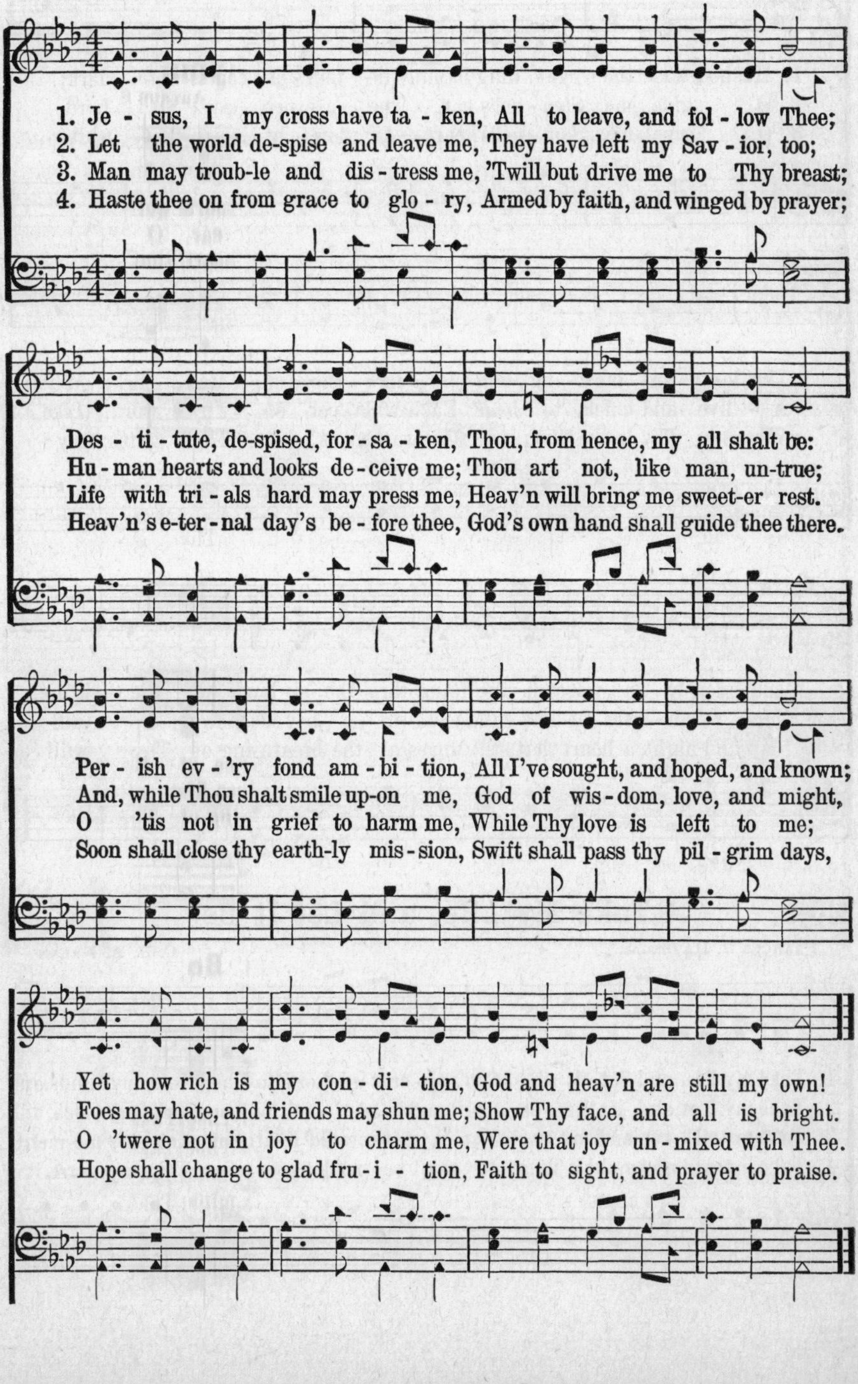
1. Je - sus, I my cross have ta - ken, All to leave, and fol - low Thee;
2. Let the world de-spise and leave me, They have left my Sav - ior, too;
3. Man may troub-le and dis - tress me, 'Twill but drive me to Thy breast;
4. Haste thee on from grace to glo - ry, Armed by faith, and winged by prayer;
Des - ti - tute, de-spised, for - sa - ken, Thou, from hence, my all shalt be:
Hu - man hearts and looks de - ceive me; Thou art not, like man, un-true;
Life with tri - als hard may press me, Heav'n will bring me sweet-er rest.
Heav'n's e-ter - nal day's be - fore thee, God's own hand shall guide thee there.
Per - ish ev - 'ry fond am - bi - tion, All I've sought, and hoped, and known;
And, while Thou shalt smile up-on me, God of wis - dom, love, and might,
O 'tis not in grief to harm me, While Thy love is left to me;
Soon shall close thy earth-ly mis - sion, Swift shall pass thy pil - grim days,
Yet how rich is my con - di - tion, God and heav'n are still my own!
Foes may hate, and friends may shun me; Show Thy face, and all is bright.
O 'twere not in joy to charm me, Were that joy un - mixed with Thee.
Hope shall change to glad fru - i - tion, Faith to sight, and prayer to praise.

253 Hushed Was the Evening Hymn

James D. Burns — Arthur S. Sullivan

1. Hushed was the eve - ning hymn, The tem - ple courts were dark;
2. O give me Sam - uel's ear,— The o - pen ear, O Lord,
3. O give me Sam - uel's heart,—A low - ly heart, that waits
The lamp was burn - ing dim Be - fore the sa - cred ark; When
A - live and quick to hear Each whis - per of Thy word, Like
Where-in Thy house Thou art, Or watch - es at Thy gates; By
sud - den-ly a voice di-vine Rang thro' the si - lence of the shrine.
him to an - swer at Thy call, And to o - bey Thee first of all!
day and night, a heart that still Moves at the breath-ing of Thy will!

254 Take My Life, and Let It Be

Frances R. Havergal — C. H. A. Malan

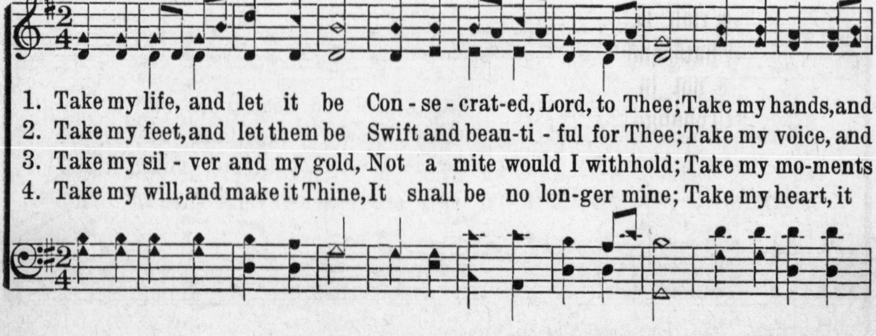
1. Take my life, and let it be Con - se - crat-ed, Lord, to Thee; Take my hands, and
2. Take my feet, and let them be Swift and beau - ti - ful for Thee; Take my voice, and
3. Take my sil - ver and my gold, Not a mite would I withhold; Take my mo-ments
4. Take my will, and make it Thine, It shall be no lon-ger mine; Take my heart, it

Take My Life, and Let It Be

let them move At the im-pulse of Thy love, At the im - pulse of Thy love.
let me sing Al-ways, on - ly, for my King, Al-ways, on - ly, for my King.
and my days, Let them flow in ceaseless praise, Let them flow in ceaseless praise.
is Thine own, It shall be Thy roy - al throne, It shall be Thy roy - al throne.

Jesus, Thy Name I Bear 255

WILLIAM COLTON CLARK FRED. WEST

1. Je - sus, Thy name I bear, Make me Thy life to share,
2. Thy Spir - it, Lord, be - stow, That I like Thee may grow,
3. Let me be brave and strong, Pa - tient to suf - fer wrong,
4. And when the day is done, Life's bat - tles fought and won,

Be Thou my Lord; Write me as one of Thine, Re-deemed by
From day to day. Let good the ill dis-place, Trans-form me
Hard-ship en - dure; Read - y at Thy com-mand To en - ter
All la - bors past, O then may I be found Where vic-tors'

grace di - vine; My heart to Thee en - twine, With lov - ing cord.
by Thy grace, With glimps-es of Thy face; For this I pray.
an - y land, Al - ways for Thee to stand, Loy - al and sure.
songs a - bound And faith - ful ones are crowned, With Thee at last.

256 Must Jesus Bear the Cross Alone?

MAITLAND. C. M. G. N. ALLEN

1. Must Je - sus bear the cross a - lone, And all the world go free?
2. Dis-owned on earth,'mid griefs and cares, He led His toil - some way;
3. The con - se - crat - ed cross I'll bear, Till from the cross set free,

No: there's a cross for ev - 'ry - one, And there's a cross for me.
But now in heav'n a crown He wears, And reigns in end - less day.
And then go home, my crown to wear, For there's a crown for me.

257 O Lord, to Thee I Cry

C. U. L. PLEADING. S. M. C. U. LINK

1. O Lord, to Thee I cry, Thou art my rock and trust;
2. O hear my ear - nest cry, Thy fa - vor I en - treat;
3. Oh, bless - ed be the Lord, He heard me when I cried.
4. From Him I help ob-tained, And now my voice I raise;

O be not si - lent lest I die, And slum - ber in the dust.
Here while I lift im - plor - ing hands, Be - fore Thy mer - cy - seat.
Je - ho - vah is my strength and shield, On Him my heart re - lied.
And while my heart ex - ults with joy, My heart is turned to praise.

Follow All the Way

ELISHA A. HOFFMAN | Arr. by IRA ORWIG HOFFMAN

TRIO

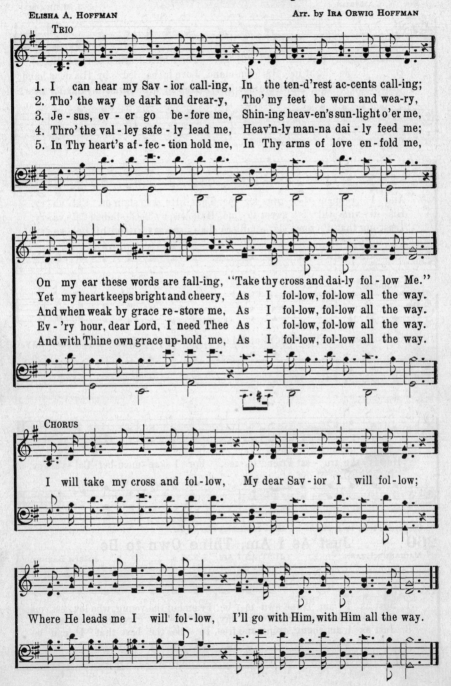

1. I can hear my Sav - ior call-ing, In the ten-d'rest ac-cents call-ing;
2. Tho' the way be dark and drear-y, Tho' my feet be worn and wea-ry,
3. Je - sus, ev - er go be-fore me, Shin-ing heav-en's sun-light o'er me,
4. Thro' the val - ley safe - ly lead me, Heav'n-ly man-na dai - ly feed me;
5. In Thy heart's af - fec - tion hold me, In Thy arms of love en-fold me,

On my ear these words are fall-ing, "Take thy cross and dai-ly fol - low Me."
Yet my heart keeps bright and cheery, As I fol-low, fol-low all the way.
And when weak by grace re-store me, As I fol-low, fol-low all the way.
Ev - 'ry hour, dear Lord, I need Thee As I fol-low, fol-low all the way.
And with Thine own grace up-hold me, As I fol-low, fol-low all the way.

CHORUS

I will take my cross and fol-low, My dear Sav-ior I will fol-low;

Where He leads me I will fol-low, I'll go with Him, with Him all the way.

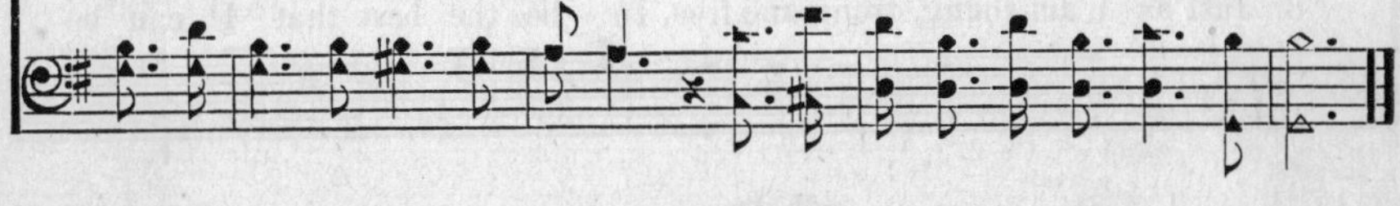

259 I Remember Calvary

Rev. W. C. Martin — J. M. Black

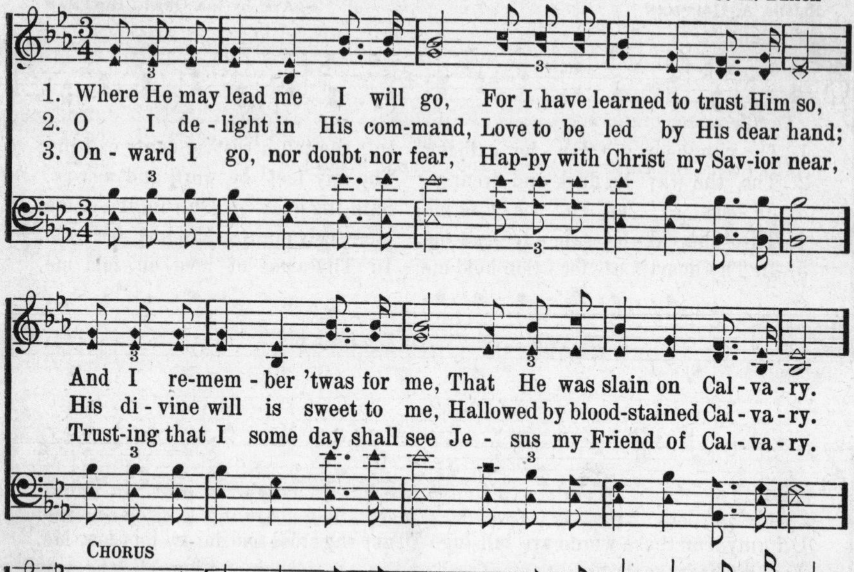

1. Where He may lead me I will go, For I have learned to trust Him so,
2. O I de-light in His com-mand, Love to be led by His dear hand;
3. On-ward I go, nor doubt nor fear, Hap-py with Christ my Sav-ior near,
And I re-mem-ber 'twas for me, That He was slain on Cal-va-ry.
His di-vine will is sweet to me, Hallowed by blood-stained Cal-va-ry.
Trust-ing that I some day shall see Je-sus my Friend of Cal-va-ry.
CHORUS
Je-sus shall lead me night and day, Je-sus shall lead me all the way,
He is the tru-est Friend to me, For I re-mem-ber Cal-va-ry.

Copyright, 1928, by J. M. Black. Hope Publishing Co., owner.

260 Just As I Am, Thine Own to Be

Marianne Hearn — JUST AS I AM. 8. 8. 8. 6. — Joseph Barnby

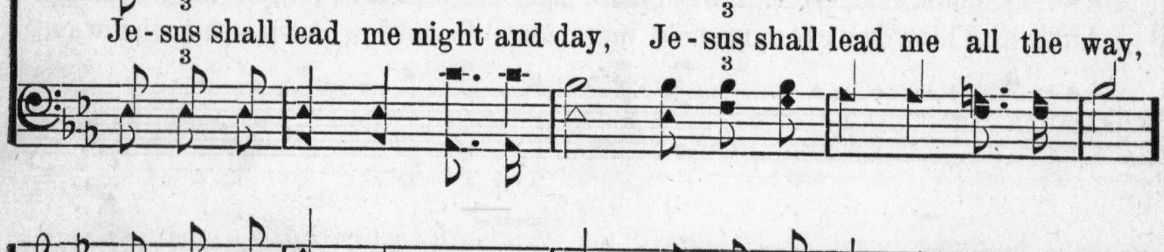

1. Just as I am, Thine own to be, Friend of the young, who lov-est me,
2. In the glad morn-ing of my day, My life to give, my vows to pay,
3. Just as I am, young, strong, and free, To be the best that I can be

Just As I Am, Thine Own to Be

Unison

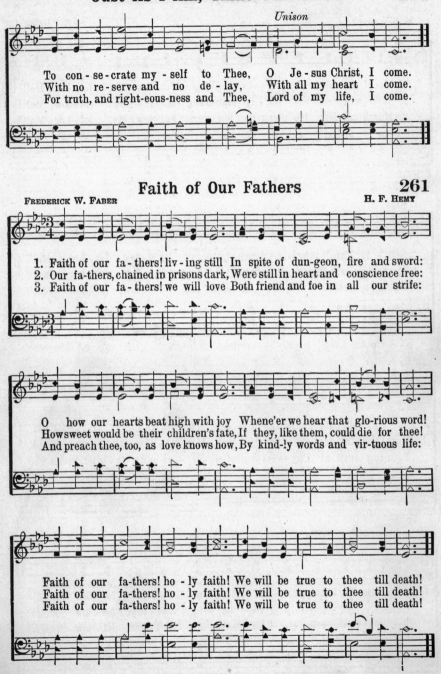

To con - se - crate my - self to Thee, O Je - sus Christ, I come.
With no re - serve and no de - lay, With all my heart I come.
For truth, and right-eous-ness and Thee, Lord of my life, I come.

Faith of Our Fathers 261

FREDERICK W. FABER H. F. HEMY

1. Faith of our fa - thers! liv - ing still In spite of dun-geon, fire and sword:
2. Our fa-thers, chained in prisons dark, Were still in heart and conscience free:
3. Faith of our fa - thers! we will love Both friend and foe in all our strife:

O how our hearts beat high with joy Whene'er we hear that glo-rious word!
How sweet would be their children's fate, If they, like them, could die for thee!
And preach thee, too, as love knows how, By kind-ly words and vir-tuous life:

Faith of our fa-thers! ho - ly faith! We will be true to thee till death!
Faith of our fa-thers! ho - ly faith! We will be true to thee till death!
Faith of our fa-thers! ho - ly faith! We will be true to thee till death!

Follow Me

M. B. SLEIGHT H. R. PALMER

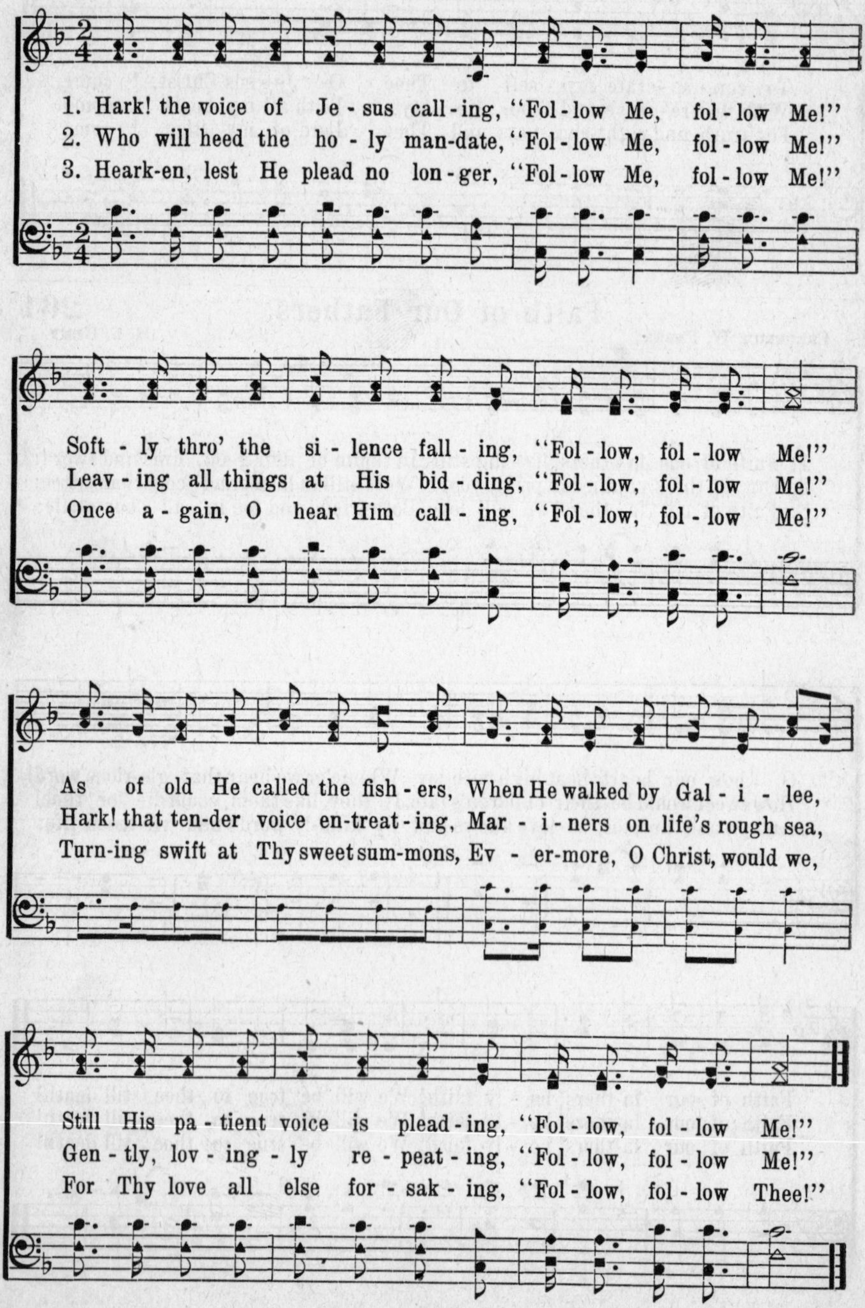
1. Hark! the voice of Je - sus call - ing, "Fol - low Me, fol - low Me!"
2. Who will heed the ho - ly man-date, "Fol - low Me, fol - low Me!"
3. Heark-en, lest He plead no lon - ger, "Fol - low Me, fol - low Me!"
Soft - ly thro' the si - lence fall - ing, "Fol - low, fol - low Me!"
Leav - ing all things at His bid - ding, "Fol - low, fol - low Me!"
Once a - gain, O hear Him call - ing, "Fol - low, fol - low Me!"
As of old He called the fish - ers, When He walked by Gal - i - lee,
Hark! that ten-der voice en-treat - ing, Mar - i - ners on life's rough sea,
Turn-ing swift at Thy sweet sum-mons, Ev - er-more, O Christ, would we,
Still His pa - tient voice is plead - ing, "Fol - low, fol - low Me!"
Gen - tly, lov - ing - ly re - peat - ing, "Fol - low, fol - low Me!"
For Thy love all else for - sak - ing, "Fol - low, fol - low Thee!"

"Follow Me," the Master Said

BEACHLEY. 7. 6. 7. 6. 7. 7. 7. 6.

Anonymous — Arthur Cottman

1. "Fol - low Me," the Mas - ter said; We will fol - low Je - sus:
2. Should the world and sin op - pose, We will fol - low Je - sus:
3. Tho' the way may dark ap - pear, We will fol - low Je - sus:
4. Ev - er keep the end in view; We will fol - low Je - sus:
By His Word and Spir - it led, We will fol - low Je - sus.
He is great - er than our foes; We will fol - low Je - sus.
He will make our path - way clear; We will fol - low Je - sus.
All His prom - is - es are true; We will fol - low Je - sus.
Still for us He lives to plead, At the throne doth in - ter - cede,
On His prom - ise we de - pend; He will suc - cor and de - fend,
In our dai - ly round of care, As we plead with God in prayer,
When this earth - ly course is run, And the Mas - ter says, "Well done!"
Of - fers help in time of need: We will fol - low Je - sus.
Help and keep us to the end: We will fol - low Je - sus.
With the cross which we must bear, We will fol - low Je - sus.
Life e - ter - nal we have won: We will fol - low Je - sus.

264 Give Me Jesus

FANNY J. CROSBY — JNO. R. SWENEY

1. Take the world, but give me Je - sus, All its joys are but a name;
2. Take the world, but give me Je - sus, Sweet-est com - fort of my soul;
3. Take the world, but give me Je - sus, Let me view His con-stant smile;
4. Take the world, but give me Je - sus, In His cross my trust shall be;
But His love a - bid - eth ev - er, Thro' e - ter - nal years the same.
With my Sav - ior watch-ing o'er me, I can sing though bil-lows roll.
Then thro'-out my pil - grim jour - ney Light will cheer me all the while.
Till, with clear - er, bright-er vi - sion, Face to face my Lord I see.
CHORUS
Oh, the height and depth of mer - cy! Oh, the length and breadth of love!
Oh, the full - ness of re-demp-tion, Pledge of end - less life a - bove!

Forward Through the Ages

FREDERICK L. HOSMER

ARTHUR S. SULLIVAN

1. For-ward thro' the a - ges In un-bro-ken line, Move the faith-ful
2. Wid - er grows the king-dom, Reign of love and light; For it we must
3. Not a - lone we con - quer, Not a - lone we fall; In each loss or
spir - its At the call di - vine; Gifts in dif-f'ring meas-ure, Hearts of
la - bor Till our faith is sight; Prophets have pro-claimed it, Mar - tyrs
tri - umph Lose or tri-umph all. Bound by God's far pur - pose In one
one ac - cord, Man - i - fold the serv - ice, One the sure re - ward.
tes - ti - fied, Po - ets sung its glo - ry, He - roes for it died.
liv - ing whole, Move we on to - geth - er To the shin - ing goal!
REFRAIN
For - ward thro' the a - ges In un - bro - ken line,
Move the faith - ful spir - its At the call di - vine.

266 When Love Shines In

Mrs. Frank A. Breck — Wm. J. Kirkpatrick

1. Je-sus comes with pow'r to gladden, When love shines in, Ev-'ry life that
2. How the world will grow with beauty, When love shines in, And the heart re-
3. Dark-est sor-row will grow brighter, When love shines in, And the heav-iest
4. We may have un-fad-ing splendor, When love shines in, And a friend-ship
woe can sad-den, When love shines in. Love will teach us how to pray,
joice in du-ty, When love shines in. Tri-als may be sanc-ti-fied,
bur-den light-er, When love shines in. 'Tis the glo-ry that will throw
true and ten-der, When love shines in. When earth vic-t'ries shall be won,
Love will drive the gloom away, Turn our darkness in-to day, When love shines in.
And the soul in peace a-bide, Life will all be glo-ri-fied, When love shines in.
Light to show us where to go; O, the heart shall blessing know, When love shines in.
And our life in Heav'n begun, There will be no need of sun, When love shines in.
CHORUS
When love shines in,...... When love shines in,...
When love shines in,........
When love shines in, When love shines in, When love shines in,....
How the heart is tuned to sing-ing, When love.. shines in;....
When love shines in;......

When Love Shines In

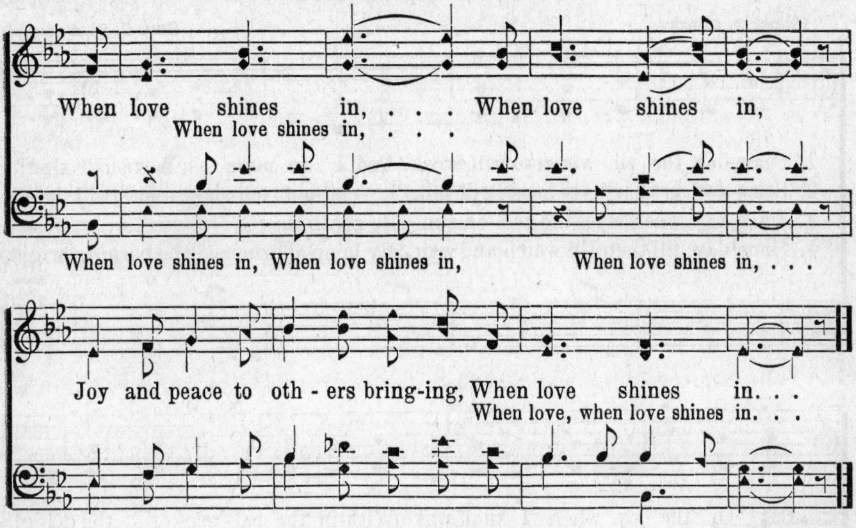
When love shines in, . . . When love shines in,
When love shines in, . . .
When love shines in, When love shines in, When love shines in, . . .
Joy and peace to oth - ers bring-ing, When love shines in. . .
When love, when love shines in. . .

Go with Me, Master 267

WALTER E. YODER

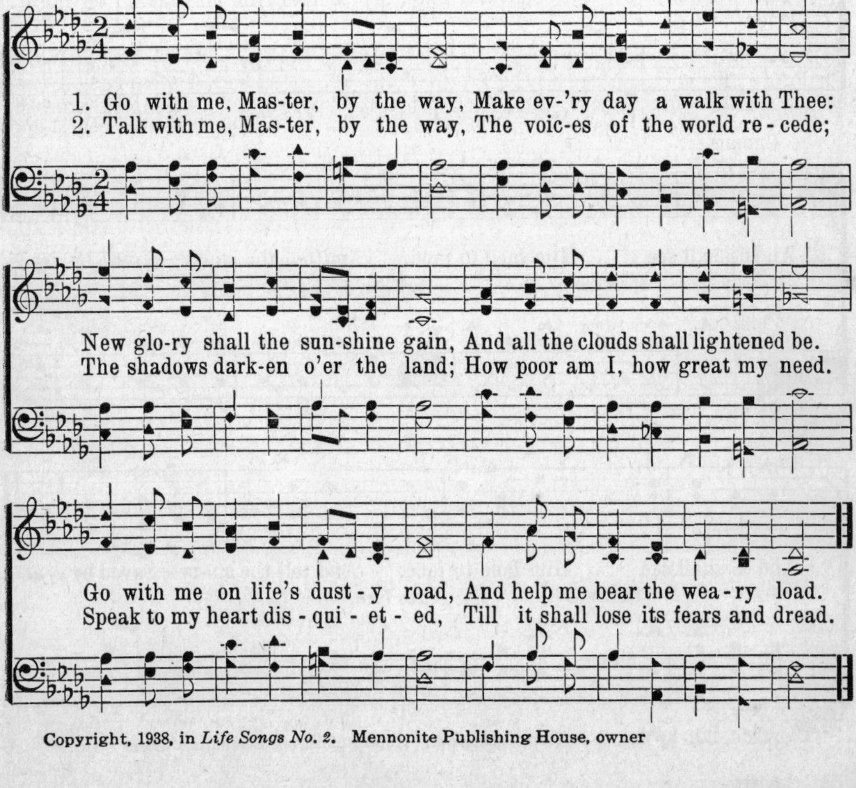
1. Go with me, Mas-ter, by the way, Make ev-'ry day a walk with Thee:
2. Talk with me, Mas-ter, by the way, The voic-es of the world re-cede;
New glo-ry shall the sun-shine gain, And all the clouds shall lightened be.
The shadows dark-en o'er the land; How poor am I, how great my need.
Go with me on life's dust - y road, And help me bear the wea - ry load.
Speak to my heart dis - qui - et - ed, Till it shall lose its fears and dread.

268 Saved By Grace

FANNY J. CROSBY — GEO. C. STEBBINS

1. Some day the sil - ver cord will break, And I no more as now shall sing;
2. Some day my earth-ly house will fall, I can-not tell how soon 'twill be,
3. Some day, when fades the gold-en sun Be-neath the ros - y - tint - ed west,
4. Some day: till then I'll watch and wait, My lamp all trimmed and burning bright,
But O, the joy when I shall wake With-in the pal - ace of the King!
But this I know—my All in All Has now a place in Heav'n for me.
My bless - ed Lord will say, "Well done!" And I shall en - ter in - to rest.
That when my Sav - ior opes the gate, My soul to Him may take its flight.
CHORUS
And I shall see Him face to face, And tell the sto-ry—Saved by grace;
shall see
to face,
And I shall see Him face to face, And tell the sto-ry—Saved by grace.
shall see
to face,
rit.

Some Time We'll Understand

MAXWELL N. CORNELIUS — JAMES MCGRANAHAN

1. Not now, but in the com-ing years, It may be in the bet-ter land,
2. We'll catch the broken thread a - gain, And fin - ish what we here be - gan;
3. We'll know why clouds instead of sun Were o - ver many a cherished plan;
4. God knows the way, He holds the key, He guides us with un - err - ing hand;
We'll read the meaning of our tears, And there, some time, we'll understand.
Heav'n will the mys-ter - ies ex - plain, And then, ah, then, we'll understand.
Why song has ceased when scarce begun; 'Tis there, some time, we'll understand.
Some time with tearless eyes we'll see; Yes, there, up there, we'll understand.
CHORUS. A little faster
Then trust in God thro' all the days; Fear not, for He doth hold thy hand;
doth hold thy hand;
A tempo
cres.
ad lib.
Though dark thy way, still sing and praise, Some time, some time, we'll understand.

270 Light After Darkness

Frances R. Havergal — Ira D. Sankey

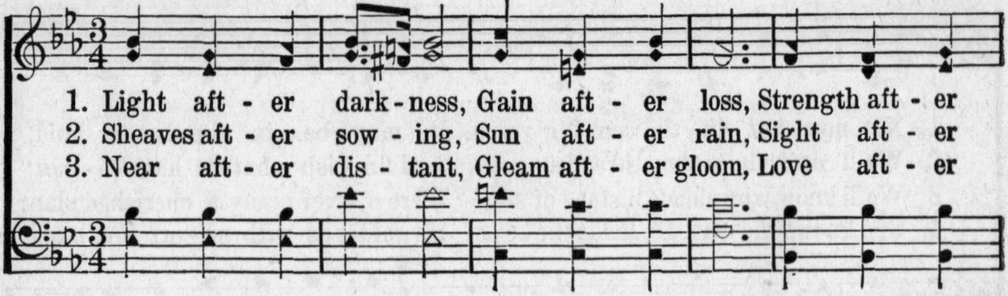
1. Light after darkness, Gain after loss, Strength after
2. Sheaves after sowing, Sun after rain, Sight after
3. Near after distant, Gleam after gloom, Love after

weakness, Crown after cross; Sweet after bitter,
mystery, Peace after pain; Joy after sorrow,
loneliness, Life after tomb; After long agony,

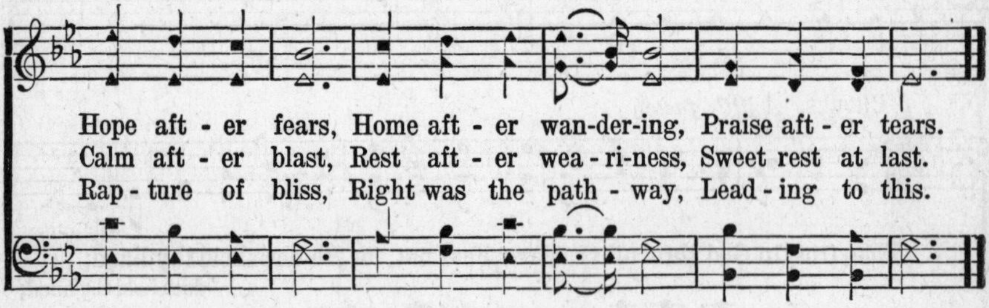
Hope after fears, Home after wandering, Praise after tears.
Calm after blast, Rest after weariness, Sweet rest at last.
Rapture of bliss, Right was the pathway, Leading to this.

271 On the Resurrection Morn

S. Baring-Gould — Ira D. Sankey

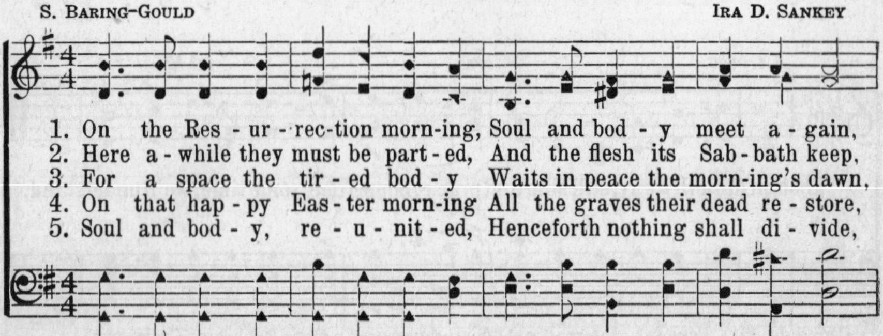
1. On the Resurrection morning, Soul and body meet again,
2. Here awhile they must be parted, And the flesh its Sabbath keep,
3. For a space the tired body Waits in peace the morning's dawn,
4. On that happy Easter morning All the graves their dead restore,
5. Soul and body, reunited, Henceforth nothing shall divide,

On the Resurrection Morn

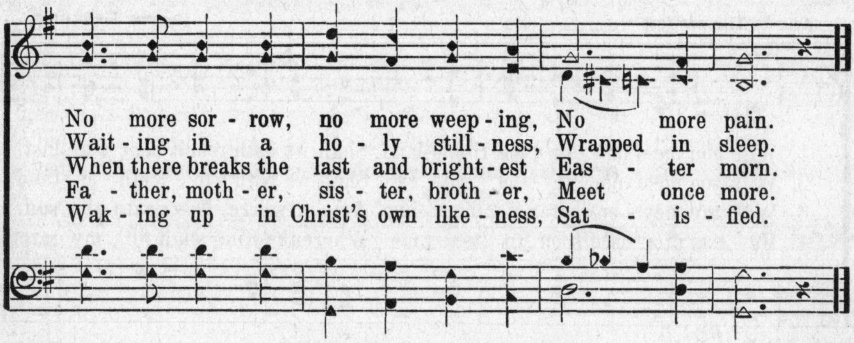
No more sor-row, no more weep-ing, No more pain.
Wait-ing in a ho-ly still-ness, Wrapped in sleep.
When there breaks the last and bright-est Eas-ter morn.
Fa-ther, moth-er, sis-ter, broth-er, Meet once more.
Wak-ing up in Christ's own like-ness, Sat-is-fied.

I Shall Be Like Him 272

W. A. S. W. A. SPENCER

1. When I shall reach the more ex-cel-lent glo-ry, And all my tri-als are passed,
2. We shall not wait till the glo-ri-ous dawning Breaks on the vi-sion so fair;
3. More and more like Him, repeat the blest sto-ry, O-ver and o-ver a-gain;
I shall be like Him, O won-der-ful sto-ry! I shall be like Him at last.
Now we may wel-come the heav-en-ly morn-ing, Now we His image may bear.
Changed by His Spir-it from glo-ry to glo-ry, I shall be sat-is-fied then.
CHORUS
I shall be like Him, I shall be like Him, And in His beau-ty shall shine;
I shall be like Him, wondrously like Him, Je-sus, my Sav-ior di-vine.

273 Meet Me in the Homeland

Ada R. Habershon — Robert Harkness

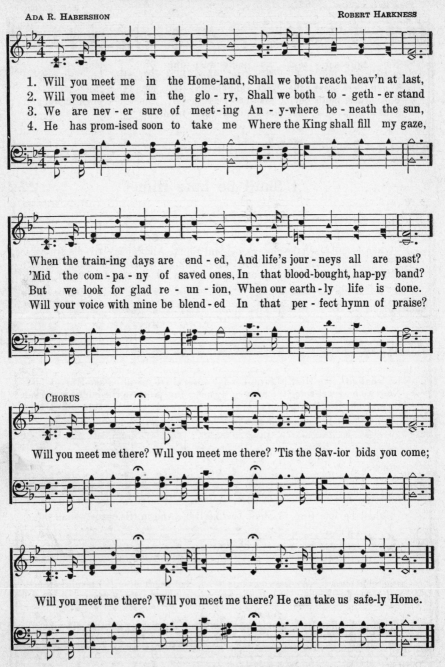

1. Will you meet me in the Home-land, Shall we both reach heav'n at last,
2. Will you meet me in the glo - ry, Shall we both to - geth - er stand
3. We are nev - er sure of meet - ing An - y-where be - neath the sun,
4. He has prom-ised soon to take me Where the King shall fill my gaze,

When the train-ing days are end - ed, And life's jour - neys all are past?
'Mid the com - pa - ny of saved ones, In that blood-bought, hap-py band?
But we look for glad re - un - ion, When our earth - ly life is done.
Will your voice with mine be blend - ed In that per - fect hymn of praise?

Chorus

Will you meet me there? Will you meet me there? 'Tis the Sav-ior bids you come;

Will you meet me there? Will you meet me there? He can take us safe-ly Home.

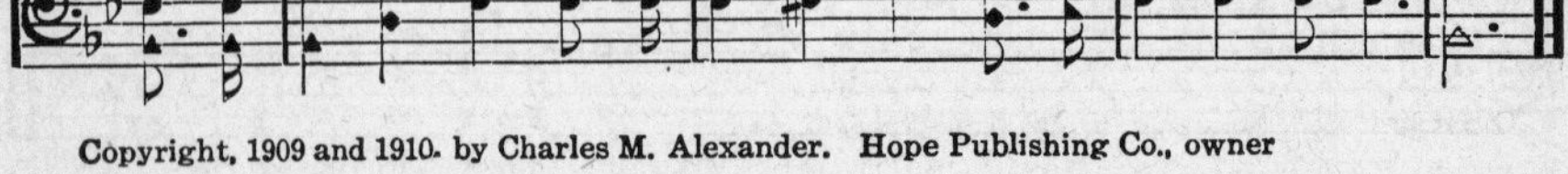

No Night There

JOHN R. CLEMENTS | H. P. DANKS

1. In the land of fade-less day Lies the "cit-y four-square,"
2. All the gates of pearl are made, In the "cit-y four-square,"
3. And the gates shall nev-er close To the "cit-y four-square,"
4. There they need no sun-shine bright, In that "cit-y four-square,"
It shall nev-er pass a-way, And there is "no night there."
All the streets with gold are laid, And there is "no night there."
There life's crys-tal riv-er flows, And there is "no night there."
For the Lamb is all the light, And there is "no night there."
CHORUS
mf
God shall "wipe a-way all tears;" There's no death, no pain, nor fears;
God shall "wipe a - way all tears;" There's no death, no pain, nor fears;
f
dim.
mf
And they count not time by years, For there is "no night there."
And they count not time by years, by years, For there is "no night..... there."

On Jordan's Stormy Banks

Rev. Samuel Stennett — T. C. O'Kane

1. On Jor-dan's storm-y banks I stand, And cast a wish - ful eye
2. O'er all those wide - ex - tend - ed plains Shines one e - ter - nal day;
3. When shall I reach that hap - py place, And be for - ev - er blest?
4. Filled with de - light, my rap - tured soul Would here no lon - ger stay;
To Ca-naan's fair and hap - py land, Where my pos - ses - sions lie.
There God the Son for - ev - er reigns, And scat - ters night a - way.
When shall I see my Fa - ther's face, And in His bos - om rest?
Tho' Jor-dan's waves a - round me roll, Fear - less I'd launch a - way.
Chorus
We will rest in the fair and hap - py land, Just a-
by and by,
cross on the ev - er-green shore, . . . Sing the song of Mo-ses and the
ev - er-green shore,
Lamb, by and by, And dwell with Je - sus ev - er - more.

My Savior First of All

FANNY J. CROSBY

JNO. R. SWENEY

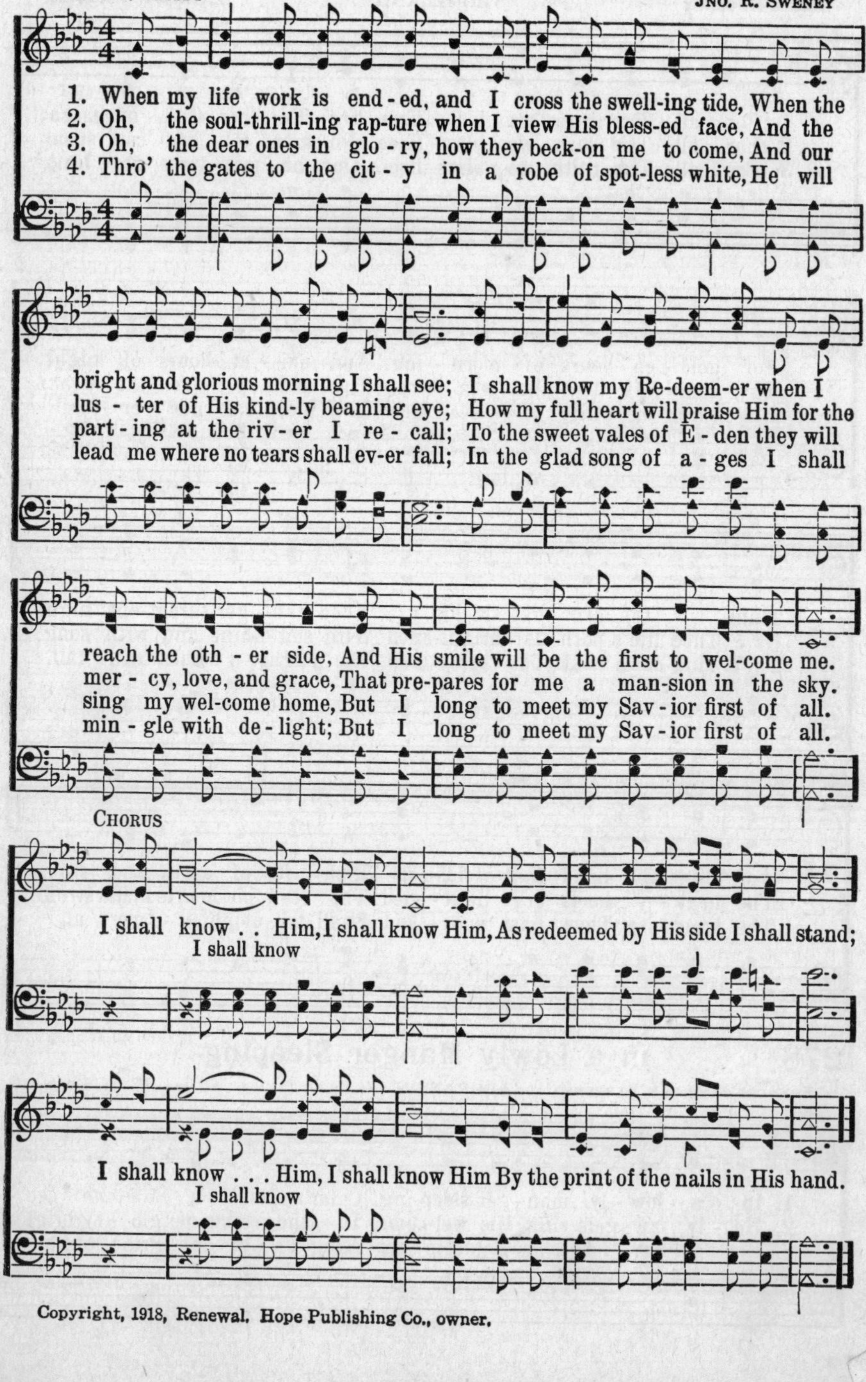
1. When my life work is end-ed, and I cross the swell-ing tide, When the
2. Oh, the soul-thrill-ing rap-ture when I view His bless-ed face, And the
3. Oh, the dear ones in glo-ry, how they beck-on me to come, And our
4. Thro' the gates to the cit-y in a robe of spot-less white, He will
bright and glorious morning I shall see; I shall know my Re-deem-er when I
lus-ter of His kind-ly beaming eye; How my full heart will praise Him for the
part-ing at the riv-er I re-call; To the sweet vales of E-den they will
lead me where no tears shall ev-er fall; In the glad song of a-ges I shall
reach the oth-er side, And His smile will be the first to wel-come me.
mer-cy, love, and grace, That pre-pares for me a man-sion in the sky.
sing my wel-come home, But I long to meet my Sav-ior first of all.
min-gle with de-light; But I long to meet my Sav-ior first of all.
CHORUS
I shall know . . Him, I shall know Him, As redeemed by His side I shall stand;
I shall know
I shall know . . . Him, I shall know Him By the print of the nails in His hand.
I shall know

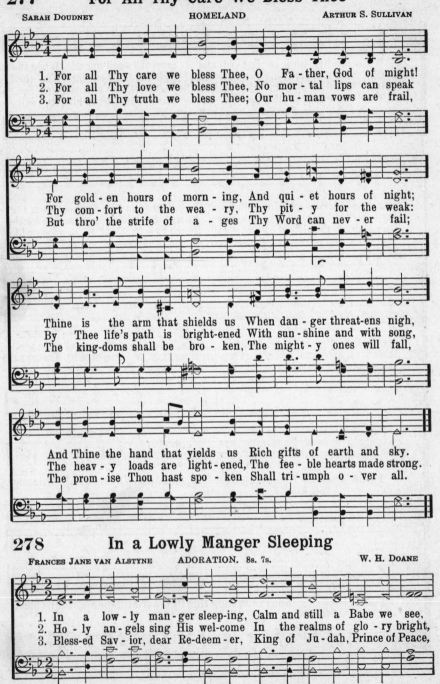

277 For All Thy Care We Bless Thee

SARAH DOUDNEY HOMELAND ARTHUR S. SULLIVAN

1. For all Thy care we bless Thee, O Fa - ther, God of might!
2. For all Thy love we bless Thee, No mor - tal lips can speak
3. For all Thy truth we bless Thee; Our hu - man vows are frail,

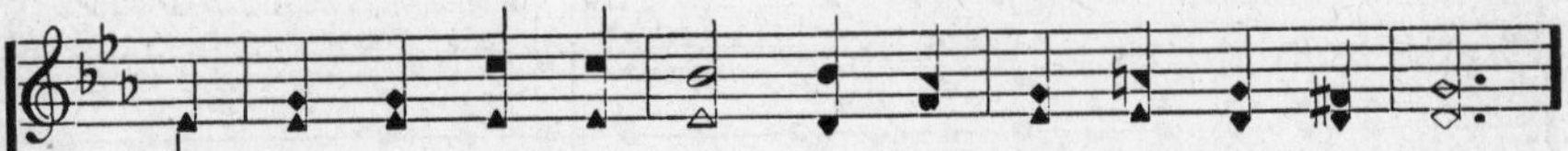

For gold - en hours of morn - ing, And qui - et hours of night;
Thy com - fort to the wea - ry, Thy pit - y for the weak:
But thro' the strife of a - ges Thy Word can nev - er fail;

Thine is the arm that shields us When dan - ger threat-ens nigh,
By Thee life's path is bright-ened With sun - shine and with song,
The king-doms shall be bro - ken, The might - y ones will fall,

And Thine the hand that yields us Rich gifts of earth and sky.
The heav - y loads are light - ened, The fee - ble hearts made strong.
The prom - ise Thou hast spo - ken Shall tri - umph o - ver all.

278 In a Lowly Manger Sleeping

FRANCES JANE VAN ALSTYNE ADORATION. 8s. 7s. W. H. DOANE

1. In a low - ly man - ger sleep - ing, Calm and still a Babe we see,
2. Ho - ly an - gels sing His wel - come In the realms of glo - ry bright,
3. Bless-ed Sav - ior, dear Re - deem - er, King of Ju - dah, Prince of Peace,

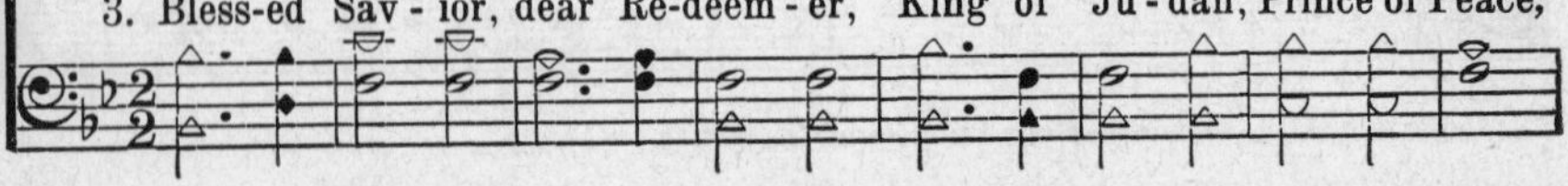

In a Lowly Manger Sleeping

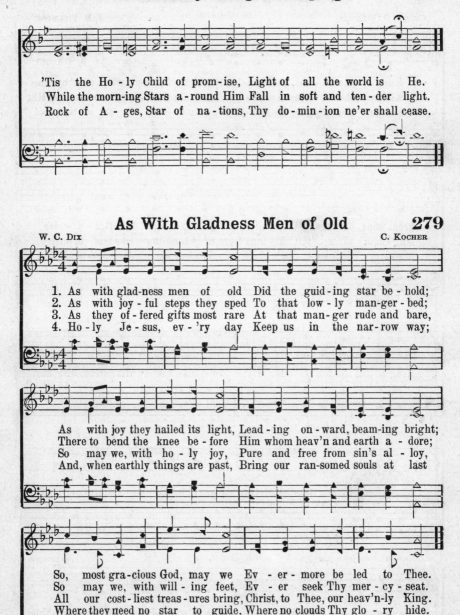

'Tis the Ho - ly Child of prom - ise, Light of all the world is He.
While the morn-ing Stars a - round Him Fall in soft and ten - der light.
Rock of A - ges, Star of na - tions, Thy do - min - ion ne'er shall cease.

As With Gladness Men of Old

W. C. DIX C. KOCHER

1. As with glad-ness men of old Did the guid - ing star be - hold;
2. As with joy - ful steps they sped To that low - ly man-ger - bed;
3. As they of - fered gifts most rare At that man - ger rude and bare,
4. Ho - ly Je - sus, ev - 'ry day Keep us in the nar - row way;

As with joy they hailed its light, Lead - ing on - ward, beam-ing bright;
There to bend the knee be - fore Him whom heav'n and earth a - dore;
So may we, with ho - ly joy, Pure and free from sin's al - loy,
And, when earthly things are past, Bring our ran-somed souls at last

So, most gra-cious God, may we Ev - er - more be led to Thee.
So may we, with will - ing feet, Ev - er seek Thy mer - cy - seat.
All our cost - liest treas - ures bring, Christ, to Thee, our heav'n-ly King.
Where they need no star to guide, Where no clouds Thy glo - ry hide.

280 King of the Ages

George O. Webster — J. H. Fillmore

1. King of the A - ges, tho' low - ly His birth, Scorned and de - nied by the great ones of earth, Child of a peas - ant in far Gal - i - lee,
2. King of the A - ges, a ba - by so weak, Com - ing in meek - ness His king - dom to seek; Com - ing, from sin's bind - ing fet - ters to free,
3. King of the A - ges, in wor - thy ac - claim Sing we our an - thems of praise to His name; Sin's night is bro - ken, earth's dark - ness shall flee;
King of the A - ges is He.
Chorus
Je - sus, low - ly His shrine; Je - sus, Mon - arch Di - vine; Hum - ble His birth - place in Beth - le - hem's stall, Com - ing our Sav - ior to be;
Je - sus, low - ly His shrine; Je - sus, Mon - arch Di - vine;

King of the Ages

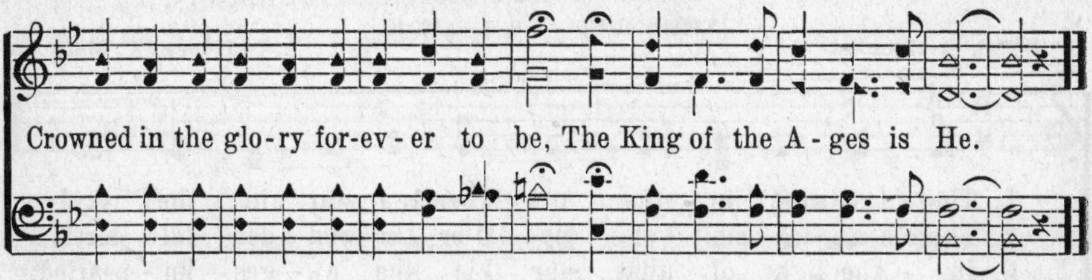
Crowned in the glo-ry for-ev-er to be, The King of the A-ges is He.

The First Noel

281

Traditional

Traditional

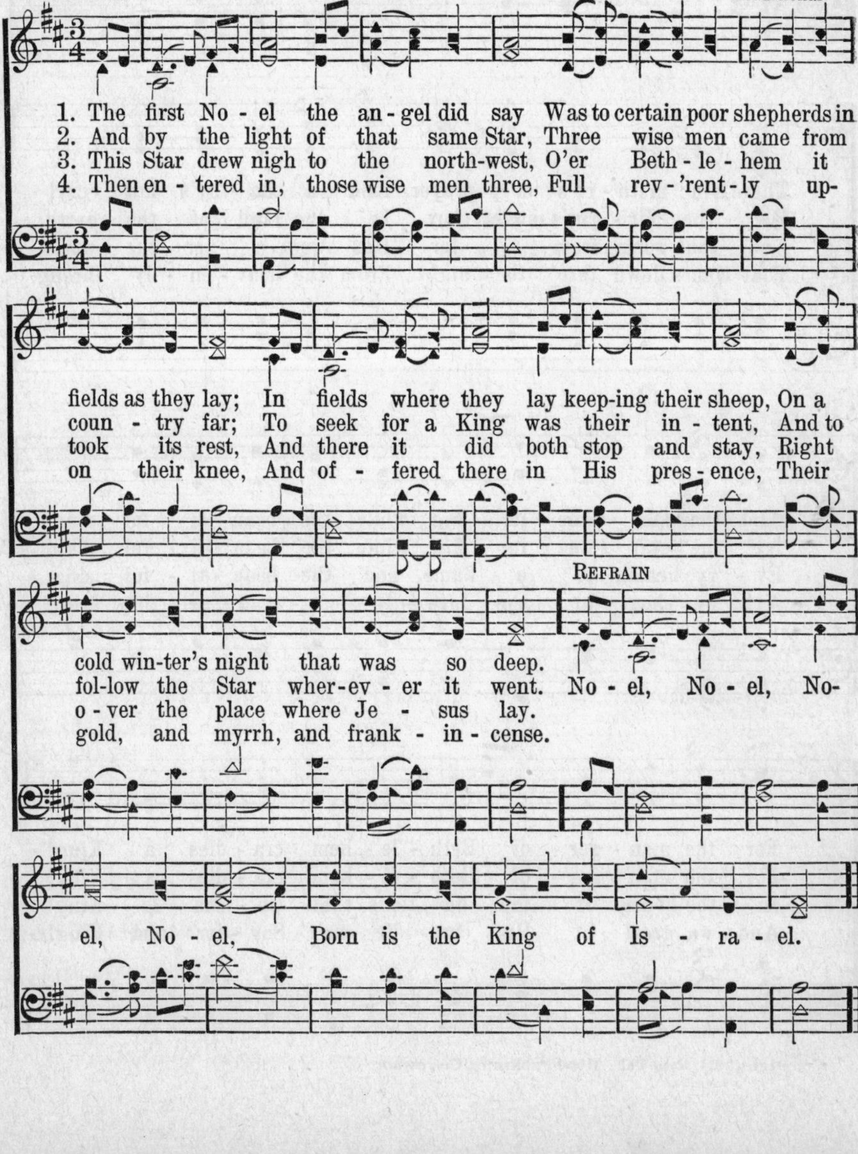
1. The first No-el the an-gel did say Was to certain poor shepherds in
2. And by the light of that same Star, Three wise men came from
3. This Star drew nigh to the north-west, O'er Beth-le-hem it
4. Then en-tered in, those wise men three, Full rev-'rent-ly up-
fields as they lay; In fields where they lay keep-ing their sheep, On a
coun-try far; To seek for a King was their in-tent, And to
took its rest, And there it did both stop and stay, Right
on their knee, And of-fered there in His pres-ence, Their
REFRAIN
cold win-ter's night that was so deep.
fol-low the Star wher-ev-er it went. No-el, No-el, No-
o-ver the place where Je-sus lay.
gold, and myrrh, and frank-in-cense.
el, No-el, Born is the King of Is-ra-el.

282 There's a Song in the Air

EMMANUEL. 6. 6. 6. 6. 12. 12.

JOSIAH G. HOLLAND — HUBERT P. MAIN

1. There's a song in the air! There's a star in the sky!
2. There's a tu - mult of joy O'er the won - der - ful birth,
3. In the light of that star Lie the a - ges im - pearled;
4. We re - joice in the light, And we ech - o the song
There's a moth - er's deep prayer, And a ba - by's low cry!
For the Vir - gin's sweet boy Is the Lord of the earth.
And that song from a - far Has swept o - ver the world.
That comes down thro' the night From the heav - en - ly throng.
And the star rains its fire while the beau - ti - ful sing,
Ay! the star rains its fire while the beau - ti - ful sing,
Ev - 'ry hearth is a - flame, and the beau - ti - ful sing,
Ay! we shout to the love - ly e - van - gel they bring,
For the man - ger of Beth - le - hem cra - dles a King!
For the man - ger of Beth - le - hem cra - dles a King!
In the homes of the na - tions, that Je - sus is King!
And we greet in His cra - dle our Sav - ior and King!

Thou Didst Leave Thy Throne

MARGARET. P. M. With Refrain

EMILY E. S. ELLIOTT — TIMOTHY R. MATTHEWS

Moderately slow. Excellent for medium voice solo

mf
1. Thou didst leave Thy throne and Thy king - ly crown, When Thou
2. Heav-en's arch - es rang when the an - gels sang, Pro-
3. Thou cam'st, O Lord, with the liv - ing Word That should
4. When heav'n's arch-es shall ring, and her choir shall sing, At Thy

cres.
cam - est to earth for me; But in Beth - le-hem's home there was
claim-ing Thy roy - al de - gree; But in low - ly birth Thou didst
set Thy peo - ple free; But with mock - ing scorn, and with
com - ing to vic - to - ry, Let Thy voice call me home, say - ing,

cres.
f
dim. e rit.
REFRAIN
found no room For Thy ho - ly na - tiv - i - ty. Oh,
come to earth, And in great hu - mil - i - ty. Oh,
crown of thorn, They bore Thee to Cal - va - ry. Oh,
"Yet there is room, There is room at My side for thee!" And my

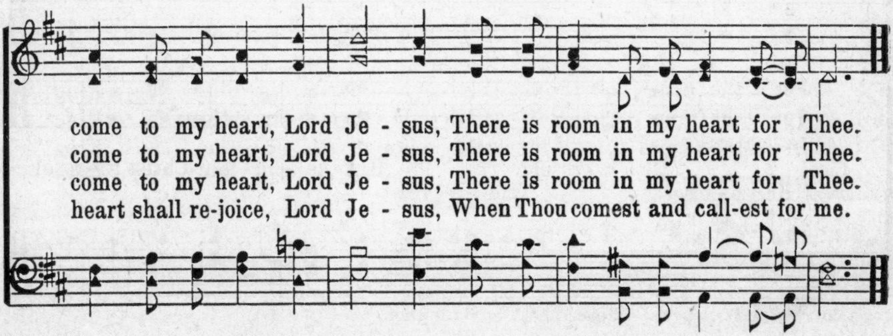
come to my heart, Lord Je - sus, There is room in my heart for Thee.
come to my heart, Lord Je - sus, There is room in my heart for Thee.
come to my heart, Lord Je - sus, There is room in my heart for Thee.
heart shall re-joice, Lord Je - sus, When Thou comest and call-est for me.

284 Christ Arose

ROBERT LOWRY — ROBERT LOWRY

1. Low in the grave He lay— Je-sus my Sav-ior! Wait-ing the com-ing day—
2. Vain-ly they watch His bed—Je-sus my Sav-ior! Vain-ly they seal the dead—
3. Death cannot keep his prey—Je-sus my Sav-ior! He tore the bars a-way—
Je-sus my Lord!
REFRAIN Faster
Up from the grave He a-rose, (He a-rose,) With a might-y tri-umph o'er His foes; (He a-rose!) He a-rose a Vic-tor from the dark do-main, And He lives for-ev-er with His saints to reign. He a-rose! He a-rose! He a-rose! He a-rose! Hal-le-lu-jah! Christ a-rose!
rit.

In the Garden

J. L. HORST　　　　H. D. WEAVER

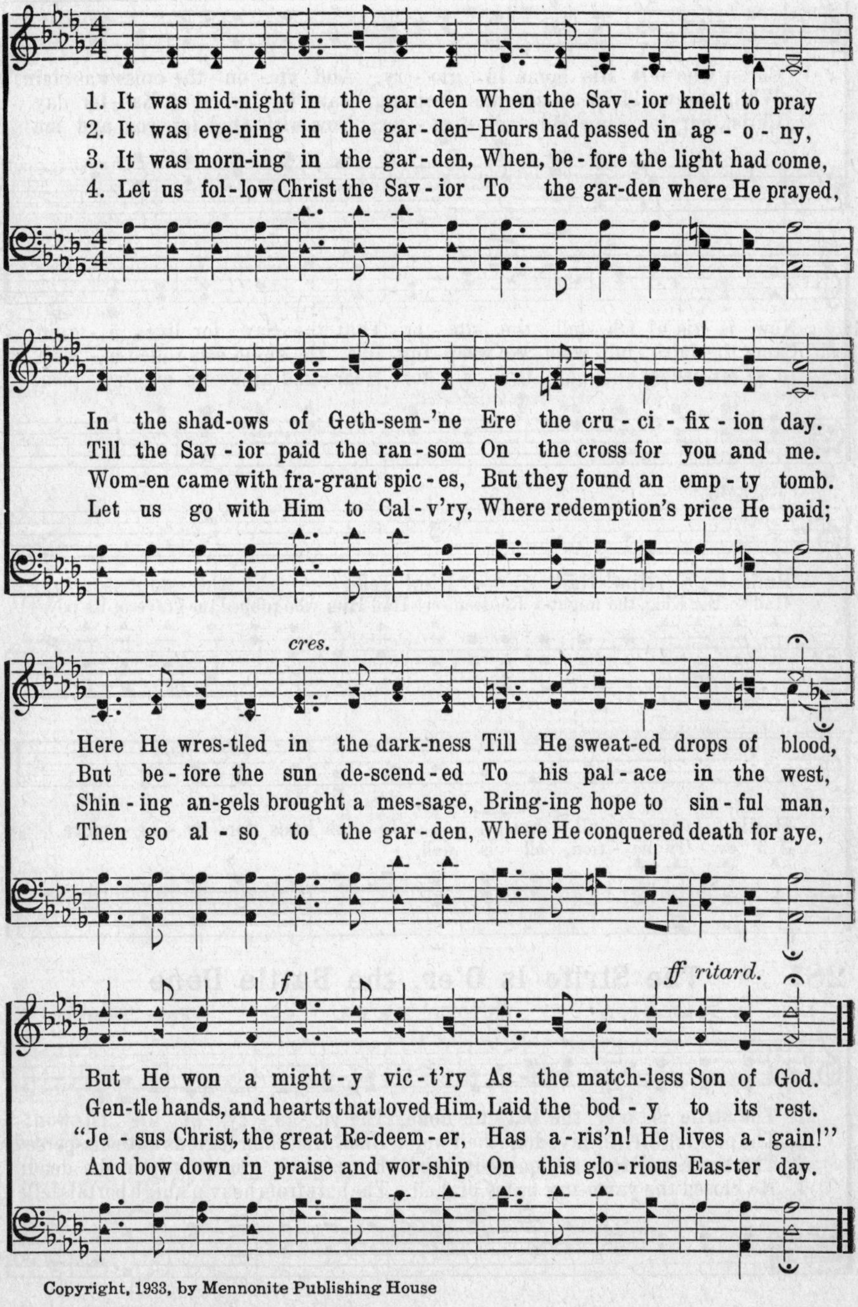
1. It was mid-night in the gar-den When the Sav-ior knelt to pray
2. It was eve-ning in the gar-den–Hours had passed in ag-o-ny,
3. It was morn-ing in the gar-den, When, be-fore the light had come,
4. Let us fol-low Christ the Sav-ior To the gar-den where He prayed,
In the shad-ows of Geth-sem-'ne Ere the cru-ci-fix-ion day.
Till the Sav-ior paid the ran-som On the cross for you and me.
Wom-en came with fra-grant spic-es, But they found an emp-ty tomb.
Let us go with Him to Cal-v'ry, Where redemption's price He paid;
cres.
Here He wres-tled in the dark-ness Till He sweat-ed drops of blood,
But be-fore the sun de-scend-ed To his pal-ace in the west,
Shin-ing an-gels brought a mes-sage, Bring-ing hope to sin-ful man,
Then go al-so to the gar-den, Where He conquered death for aye,
f
ff ritard.
But He won a might-y vic-t'ry As the match-less Son of God.
Gen-tle hands, and hearts that loved Him, Laid the bod-y to its rest.
"Je-sus Christ, the great Re-deem-er, Has a-ris'n! He lives a-gain!"
And bow down in praise and wor-ship On this glo-rious Eas-ter day.

286 Christ Is Risen

A. B. K. A. B. Kolb

Joyfully

1. Christ who left His home in glo - ry, And up - on the cross was slain,
2. While the world in peace was sleep-ing, Ear - ly on that Eas - ter day,
3. Christ, our lov - ing Me - di - a - tor, Now with God for you and me
Now is ris'n! Oh, tell the sto - ry That the Sav - ior lives a - gain.
Came the faith - ful wom - en weep - ing, But the stone was rolled a - way.
In - ter-cedes, and our Cre - a - tor Hears and an-swers ev - 'ry plea.
Refrain
Hail Him! Hail Him! Tell the sto - ry!
Hail to the King, the might-y Re-deem-er! Hail Him who robbed the grave of its pow'r!
Hail! all hail! . . . Je - sus lives for - ev - er - more.
Tell ev - 'ry na - tion, all is well,

287 The Strife Is O'er, the Battle Done

Latin. Tr. Francis Pott VICTORY. 8. 8. 8. 4. From "Palestrina"

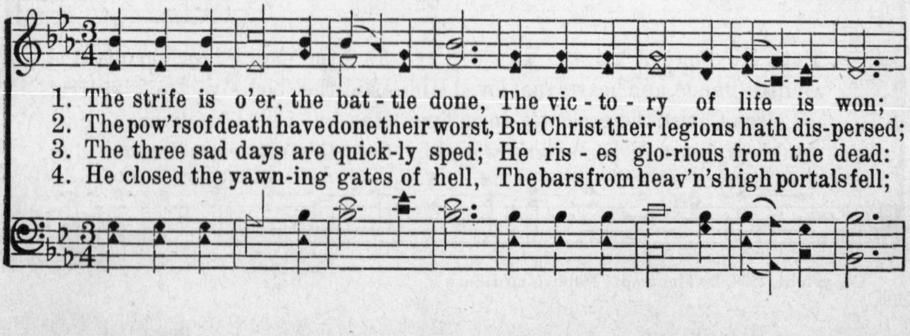
1. The strife is o'er, the bat - tle done, The vic - to - ry of life is won;
2. The pow'rs of death have done their worst, But Christ their legions hath dis-persed;
3. The three sad days are quick-ly sped; He ris - es glo-rious from the dead:
4. He closed the yawn-ing gates of hell, The bars from heav'n's high portals fell;

The Strife Is O'er, the Battle Done

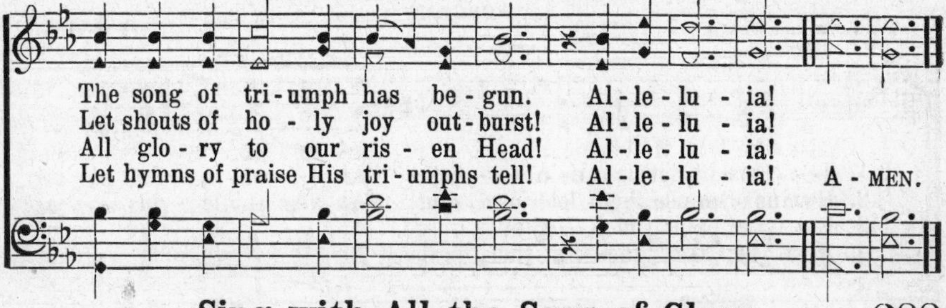
The song of tri-umph has be-gun. Al-le-lu-ia!
Let shouts of ho-ly joy out-burst! Al-le-lu-ia!
All glo-ry to our ris-en Head! Al-le-lu-ia!
Let hymns of praise His tri-umphs tell! Al-le-lu-ia! A-MEN.

Sing with All the Sons of Glory 288

HYMN TO JOY. 8s. 7s. D.

WILLIAM J. IRONS — From LUDWIG VAN BEETHOVEN

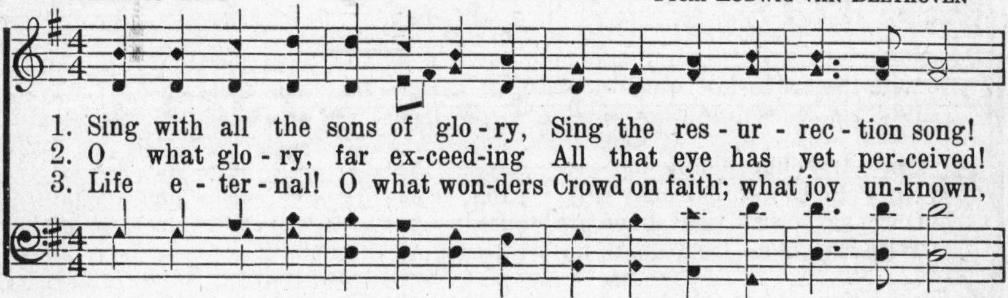
1. Sing with all the sons of glo-ry, Sing the res-ur-rec-tion song!
2. O what glo-ry, far ex-ceed-ing All that eye has yet per-ceived!
3. Life e-ter-nal! O what won-ders Crowd on faith; what joy un-known,

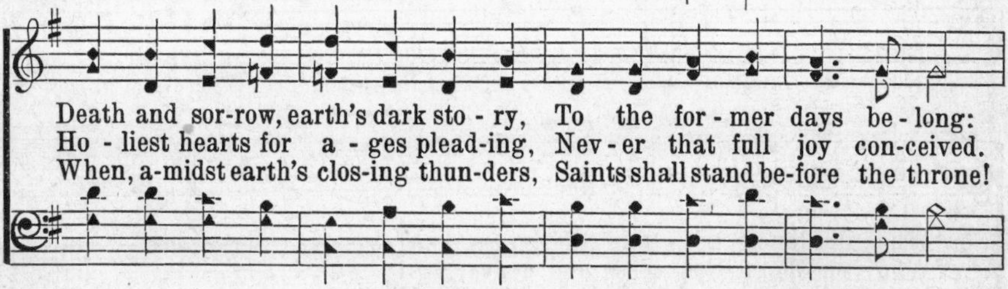
Death and sor-row, earth's dark sto-ry, To the for-mer days be-long:
Ho-liest hearts for a-ges plead-ing, Nev-er that full joy con-ceived.
When, a-midst earth's clos-ing thun-ders, Saints shall stand be-fore the throne!

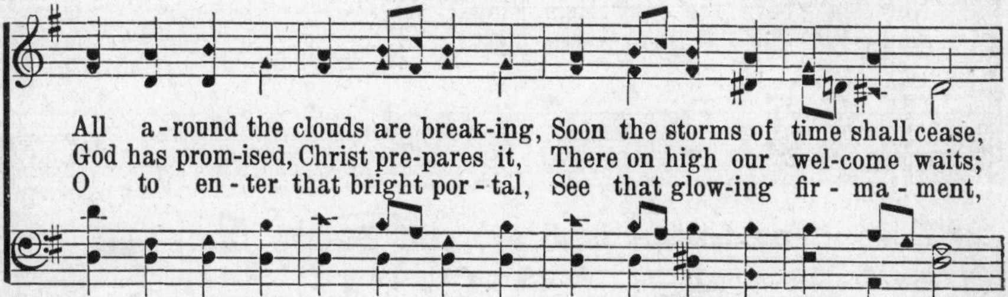
All a-round the clouds are break-ing, Soon the storms of time shall cease,
God has prom-ised, Christ pre-pares it, There on high our wel-come waits;
O to en-ter that bright por-tal, See that glow-ing fir-ma-ment,

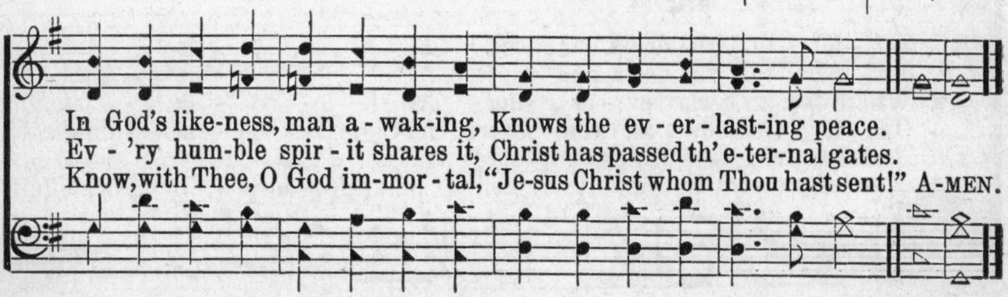
In God's like-ness, man a-wak-ing, Knows the ev-er-last-ing peace.
Ev-'ry hum-ble spir-it shares it, Christ has passed th' e-ter-nal gates.
Know, with Thee, O God im-mor-tal, "Je-sus Christ whom Thou hast sent!" A-MEN.

289 Jesus Christ Is Risen Today

WORGAN

Tr. TATE and BRADY | Lyra Davidica

1. Je - sus Christ is ris'n to - day, Al - - le - lu - ia!
2. Hymns of praise then let us sing, Al - - le - lu - ia!
3. But the pains which He en - dured, Al - - le - lu - ia!
4. Now be God the Fa - ther praised, Al - - le - lu - ia!

Our tri - um - phant ho - ly day, Al - - le - lu - ia!
Un - to Christ, our heav'n-ly King, Al - - le - lu - ia!
Our sal - va - tion have pro - cured; Al - - le - lu - ia!
With the Son, from death up - raised, Al - - le - lu - ia!

Who did once up - on the cross, Al - - le - lu - ia!
Who en - dured the cross and grave, Al - - le - lu - ia!
Now a - bove the sky He's King, Al - - le - lu - ia!
And the Spir - it, ev - er blest, Al - - le - lu - ia!

Suf - fer to re - deem our loss. Al - - le - lu - ia!
Sin - ners to re - deem and save. Al - - le - lu - ia!
Where the an - gels ev - er sing, Al - - le - lu - ia!
One true God, by all con - fessed. Al - - le - lu - ia!

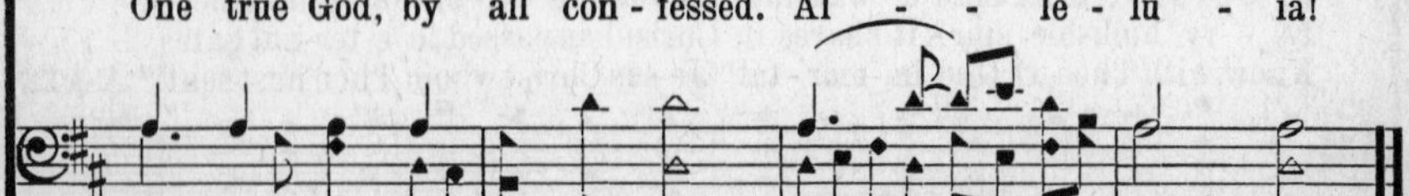

For Christ and the Church

E. E. Hewitt — Wm. J. Kirkpatrick

1. "For Christ and the Church" let our voi - ces ring, Let us hon - or the
2. "For Christ and the Church" be our ear-nest prayer, Let us fol - low His
3. "For Christ and the Church" willing of-f'rings make, Time and tal - ents and
4. "For Christ and the Church" let us cast a - side, By His con - quer - ing
name of our own bless - ed King; Let us work with a will in the
ban - ner, the cross dai - ly bear; Let us yield, whol - ly yield, to the
gold for the dear Mas-ter's sake; We will ren - der the best we can
grace, chains of self, fear, and pride; May our lives be en-riched by an
strength of youth, And loy - al - ly stand for the king - dom of truth.
Spir - it's pow'r, And faith - ful - ly serve Him in life's bright-est hour.
bring to Him, The heart's wealth of love, that will nev - er grow dim.
aim so grand; Then hap - py the call to the Sav-ior's right hand.
CHORUS
For Christ, our dear Re-deem - er, For Christ, who died to save;
For Christ, For Christ,
For the Church . . His blood hath purchased; Lord, make us pure and brave.
For the Church.

291 More Like the Master

C. H. G. — Chas. H. Gabriel

1. More like the Mas-ter I would ev-er be, More of His meek-ness,
2. More like the Mas-ter is my dai-ly prayer; More strength to car-ry
3. More like the Mas-ter I would live and grow; More of His love to
more hu-mil-i-ty; More zeal to la-bor, more cour-age to be true,
cross-es I must bear; More ear-nest ef-fort to bring His kingdom in;
oth-ers I would show; More self-de-ni-al, like His in Gal-i-lee,
rit.
Chorus
More con-se-cra-tion for work He bids me do. . . . . Take Thou my
More of His Spir-it, the wan-der-er to win. . . . .
More like the Mas-ter I long to ev-er be. . . . . Take my heart, O
heart, . . I would be Thine a-lone; . . Take Thou my heart . . and
take my heart, I would be Thine a-lone; Take my heart, O take my heart and
make it all Thine own; . . Purge me from sin, . . . O Lord, I now im-
make it all Thine own; Purge Thou me from ev-'ry sin, O Lord, I

More Like the Master

plore, . . . Wash me and keep . . . . me Thine for-ev - er - more.
now im-plore, Wash and keep, O wash and keep me Thine for-ev - er - more.

Saved to Serve

292

El Nathan — James McGranahan

1. Go - ing forth at Christ's com-mand, Go - ing forth to ev - 'ry land;
2. Serv-ing God thro' all our days, Toil-ing not for purse or praise;
3. Seek-ing on - ly souls to win, From the dead-ly pow'r of sin;
Full sal - va - tion mak - ing known, Thro' the blood of God's dear Son.
But to mag - ni - fy His name, While the gos - pel we pro - claim.
We would guide their steps a - right, Out of dark-ness in - to light.
Chorus
"Saved to serve!" the watch-word ring, Saved to serve our glo - rious King;
Tell the sto - ry o'er and o'er, Saved to serve for - ev - er - more.

293 Ye Fair Green Hills of Galilee

STELLA. English. 8. 8. 8. 8. 8. 8.

EUSTACE R. CONDER — Founded on an old English Melody

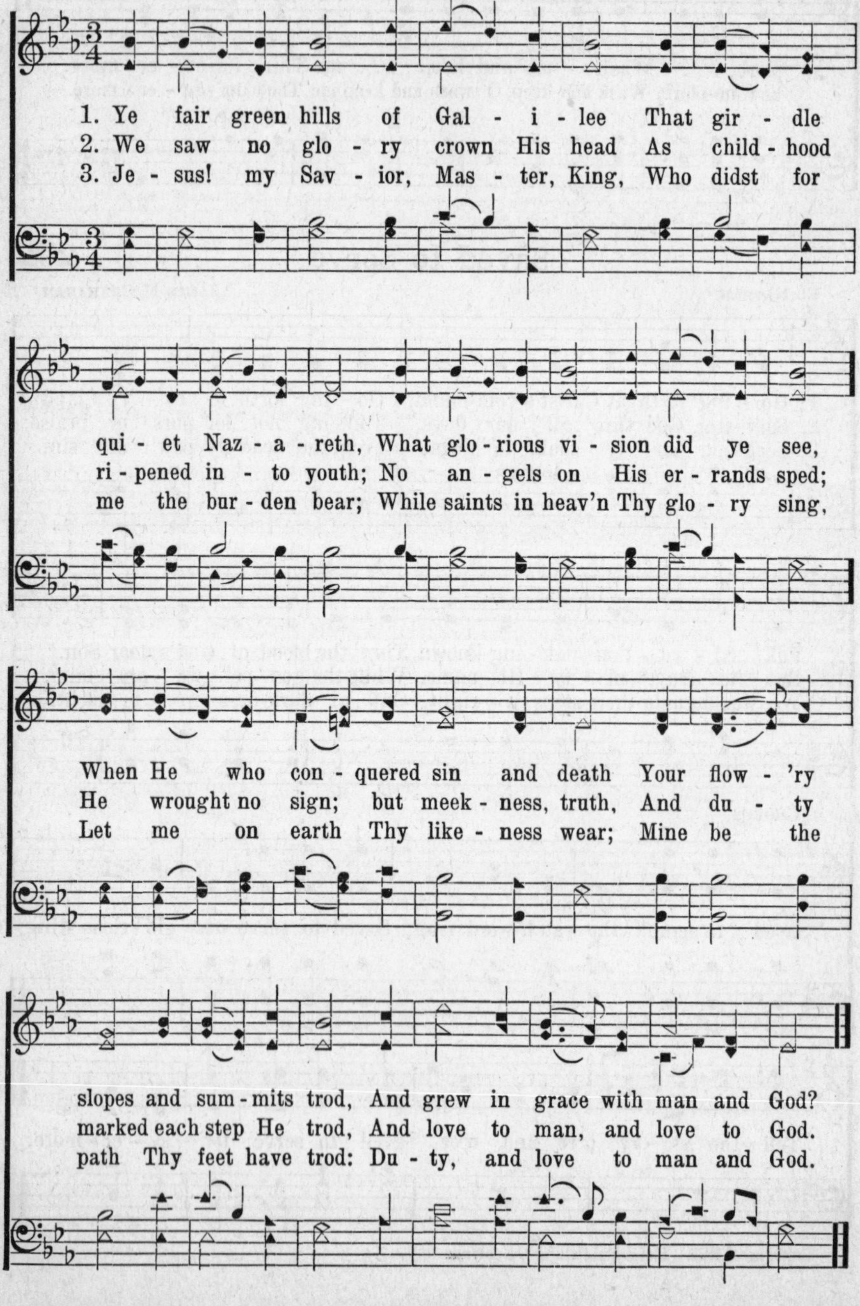
1. Ye fair green hills of Gal - i - lee That gir - dle
2. We saw no glo - ry crown His head As child - hood
3. Je - sus! my Sav - ior, Mas - ter, King, Who didst for
qui - et Naz - a - reth, What glo - rious vi - sion did ye see,
ri - pened in - to youth; No an - gels on His er - rands sped;
me the bur - den bear; While saints in heav'n Thy glo - ry sing,
When He who con - quered sin and death Your flow - 'ry
He wrought no sign; but meek - ness, truth, And du - ty
Let me on earth Thy like - ness wear; Mine be the
slopes and sum - mits trod, And grew in grace with man and God?
marked each step He trod, And love to man, and love to God.
path Thy feet have trod: Du - ty, and love to man and God.

When, His Salvation Bringing 294

TOURS. 7. 6. 7. 6. 7. 6. 7. 6.

JOHN KING BERTHOLD TOURS

1. When, His sal - va - tion bring - ing, To Zi - on Je - sus came,
2. And since the Lord re - tain - eth His love for chil - dren still,
3. For should we fail pro - claim - ing Our great Re - deem - er's praise,

The chil - dren all stood sing - ing Ho - san - na to His name:
Tho' now as King He reign - eth On Zi - on's heav'n-ly hill,
The stones, our si - lence sham - ing, Would their ho - san - nas raise.

Nor did their zeal of - fend Him, But, as He rode a - long,
We'll gath - er round His ban - ner Who sits up - on His throne,
But shall we on - ly ren - der The trib - ute of our words?

He let them still at - tend Him, And smiled to hear their song.
And cry a - loud, "Ho - san - na To Da - vid's roy - al Son!"
No: while our hearts are ten - der, They, too, shall be the Lord's.

I Love to Tell the Story

CATHERINE HANKEY

WILLIAM G. FISCHER

1. I love to tell the sto - ry Of un - seen things a - bove, Of
2. I love to tell the sto - ry, More won - der - ful it seems Than
3. I love to tell the sto - ry, 'Tis pleas - ant to re - peat What
4. I love to tell the sto - ry, For those who know it best Seem
Je - sus and His glo - ry, Of Je - sus and His love. I love to
all the gold - en fan - cies Of all our gold - en dreams. I love to
seems, each time I tell it, More won - der - ful - ly sweet. I love to
hun - ger - ing and thirst - ing To hear it like the rest. And when, in
tell the sto - ry, Be - cause I know 'tis true; It sat - is - fies my
tell the sto - ry, It did so much for me; And that is just the
tell the sto - ry, For some have nev - er heard The mes - sage of sal-
scenes of glo - ry, I sing the new, new song, 'Twill be the old, old
longings As noth - ing else can do.
rea - son I tell it now to thee.
va - tion From God's own ho - ly word.
sto - ry That I have loved so long.
CHORUS
I love to tell the sto - ry, 'Twill
be my theme in glo - ry To tell the old, old sto - ry Of Jesus and His love.

Ho! Reapers of Life's Harvest

I. B. W. I. B. WOODBURY

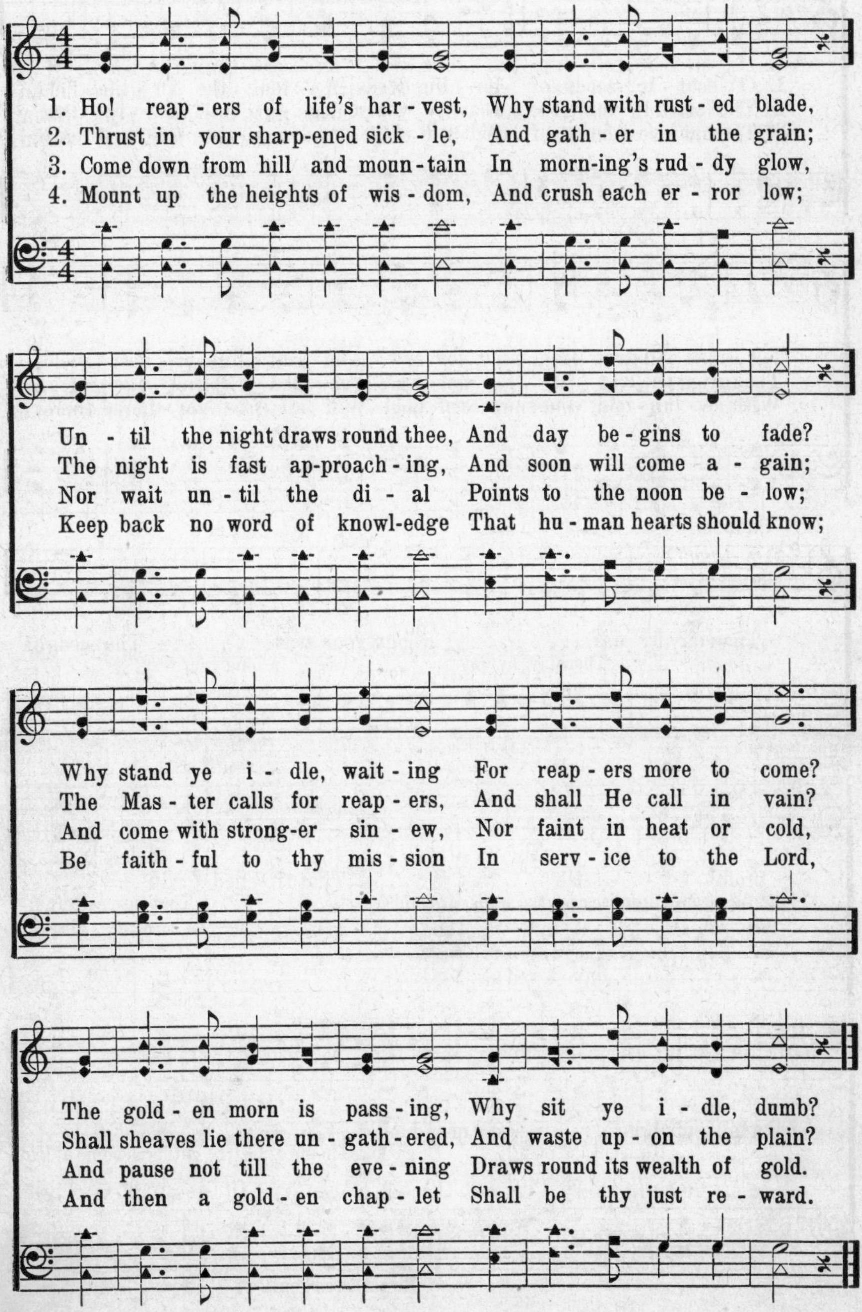
1. Ho! reap - ers of life's har - vest, Why stand with rust - ed blade,
2. Thrust in your sharp-ened sick - le, And gath - er in the grain;
3. Come down from hill and moun - tain In morn-ing's rud - dy glow,
4. Mount up the heights of wis - dom, And crush each er - ror low;
Un - til the night draws round thee, And day be - gins to fade?
The night is fast ap-proach - ing, And soon will come a - gain;
Nor wait un - til the di - al Points to the noon be - low;
Keep back no word of knowl-edge That hu - man hearts should know;
Why stand ye i - dle, wait - ing For reap - ers more to come?
The Mas - ter calls for reap - ers, And shall He call in vain?
And come with strong-er sin - ew, Nor faint in heat or cold,
Be faith - ful to thy mis - sion In serv - ice to the Lord,
The gold - en morn is pass - ing, Why sit ye i - dle, dumb?
Shall sheaves lie there un - gath - ered, And waste up - on the plain?
And pause not till the eve - ning Draws round its wealth of gold.
And then a gold - en chap - let Shall be thy just re - ward.

297 O Scatter Seeds of Loving Deeds

JESSIE H. BROWN — FRED. A. FILLMORE

1. O scat - ter seeds of lov - ing deeds, A - long the fer - tile field,
2. Tho' sown in tears thro' wear - y years, The seed will sure - ly live;
3. The har - vest-home of God will come, And aft - er toil and care,
For grain will grow from what you sow, And fruit - ful har - vest yield.
Tho' great the cost, it is not lost, For God will fruit - age give.
With joy un - told, your sheaves of gold Will all be gar - nered there.
CHORUS
Then day by day . . . . a-long your way, ... The seeds of
Then day by day a-long your way,
prom - - - ise cast, , ... That rip-ened grain . . . . . .
The seeds of promise cast, the seeds of promise cast, That rip-ened grain
from hill and plain, . . . Be gathered home . . . . . at last. . . . . . .
from hill and plain, Be gathered home at last, be gathered home at last.
Be gathered home at last. . . . . . .

Lord of Life

SICILIAN MARINERS' HYMN. 8. 7. 8. 7. 8. 7.

CHRISTIAN BURKE | Arr. from a Sicilian Melody

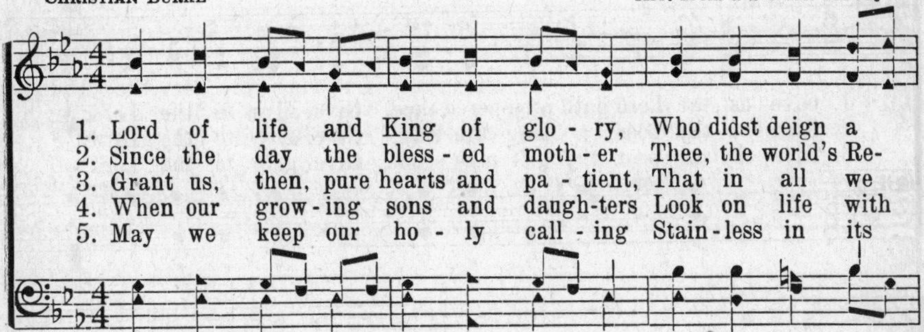
1. Lord of life and King of glo - ry, Who didst deign a
2. Since the day the bless - ed moth - er Thee, the world's Re-
3. Grant us, then, pure hearts and pa - tient, That in all we
4. When our grow - ing sons and daugh - ters Look on life with
5. May we keep our ho - ly call - ing Stain - less in its

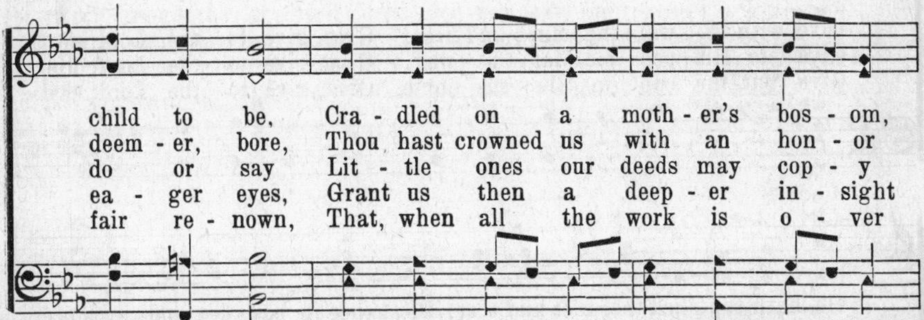
child to be, Cra - dled on a moth - er's bos - om,
deem - er, bore, Thou hast crowned us with an hon - or
do or say Lit - tle ones our deeds may cop - y
ea - ger eyes, Grant us then a deep - er in - sight
fair re - nown, That, when all the work is o - ver

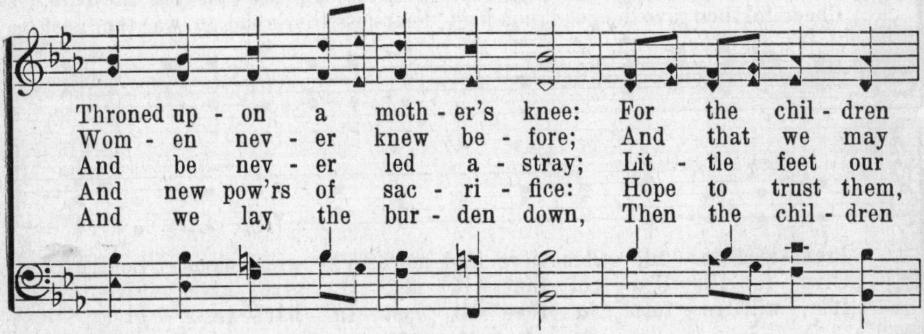
Throned up - on a moth - er's knee: For the chil - dren
Wom - en nev - er knew be - fore; And that we may
And be nev - er led a - stray; Lit - tle feet our
And new pow'rs of sac - ri - fice: Hope to trust them,
And we lay the bur - den down, Then the chil - dren

Thou hast giv - en We must an - swer un - to Thee.
bear it meet - ly, We must seek Thine aid the more.
steps may fol - low In a safe and nar - row way.
faith to guide them, Love that noth - ing good de - nies.
Thou hast giv - en Still may be our joy and crown.

Words used by permission of The Mothers' Union

299 Give to the Lord

PALMER HARTSOUGH J. H. FILLMORE

1. Give as the Lord hath pros-pered thee, Give, give to the Lord;
2. Give to the poor a - long the way, Give, give to the Lord;
3. Give, tho' so poor thy gift may seem, Give, give to the Lord;
Give with a will - ing mind and free, Give, give to the Lord;
Give to His peo - ple far a - way, Give, give to the Lord;
Give but the cup in Je - sus' name, Give, give to the Lord;
He hath sup-plied thee o'er and o'er, Blest thee in bas - ket and in store,
Give to His need - y as they cry, Give to His peo - ple ere they die,
Cheer-ful then give the good thou hast, Fear-less thy bread on wa - ters cast,
Prom - ised to fill thee more and more, Thy gra - cious Lord.
Give to His Gos - pel that it fly, O give, give, give.
It will re - turn to thee at last In har - vests great.
CHORUS
Give, give with a will - ing hand, Give, give with a lib - 'ral hand,

Give to the Lord

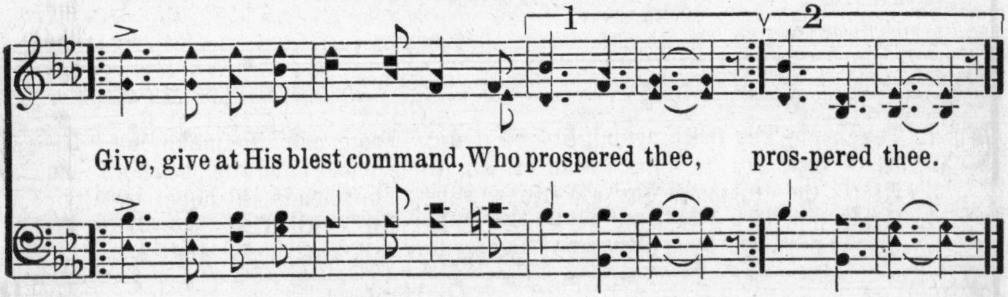
1
2
Give, give at His blest command, Who prospered thee, pros-pered thee.

Master, No Offering Costly 300

LOVE'S OFFERING. 6. 4. 6. 4. 6. 6. 4.

E. P. P. Edwin P. Parker

1. Mas - ter, no of - fer - ing Cost - ly and sweet May we, like Mag - da - lene, Lay at Thy feet; Yet may love's in - cense rise, Sweet - er than sac - ri - fice, Dear Lord, to Thee, Dear Lord, to Thee.
2. Dai - ly our lives would show Weak-ness made strong, Toil - some and gloom - y ways Bright-ened with song; Some deeds of kind-ness done, Some souls by pa-tience won, Dear Lord, to Thee, Dear Lord, to Thee.
3. Some word of hope for hearts Bur-dened with fears, Some balm of peace for eyes Blind - ed with tears; Some dews of mer - cy shed, Some way-ward foot-steps led, Dear Lord, to Thee, Dear Lord, to Thee.
4. Thus in Thy serv - ice, Lord, Till e - ven - tide Clos - es the day of life, May we a - bide; And when earth's la - bors cease, Bid us de - part in peace, Dear Lord, to Thee, Dear Lord, to Thee.

301 Teach Me Thy Truth

EDITH WITMER — GOSHEN — WALTER E. YODER

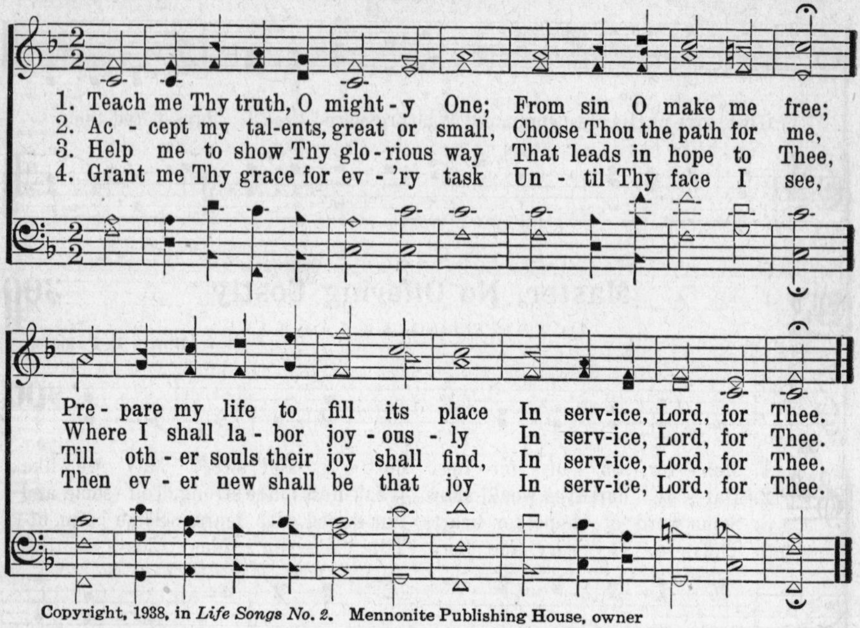
1. Teach me Thy truth, O might - y One; From sin O make me free;
2. Ac - cept my tal-ents, great or small, Choose Thou the path for me,
3. Help me to show Thy glo - rious way That leads in hope to Thee,
4. Grant me Thy grace for ev - 'ry task Un - til Thy face I see,
Pre - pare my life to fill its place In serv-ice, Lord, for Thee.
Where I shall la - bor joy - ous - ly In serv-ice, Lord, for Thee.
Till oth - er souls their joy shall find, In serv-ice, Lord, for Thee.
Then ev - er new shall be that joy In serv-ice, Lord, for Thee.

302 Fight the Good Fight with All Thy Might

JOHN S. B. MONSELL — PENTECOST. L. M. — WILLIAM BOYD

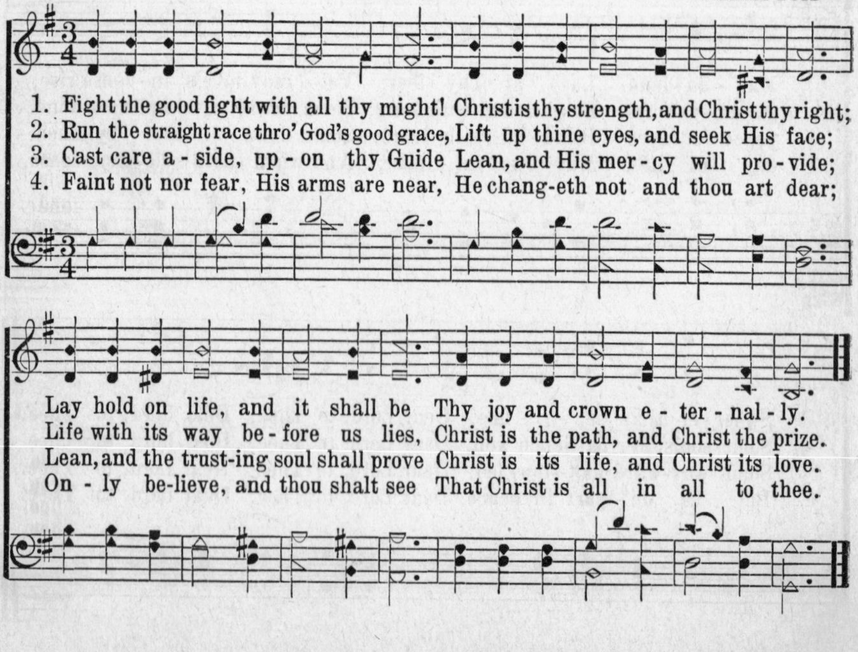
1. Fight the good fight with all thy might! Christ is thy strength, and Christ thy right;
2. Run the straight race thro' God's good grace, Lift up thine eyes, and seek His face;
3. Cast care a - side, up - on thy Guide Lean, and His mer - cy will pro - vide;
4. Faint not nor fear, His arms are near, He chang-eth not and thou art dear;
Lay hold on life, and it shall be Thy joy and crown e - ter - nal - ly.
Life with its way be - fore us lies, Christ is the path, and Christ the prize.
Lean, and the trust-ing soul shall prove Christ is its life, and Christ its love.
On - ly be-lieve, and thou shalt see That Christ is all in all to thee.

Let the Lower Lights Be Burning

P. P. Bliss | P. P. Bliss

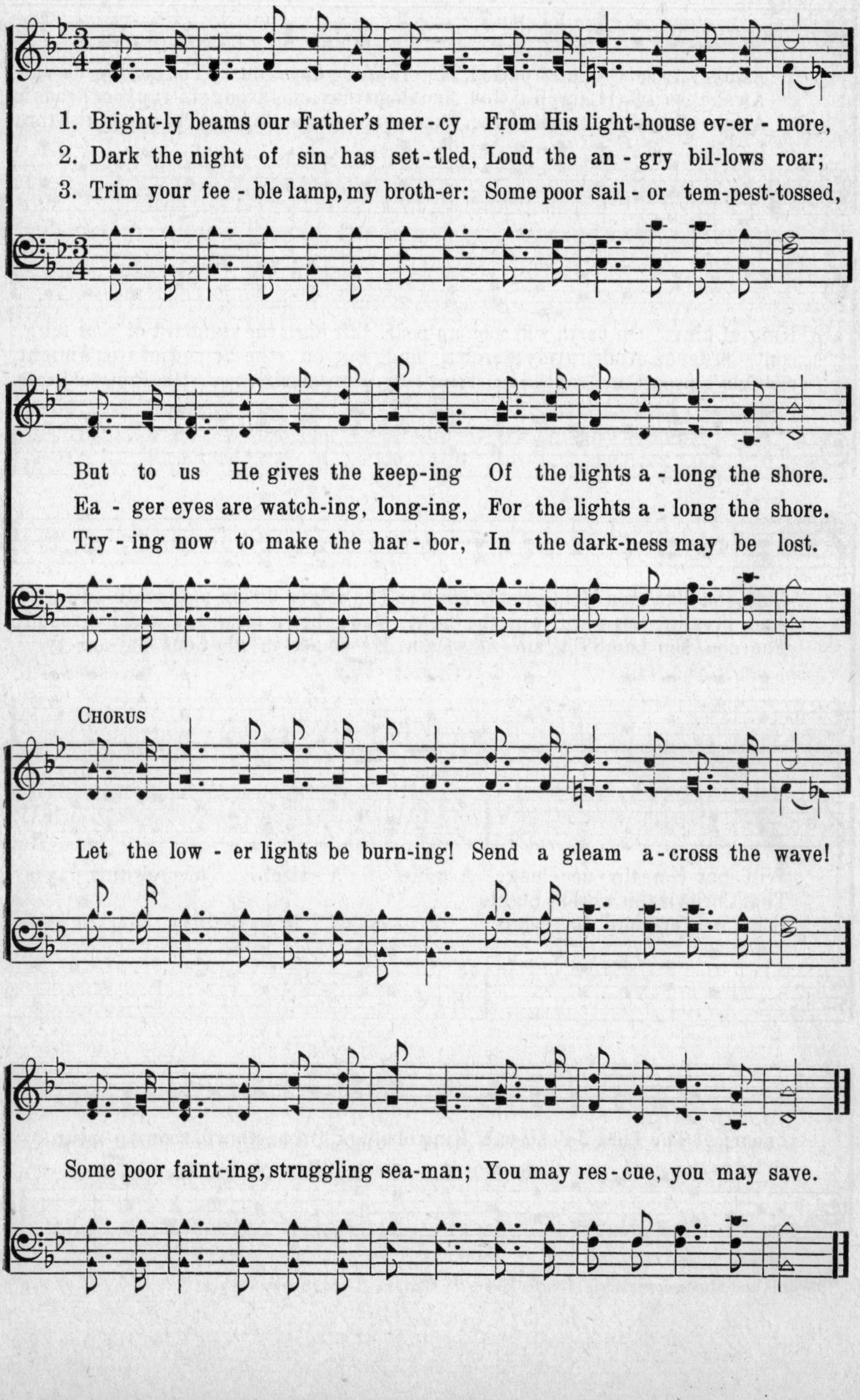
1. Bright-ly beams our Father's mer - cy From His light-house ev-er - more,
2. Dark the night of sin has set-tled, Loud the an - gry bil-lows roar;
3. Trim your fee - ble lamp, my broth-er: Some poor sail - or tem-pest-tossed,
But to us He gives the keep-ing Of the lights a - long the shore.
Ea - ger eyes are watch-ing, long-ing, For the lights a - long the shore.
Try - ing now to make the har - bor, In the dark-ness may be lost.
Chorus
Let the low - er lights be burn-ing! Send a gleam a - cross the wave!
Some poor faint-ing, struggling sea-man; You may res - cue, you may save.

Awake! Arise!

HENRY H. SAVAGE — HARRY D. CLARKE

1. Awake! Arise! O Church of God, The crowning day is near; The Lord Je-ho-vah,
2. Awake! Arise! O Church of God, And shout the victor's song; Lift up your heads in
3. Awake! Arise! O Church of God, The morning draweth nigh; The ear of faith thro'
King of kings, On earth will soon ap-pear. Lift high the standard of your faith,
con - fi-dence, And bravely march a - long. Put on the ar-mor of God's might,
midnight's gloom Can hear the watchman's cry. He comes! He comes! the Prince of Peace,
Quit you like men, for Christ be strong; The reign of sin and death on earth
And, pressing on-ward, win the fight; Make known to all the world a-round
The cho-sen Lamb for sin-ners slain; He comes in glo-rious maj-es-ty,
Will not con-tin-ue long.
That Christ is this world's Light.
For-ev-er-more to reign.
CHORUS
A-wake! A-rise! The crowning day is
A-wake! A-rise! the
near; The Lord Je-ho-vah, King of kings, On earth will soon ap-pear.
day is near;

Words and Music copyright, 1928, by Harry D. Clarke. Used by permission

Jesus Saves

RISCILLA J. OWENS
WM. J. KIRKPATRICK

1. We have heard the joy - ful sound: Je - sus saves! Je - sus saves!
2. Waft it on the roll - ing tide; Je - sus saves! Je - sus saves!
3. Sing a - bove the bat - tle strife, Je - sus saves! Je - sus saves!
4. Give the winds a might - y voice, Je - sus saves! Je - sus saves!
Spread the ti - dings all a - round: Je - sus saves! Je - sus saves!
Tell to sin - ners far and wide: Je - sus saves! Je - sus saves!
By His death and end - less life, Je - sus saves! Je - sus saves!
Let the na - tions now re - joice,— Je - sus saves! Je - sus saves!
Bear the news to ev - 'ry land, Climb the steeps and cross the waves;
Sing, ye is - lands of the sea; Ech - o back, ye o - cean caves;
Sing it soft - ly thro' the gloom, When the heart for mer - cy craves;
Shout sal - va - tion full and free; High - est hills and deep - est caves;
On - ward!—'tis our Lord's com - mand; Je - sus saves! Je - sus saves!
Earth shall keep her ju - bi - lee: Je - sus saves! Je - sus saves!
Sing in tri - umph o'er the tomb,— Je - sus saves! Je - sus saves!
This our song of vic - to - ry,— Je - sus saves! Je - sus saves!

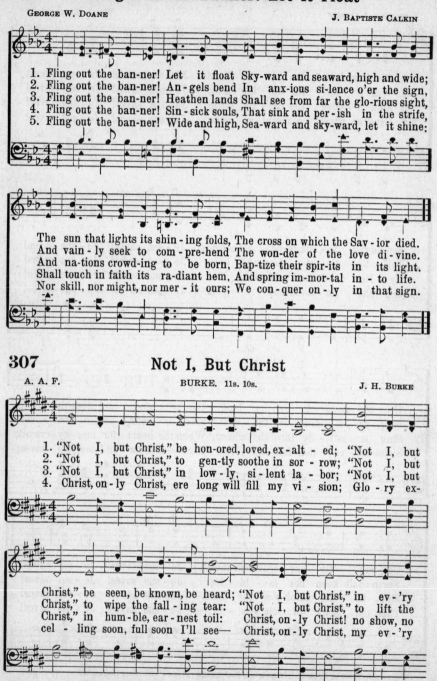

306 Fling Out the Banner! Let It Float

GEORGE W. DOANE — J. BAPTISTE CALKIN

1. Fling out the ban-ner! Let it float Sky-ward and seaward, high and wide;
2. Fling out the ban-ner! An-gels bend In anx-ious si-lence o'er the sign,
3. Fling out the ban-ner! Heathen lands Shall see from far the glo-rious sight,
4. Fling out the ban-ner! Sin-sick souls, That sink and per-ish in the strife,
5. Fling out the ban-ner! Wide and high, Sea-ward and sky-ward, let it shine:

The sun that lights its shin-ing folds, The cross on which the Sav-ior died.
And vain-ly seek to com-pre-hend The won-der of the love di-vine.
And na-tions crowd-ing to be born, Bap-tize their spir-its in its light.
Shall touch in faith its ra-diant hem, And spring im-mor-tal in-to life.
Nor skill, nor might, nor mer-it ours; We con-quer on-ly in that sign.

307 Not I, But Christ

A. A. F. — BURKE. 11s. 10s. — J. H. BURKE

1. "Not I, but Christ," be hon-ored, loved, ex-alt-ed; "Not I, but
2. "Not I, but Christ," to gen-tly soothe in sor-row; "Not I, but
3. "Not I, but Christ," in low-ly, si-lent la-bor; "Not I, but
4. Christ, on-ly Christ, ere long will fill my vi-sion; Glo-ry ex-

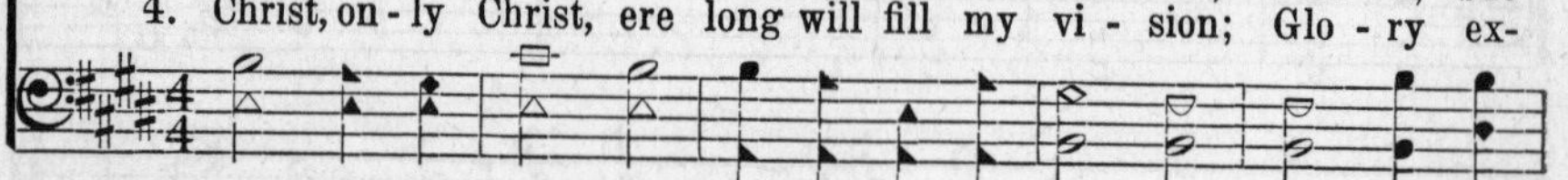

Christ," be seen, be known, be heard; "Not I, but Christ," in ev-'ry
Christ," to wipe the fall-ing tear: "Not I, but Christ," to lift the
Christ," in hum-ble, ear-nest toil: Christ, on-ly Christ! no show, no
cel-ling soon, full soon I'll see— Christ, on-ly Christ, my ev-'ry

Not I, But Christ

look and ac - tion, "Not I, but Christ," in ev - 'ry tho't and word.
wea - ry bur - den; "Not I, but Christ," to hush a - way all fear.
os - ten - ta - tion; Christ, none but Christ, the gath-'rer of the spoil.
wish ful - fill - ing— Christ, on - ly Christ, my All in All to be.

The Call for Reapers 308

J. O. Thompson — J. B. O. Clemm

Spirited

1. Far and near the fields are teem - ing With the waves of rip - ened grain;
2. Send them forth with morn's first beaming, Send them in the noontide's glare;
3. O thou, whom thy Lord is send - ing, Gath - er now the sheaves of gold,

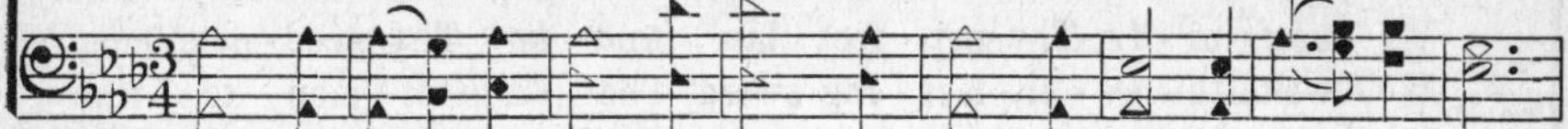

Far and near their gold is gleam-ing O'er the sun - ny slope and plain.
When the sun's last rays are gleam-ing, Bid them gath - er ev - 'ry-where.
Heav'nward then at eve-ning wend - ing, Thou shalt come with joy un - told.

Refrain

Lord of har-vest, send forth reap-ers! Hear us, Lord, to Thee we cry;

Send them now the sheaves to gath - er, Ere the har - vest time pass by.

309 The Isles Await the King

SILVANUS

SILVANUS YODER — Is. 42: 4 — WALTER E. YODER

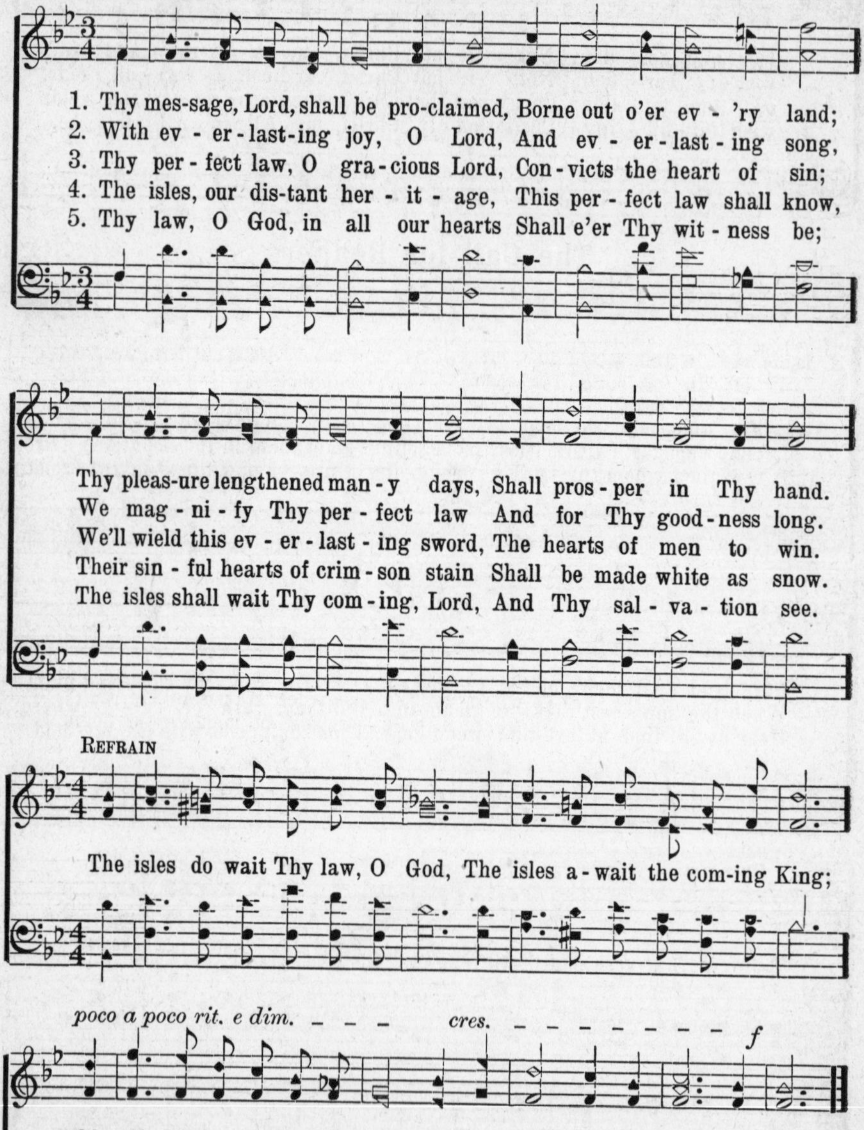
1. Thy mes-sage, Lord, shall be pro-claimed, Borne out o'er ev - 'ry land;
2. With ev - er-last-ing joy, O Lord, And ev - er-last - ing song,
3. Thy per - fect law, O gra-cious Lord, Con-victs the heart of sin;
4. The isles, our dis-tant her - it - age, This per-fect law shall know,
5. Thy law, O God, in all our hearts Shall e'er Thy wit - ness be;
Thy pleas-ure lengthened man - y days, Shall pros-per in Thy hand.
We mag - ni - fy Thy per - fect law And for Thy good-ness long.
We'll wield this ev - er - last - ing sword, The hearts of men to win.
Their sin - ful hearts of crim - son stain Shall be made white as snow.
The isles shall wait Thy com - ing, Lord, And Thy sal - va - tion see.
REFRAIN
The isles do wait Thy law, O God, The isles a-wait the com-ing King;
poco a poco rit. e dim. cres. f
Of all Thy o-ver-flow-ing love, The re-deemed of the earth shall sing.

Anywhere With Jesus

JESSIE H. BROWN and MRS. C. M. ALEXANDER

D. B. TOWNER

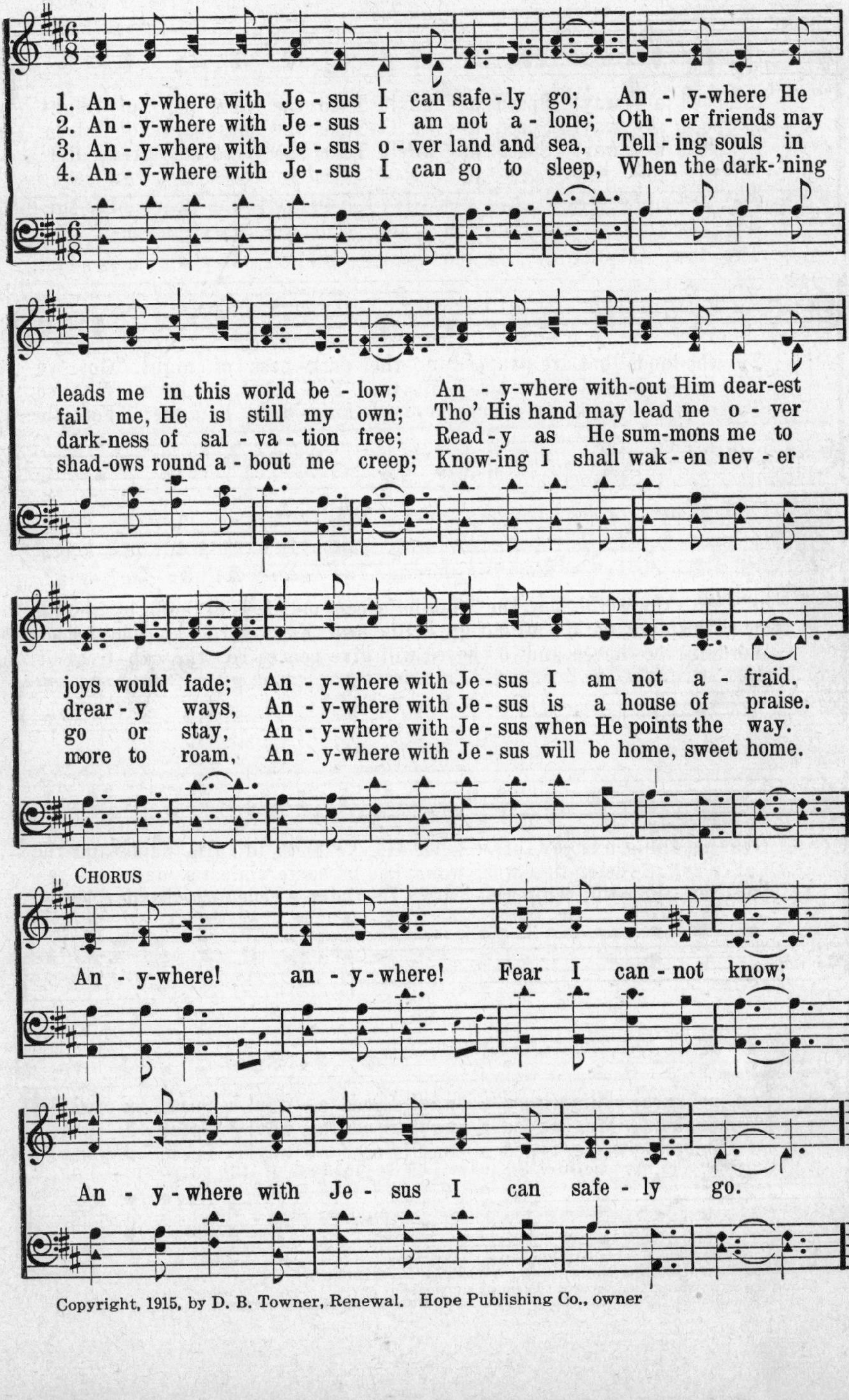
1. An - y-where with Je - sus I can safe-ly go; An - y-where He
2. An - y-where with Je - sus I am not a - lone; Oth - er friends may
3. An - y-where with Je - sus o - ver land and sea, Tell - ing souls in
4. An - y-where with Je - sus I can go to sleep, When the dark-'ning
leads me in this world be - low; An - y-where with-out Him dear-est
fail me, He is still my own; Tho' His hand may lead me o - ver
dark-ness of sal - va - tion free; Read-y as He sum-mons me to
shad-ows round a - bout me creep; Know-ing I shall wak-en nev - er
joys would fade; An - y-where with Je - sus I am not a - fraid.
drear - y ways, An - y-where with Je - sus is a house of praise.
go or stay, An - y-where with Je - sus when He points the way.
more to roam, An - y-where with Je - sus will be home, sweet home.
CHORUS
An - y-where! an - y - where! Fear I can - not know;
An - y - where with Je - sus I can safe - ly go.

311 Speed Away

W. E. M. Hackleman

Theme from Woodbury
Har. by W. E. M. H.

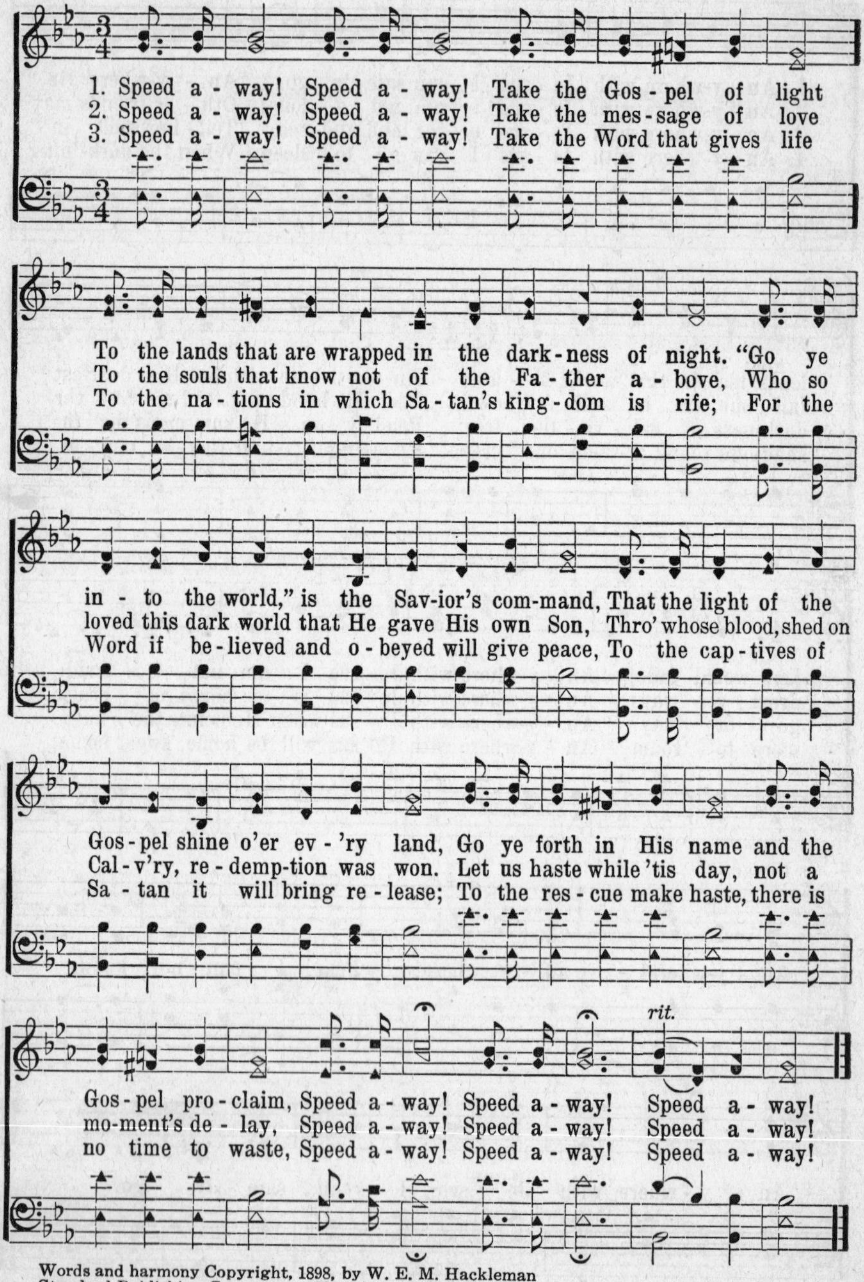
1. Speed a - way! Speed a - way! Take the Gos - pel of light
2. Speed a - way! Speed a - way! Take the mes - sage of love
3. Speed a - way! Speed a - way! Take the Word that gives life
To the lands that are wrapped in the dark - ness of night. "Go ye
To the souls that know not of the Fa - ther a - bove, Who so
To the na - tions in which Sa - tan's king - dom is rife; For the
in - to the world," is the Sav - ior's com - mand, That the light of the
loved this dark world that He gave His own Son, Thro' whose blood, shed on
Word if be - lieved and o - beyed will give peace, To the cap - tives of
Gos - pel shine o'er ev - 'ry land, Go ye forth in His name and the
Cal - v'ry, re - demp - tion was won. Let us haste while 'tis day, not a
Sa - tan it will bring re - lease; To the res - cue make haste, there is
rit.
Gos - pel pro - claim, Speed a - way! Speed a - way! Speed a - way!
mo - ment's de - lay, Speed a - way! Speed a - way! Speed a - way!
no time to waste, Speed a - way! Speed a - way! Speed a - way!

Christ Returneth

H. L. Turner — James McGranahan

1. It may be at morn, when the day is a-wak-ing, When sunlight thro'
2. It may be at mid-day, it may be at twi-light, It may be, per-
3. While its hosts cry Hosanna, from heaven de-scend-ing, With glo-ri-fied
4. Oh, joy! oh, de-light! should we go with-out dy-ing, No sick-ness, no
dark-ness and shad-ow is break-ing, That Je-sus will come in the
chance, that the black-ness of mid-night Will burst in-to light in the
saints and the an-gels at-tend-ing, With grace on His brow, like a
sad-ness, no dread and no cry-ing, Caught up thro' the clouds with our
full-ness of glo-ry, To re-ceive from the world "His own."
blaze of His glo-ry, When Je-sus re-ceives "His own."
ha-lo of glo-ry, Will Je-sus re-ceive "His own."
Lord in-to glo-ry, When Je-sus re-ceives "His own."
Chorus
O Lord Je-sus, how long, how long Ere we shout the glad song, Christ re-
rit.
turn-eth! Hal-le-lu-jah! hal-le-lu-jah! A-men, Hal-le-lu-jah! A-men.

313 Will Jesus Find Us Watching?

Fanny J. Crosby — W. H. Doane

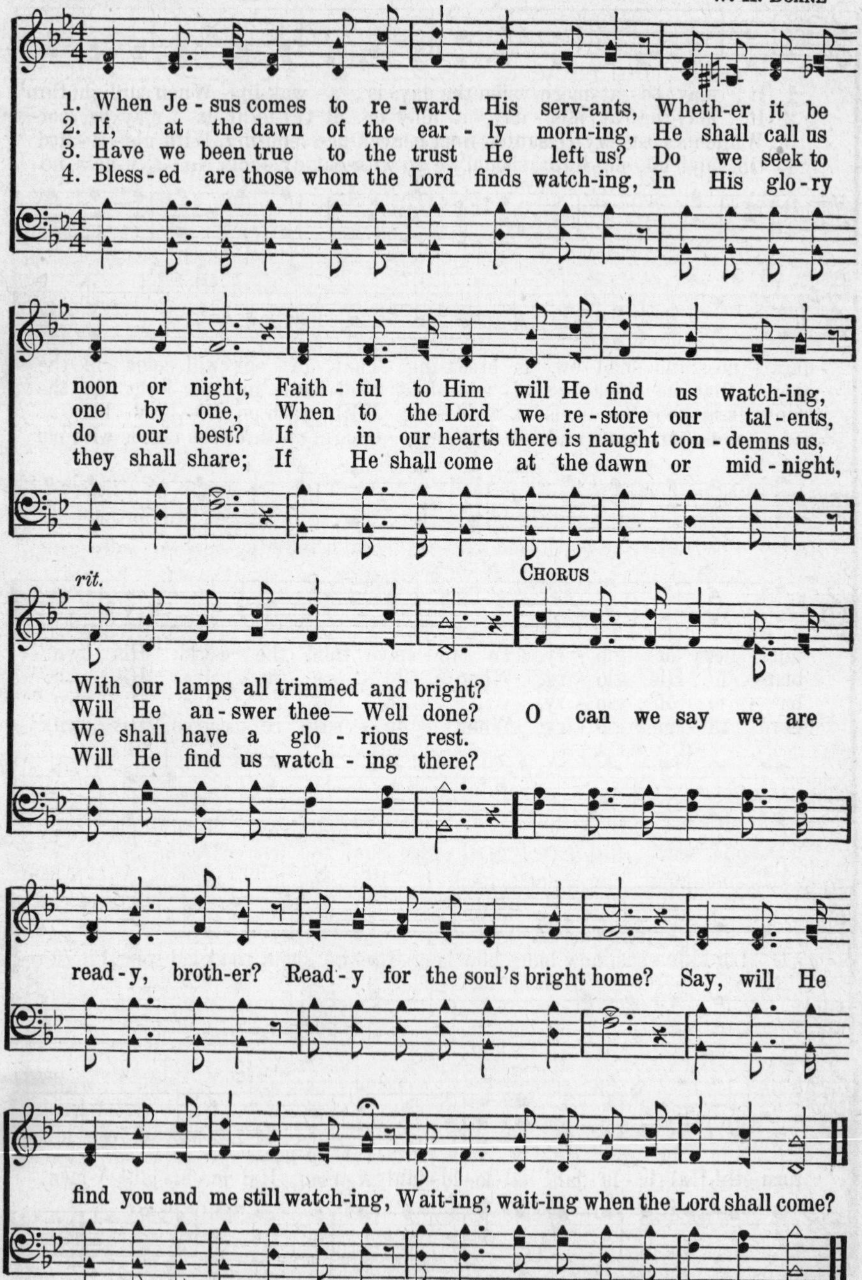
1. When Je - sus comes to re - ward His serv-ants, Wheth-er it be
2. If, at the dawn of the ear - ly morn-ing, He shall call us
3. Have we been true to the trust He left us? Do we seek to
4. Bless-ed are those whom the Lord finds watch-ing, In His glo - ry
noon or night, Faith - ful to Him will He find us watch-ing,
one by one, When to the Lord we re - store our tal - ents,
do our best? If in our hearts there is naught con - demns us,
they shall share; If He shall come at the dawn or mid - night,
rit.
Chorus
With our lamps all trimmed and bright?
Will He an - swer thee— Well done? O can we say we are
We shall have a glo - rious rest.
Will He find us watch - ing there?
read - y, broth - er? Read - y for the soul's bright home? Say, will He
find you and me still watch-ing, Wait-ing, wait-ing when the Lord shall come?

Lo! He Comes

CHARLES WESLEY, alt. — LOUIS VON ESCH

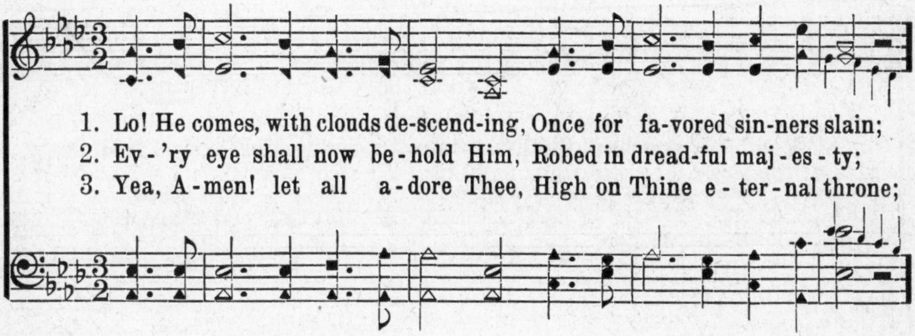
1. Lo! He comes, with clouds de-scend-ing, Once for fa-vored sin-ners slain;
2. Ev-'ry eye shall now be-hold Him, Robed in dread-ful maj-es-ty;
3. Yea, A-men! let all a-dore Thee, High on Thine e-ter-nal throne;

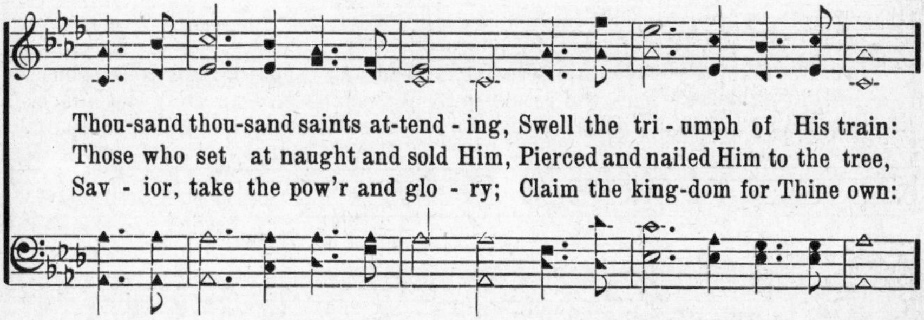
Thou-sand thou-sand saints at-tend-ing, Swell the tri-umph of His train:
Those who set at naught and sold Him, Pierced and nailed Him to the tree,
Sav-ior, take the pow'r and glo-ry; Claim the king-dom for Thine own:

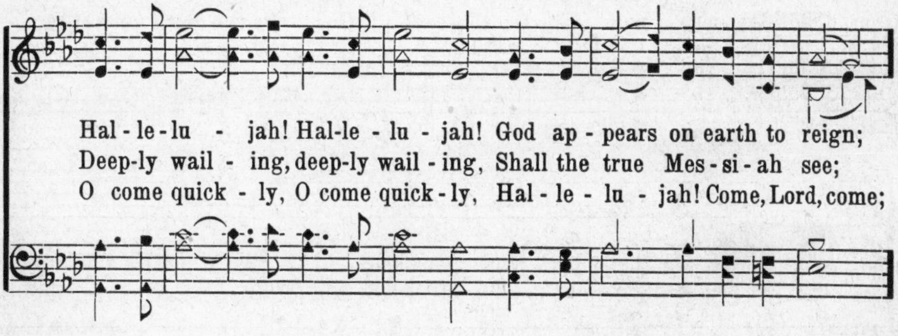
Hal-le-lu-jah! Hal-le-lu-jah! God ap-pears on earth to reign;
Deep-ly wail-ing, deep-ly wail-ing, Shall the true Mes-si-ah see;
O come quick-ly, O come quick-ly, Hal-le-lu-jah! Come, Lord, come;

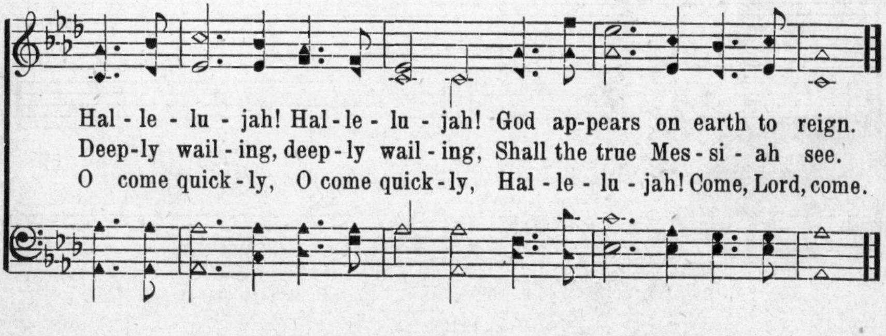
Hal-le-lu-jah! Hal-le-lu-jah! God ap-pears on earth to reign.
Deep-ly wail-ing, deep-ly wail-ing, Shall the true Mes-si-ah see.
O come quick-ly, O come quick-ly, Hal-le-lu-jah! Come, Lord, come.

315 Beloved, Now Are We

El Nathan — James McGranahan

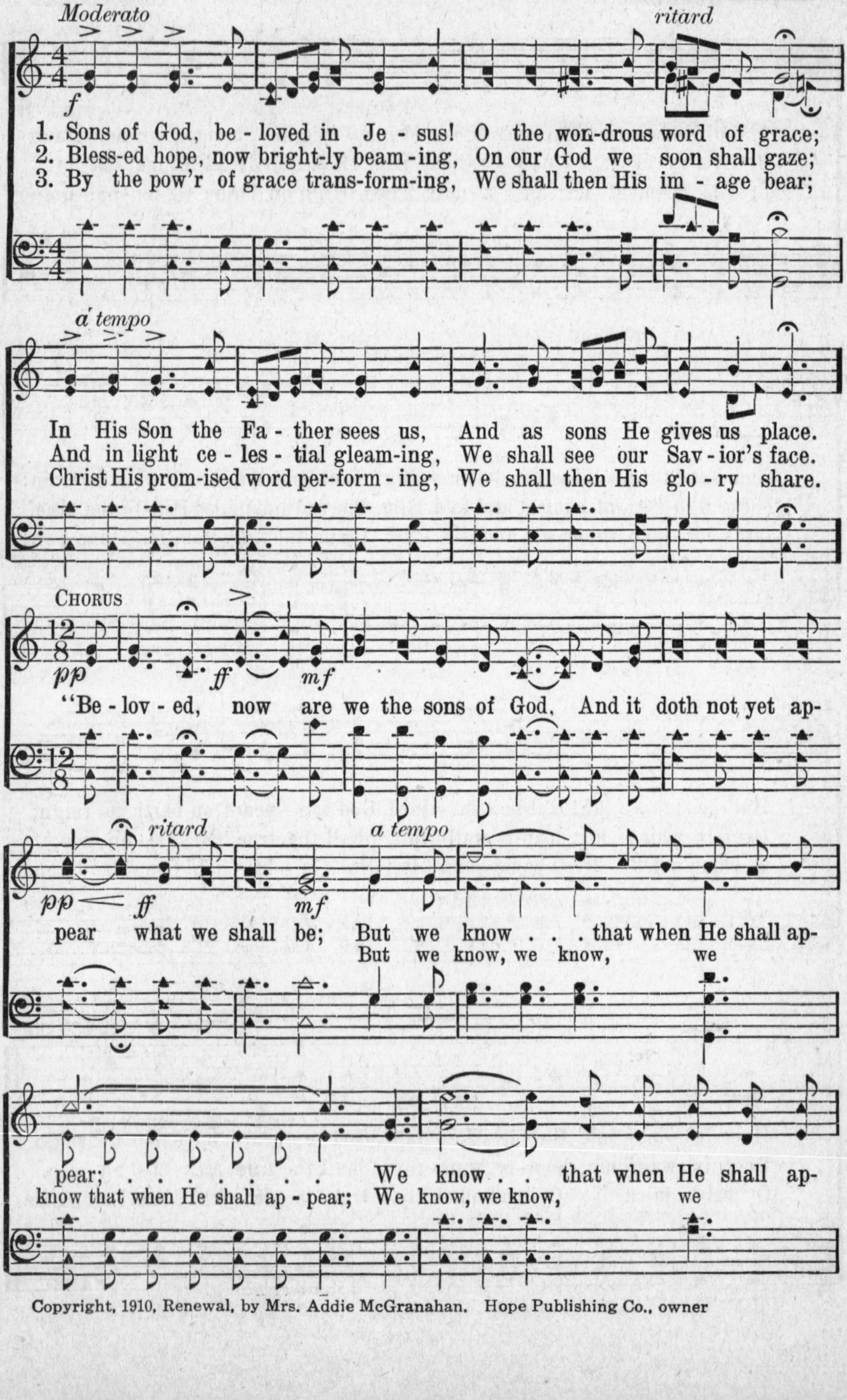
Moderato
ritard
1. Sons of God, be - loved in Je - sus! O the won-drous word of grace;
2. Bless-ed hope, now bright-ly beam - ing, On our God we soon shall gaze;
3. By the pow'r of grace trans-form-ing, We shall then His im - age bear;
a tempo
In His Son the Fa - ther sees us, And as sons He gives us place.
And in light ce - les - tial gleam-ing, We shall see our Sav - ior's face.
Christ His prom-ised word per-form - ing, We shall then His glo - ry share.
Chorus
"Be - lov - ed, now are we the sons of God, And it doth not yet ap-
ritard
a tempo
pear what we shall be; But we know . . . that when He shall ap-
But we know, we know, we
pear; . . . . We know . . that when He shall ap-
know that when He shall ap - pear; We know, we know, we

Beloved, Now Are We

ff
pear, ... We shall be like Him, we shall be
know that when He shall ap - pear,

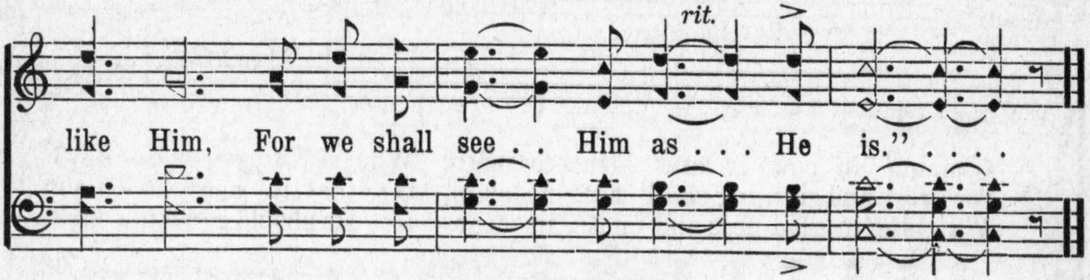
rit.
like Him, For we shall see . . Him as . . . He is." . . .

Till He Come 316

EDWARD H. BICKERSTETH ALETTA. 7. 7. 7. 7. 7. 7. WILLIAM B. BRADBURY

1. "Till He come!" O let the words Lin - ger on the trem-bling chords;
2. When the wea - ry ones we love En - ter on their rest a - bove,
3. See, the feast of love is spread, Drink the wine, and break the bread;

Let the lit - tle while be-tween In their gold - en light be seen;
When their words of love and cheer Fall no lon - ger on our ear,
Sweet me - mo - rials,—till the Lord Call us round His heav'n-ly board;

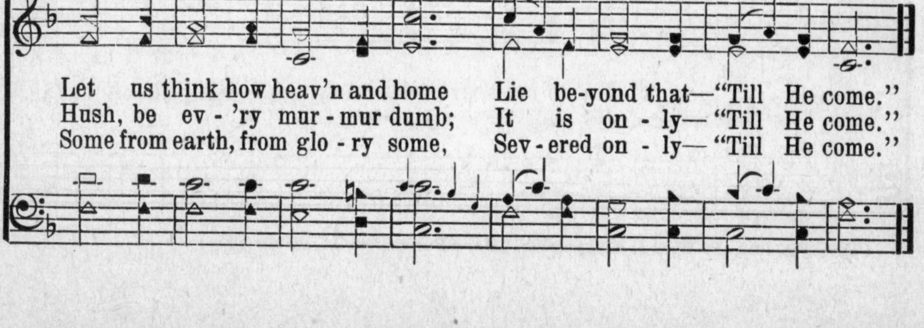
Let us think how heav'n and home Lie be-yond that—"Till He come."
Hush, be ev - 'ry mur - mur dumb; It is on - ly— "Till He come."
Some from earth, from glo - ry some, Sev - ered on - ly— "Till He come."

317 What If It Were To-day?

Mrs. C. H. M. | Mrs. C. H. Morris

1. Je - sus is com-ing to earth a - gain, What if it were to - day?
2. Sa - tan's do - min-ion will then be o'er, O that it were to - day!
3. Faith-ful and true would He find us here If He should come to - day?
Com-ing in pow-er and love to reign, What if it were to - day?
Sor - row and sigh-ing shall be no more, O that it were to - day!
Watching in glad-ness and not in fear, If He should come to - day?
Com-ing to claim His cho - sen Bride, All the re-deemed and pu - ri - fied,
Then shall the dead in Christ a - rise, Caught up to meet Him in the skies,
Signs of His com - ing mul - ti - ply, Morning light breaks in east-ern sky,
rit.
a tempo
O - ver this whole earth scat - tered wide, What if it were to - day?
When shall these glo - ries meet our eyes? What if it were to - day?
Watch, for the time is draw - ing nigh, What if it were to - day?
CHORUS
Glo - ry, glo - ry! Joy to my heart 'twill bring; . . Glo - ry, glo - ry!
Joy to my heart 'twill bring;

What If It Were To-day?

When we shall crown Him King; . . . Glo - ry, glo - ry! Haste to pre-pare the
When we shall crown Him King; Haste to pre-

way; . . . . Glo - ry, glo - ry! Je - sus will come some day.
pare the way;

Jesus Came, the Heavens Adoring 318

GODFREY THRING PRAISE MY SOUL JOHN GOSS

1. Je - sus came, the heav'ns a-dor - ing, Came with peace from realms on high;
2. Je - sus comes a - gain in mer - cy, When our hearts are bowed with care;
3. Je - sus comes to hearts re-joic - ing, Bring-ing news of sins for-giv'n;
4. Je - sus comes on clouds tri-um-phant, When the heav'ns shall pass a - way;

Je - sus came for man's re - demp-tion, Low-ly came on earth to die;
Je - sus comes a - gain in an - swer To an ear-nest, heart-felt prayer;
Je - sus comes in sounds of glad-ness, Lead-ing souls re-deemed to heav'n;
Je - sus comes a - gain in glo - ry, Let us then our hom-age pay,

Al - le - lu - ia! Al - le - lu - ia! Came in deep hu - mil - i - ty.
Al - le - lu - ia! Al - le - lu - ia! Comes to save us from de - spair.
Al - le - lu - ia! Al - le - lu - ia! Now the gate of death is riv'n.
Al - le - lu - ia! Ev - er sing-ing Till the dawn of end-less day.

319 Praise God, from Whom All Blessings Flow

SILOAM DOXOLOGY. L. M.

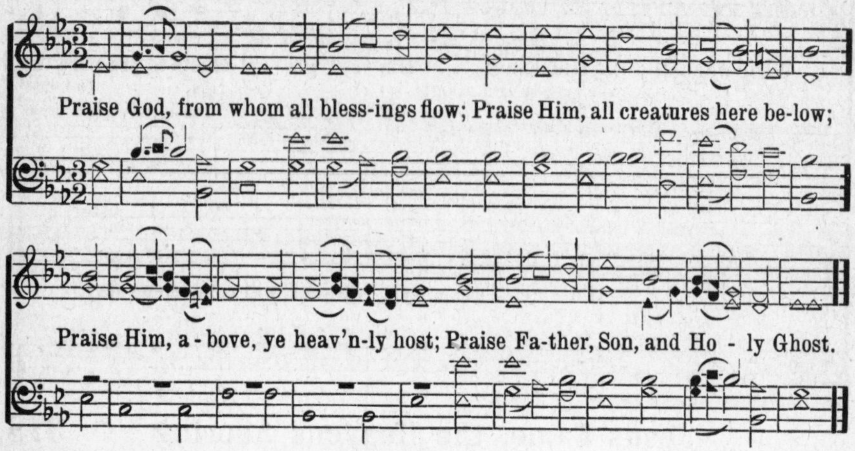
Praise God, from whom all bless-ings flow; Praise Him, all creatures here be-low;
Praise Him, a - bove, ye heav'n-ly host; Praise Fa-ther, Son, and Ho - ly Ghost.

320 Gloria Patri

Gregorian

Glory be to the Father, and to the Son, and to the Ho-ly Ghost;
As it was in the beginning, is now, and ev-er shall be, world with-out end. A - men.

321 Our Father, Who Art in Heaven

HORATIO R. PALMER

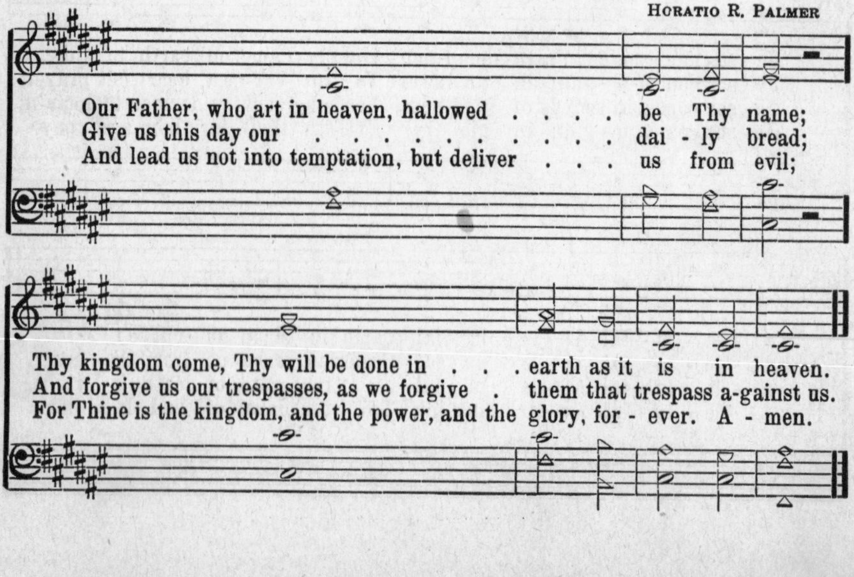
Our Father, who art in heaven, hallowed . . . . be Thy name;
Give us this day our . . . . dai - ly bread;
And lead us not into temptation, but deliver . . . us from evil;
Thy kingdom come, Thy will be done in . . . . earth as it is in heaven.
And forgive us our trespasses, as we forgive . them that trespass a-gainst us.
For Thine is the kingdom, and the power, and the glory, for - ever. A - men.

Familiar Hymns

322 We Praise Thee, O God

Key—G.

We praise Thee, O God! for the Son of thy love,
For Jesus who died, and is now gone above.

Cho.—Hallelujah! Thine the glory!
Hallelujah! Amen;
Hallelujah! Thine the glory,
Revive us again.

We praise Thee, O God, for Thy Spirit of light,
Who has shown us our Saviour, and scattered our night.

All glory and praise to the Lamb that was slain,
Who has borne all our sins, and has cleansed every stain.

All glory and praise to the God of all grace,
Who has bought us, and sought us, and guided our ways.

Revive us again; fill each heart with Thy love;
May each soul be rekindled with fire from above.

323 Love Divine

Key—B flat.

Love divine, all love excelling,
Joy of heaven, to earth come down!
Fix in us thy humble dwelling;
All thy faithful mercies crown.
Jesus, Thou art all compassion,
Pure, unbounded love Thou art;
Visit us with Thy salvation;
Enter every trembling heart.

Breathe, oh, breathe Thy loving Spirit
Into every troubled breast!
Let us all in Thee inherit,
Let us find that promised rest.
Take away the love of sinning;
Alpha and Omega be;
End of faith, as its beginning,
Set our hearts at liberty.

324 We're Marching to Zion

Key—G.

Come, we that love the Lord,
And let our joys be known,
||:Join in a song with sweet accord,:||
||:And thus surround the throne.:||

Cho.—We're marching to Zion,
Beautiful, beautiful Zion;
We're marching upward to Zion,
The beautiful city of God.

Let those refuse to sing
Who never knew our God;
||:But children of the heavenly King,:||
||:May speak their joys abroad.:||

The hill of Zion yields
A thousand sacred sweets,
||:Before we reach the heav'nly fields,:||
||:Or walk the golden streets.:||

Then let our songs abound,
And ev'ry tear be dry;
||:We're marching thro' Immanuel's ground,:||
||:To fairer worlds on high.:||

325 Rock of Ages

Key—B flat.

Rock of Ages, cleft for me,
Let me hide myself in Thee;
Let the water and the blood,
From Thy riven side which flow'd,
Be of sin the double cure,
Cleanse me from its guilt and pow'r.

Not the labor of my hands
Can fulfil the law's demands;
Could my zeal no respite know,
Could my tears forever flow,
All for sin could not atone;
Thou must save, and Thou alone.

Nothing in my hand I bring,
Simply to Thy cross I cling;
Naked, come to Thee for dress,
Helpless, look to Thee for grace;
Foul, I to the fountain fly,
Wash, me, Saviour, or I die.

While I draw this fleeting breath,
When mine eyes shall close in death,
When I soar to worlds unknown,
See Thee on Thy judgment throne—
Rock of Ages, cleft for me,
Let me hide myself in Thee.

326 In the Cross of Christ

Key—C.

In the cross of Christ I glory,
Tow'ring o'er the wrecks of time;
All the light of sacred story
Gathers 'round its head sublime.

When the woes of life o'ertake me,
Hopes deceive, and fears annoy,
Never shall the cross forsake me:
Lo! it glows with peace and joy.

When the sun of bliss is beaming
Light and love upon my way,
From the cross the radiance streaming,
Adds more luster to the day.

Bane and blessing, pain and pleasure,
By the cross are sanctified;
Peace is there, that knows no measure,
Joys that through all time abide.

327 Saviour, Like a Shepherd

Key—E flat.

Saviour, like a shepherd lead us,
Much we need Thy tenderest care;
In Thy pleasant pastures feed us,
For our use Thy folds prepare.
||:Blessed Jesus, blessed Jesus,
Thou hast bought us, Thine we are.:||

We are Thine, do Thou befriend us,
Be the Guardian of our way;
Keep Thy flock, from sin defend us,
Seek us when we go astray.
||:Blessed Jesus, blessed Jesus,
Hear, O hear us when we pray.:||

Thou hast promised to receive us,
Poor and sinful though we be;
Thou hast mercy to relieve us,
Grace to cleanse, and power to free.
||:Blessed Jesus, blessed Jesus,
We will early turn to Thee.:||

328 When I Survey the Wondrous Cross

Key—G.

When I survey the wondrous cross,
  On which the Prince of glory died,
My richest gain I count but loss,
  And pour contempt on all my pride.

Cho.—O wondrous cross where Jesus died,
    And for my sins was crucified;
  My longing eyes look up to Thee,
    Thou blessed Lamb of Calvary.

Forbid it, Lord, that I should boast,
  Save in the death of Christ, my Lord;
All the vain things that charm me most,
  I sacrifice them to His blood.

See, rfom His head, His hands, His feet,
  Sorrow and love flow mingled down;
Did e'er such love and sorrow meet,
  Or thorns compose so rich a crown?

Were the whole realm of nature mine,
  That were a present far too small;
Love so amazing, so divine,
  Demands my soul, my life, my all.

329 Nearer, My God, to Thee

Key—G.

Nearer, my God, to Thee,
  Nearer to Thee!
E'en tho' it be a cross
  That raiseth me;
Still all my song shall be,

Ref.—||:Nearer, my God, to Thee,:||
    Nearer to Thee!

Tho' like a wanderer,
  Daylight all gone,
Darkness be over me,
  My rest a stone;
Yet in my dreams I'd be,—Ref.

There let my way appear
  Steps up to heaven;
All that Thou sendest me
  In mercy given;
Angels to beckon me,—Ref.

Then with my waking thoughts
  Bright with Thy praise,
Out of my stony griefs
  Bethel I'll raise;
So by my woes to be,—Ref.

Or if on joyful wing,
  Cleaving the sky,
Caught up to meet my King,
  Swiftly I fly;
Still all my song shall be,—Ref.

330 My Faith Looks Up to Thee

Key—E flat.

My faith looks up to Thee,
Thou Lamb of Calvary,
  Saviour Divine!
Now hear me while I pray;
Take all my guilt away;
Oh, let me from this day,
  Be wholly Thine!

May Thy rich grace impart
Strength to my fainting heart,—
  My zeal inspire!
As Thou hast died for me,
Oh, may my love to Thee
Pure, warm and changeless be—
  A living fire!

While life's dark maze I tread,
And griefs around me spread,
  Be Thou my Guide;
Bid darkness turn to day,
Wipe sorrow's tears away,
Nor let me ever stray
  From Thee aside.

When ends life's transient dream,
When death's cold sullen stream
  Shall o'er me roll,
Blest Saviour, then, in love,
Fear and distrust remove;
Oh, bear me safe above—
  A ransomed soul.

331 He Leadeth Me

Key—D.

He leadeth me! oh! blessed thought,
Oh! words with heavenly comfort fraught;
Whate'er I do, where'er I be,
Still 'tis God's hand that leadeth me.

Ref. —He leadeth me! He leadeth me!
    By His own hand He leadeth me;
    His faithful follower I would be,
    For by His hand He leadeth me.

Sometimes 'mid scenes of deepest gloom,
Sometimes where Eden's bowers bloom,
By waters still, o'er troubled sea,—
Still 'tis God's hand that leadeth me.

Lord, I would clasp Thy hand in mine,
Nor ever murmur nor repine—
Content, whatever lot I see,
Since 'tis my God that leadeth me.

And when my task on earth is done,
When, by Thy grace, the victory's won,
E'en death's cold wave I will not flee,
Since God through Jordan leadeth me.

332 Sweet Hour of Prayer

Key—D.

Sweet hour of prayer! sweet hour of prayer!
That calls me from a world of care,
And bids me at my Father's throne
Make all my wants and wishes known:
In seasons of distress and grief,
My soul has often found relief;
||:And oft escaped the tempter's snare,
  By thy return, sweet hour of prayer.:||

Sweet hour of prayer! sweet hour of prayer!
Thy wings shall my petition bear
To Him whose truth and faithfulness
Engage the waiting soul to bless:
And since He bids me seek His face,
Believe His word, and trust His grace,
||:I'll cast on Him my every care,
  And wait for thee, sweet hour of prayer.:||

Sweet hour of prayer! sweet hour of prayer!
May I thy consolation share,
Till, from Mt. Pisgah's lofty height,
I view my home and take my flight:
This robe of flesh I'll drop, and rise
To seize the everlasting prize;
||:And shout, while passing through the air,
  Farewell, farewell, sweet hour of prayer!:||

333 A Charge to Keep

Key—C.

A charge to keep I have,
A God to glorify;
A never-dying soul to save,
And fit it for the sky.

To serve the present age,
My calling to fulfill,—
Oh, may it all my powers engage
To do my Master's will.

Arm me with jealous care,
As in Thy sight to live;
And oh, Thy servant, Lord, prepare
A strict account to give.

Help me to watch and pray,
And on Thyself rely;
Assured if I my trust betray,
I shall forever die.

334 I Need Thee

Key—A flat.

I need Thee ev'ry hour,
Most gracious Lord;
No tender voice like Thine
Can peace afford.

Ref.—I need Thee, oh! I need Thee;
Ev'ry hour I need Thee;
O bless me now, my Saviour!
I come to Thee.

I need Thee ev'ry hour;
Stay Thou near by;
Temptations lose their pow'r
When Thou art nigh.

I need Thee ev'ry hour,
In joy or pain;
Come quickly and abide,
Or life is vain.

I need Thee ev'ry hour,
Teach me Thy will;
And Thy rich promises
In me fulfill.

I need Thee ev'ry hour,
Most Holy One;
Oh, make me Thine indeed,
Thou blessed Son.

335 The Gate Ajar For Me

Key—C.

There is a gate that stands ajar,
And thro' its portals gleaming
A radiance from the Cross afar,
The Saviour's love revealing.

Ref.—Oh, depth of mercy! can it be
That gate was left ajar for me?
For me?...... for me?......
Was left ajar for me?

That gate ajar stands free for all
Who seek thro' it salvation;
The rich and poor, the great and small,
Of ev'ry tribe and nation.

Press onward then, tho' foes may frown,
While mercy's gate is open:
Accept the cross, and win the crown,
Love's everlasting token.

Beyond the river's brink we'll lay
The cross that here is given,
And bear the crown of life away,
And love Him more in heaven.

336 Am I a Soldier

Key—G.

Am I a soldier of the cross—
A foll'wer of the Lamb,—
And shall I fear to own His cause,
Or blush to speak His name?

Must I be carried to the skies
On flow'ry beds of ease;
While others fought to win the prize,
And sail'd thro' bloody seas?

Are there no foes for me to face?
Must I not stem the flood?
Is this vile world a friend to grace,
To help me on to God?

Since I must fight if I would reign,
Increase my courage, Lord;
I'll bear the toil, endure the pain,
Supported by Thy word.

337 Abide With Me

Key—E flat.

Abide with me! Fast falls the eventide,
The darkness deepens—Lord, with me abide!
When other helpers fail, and comforts flee,
Help of the helpless, oh, abide with me!

Swift to its close ebbs out life's little day;
Earth's joys grow dim, its glories pass away;
Change and decay in all around I see;
O Thou, who changest not, abide with me!

I need Thy presence ev'ry passing hour,
What but Thy grace can foil the tempter's power?
Who, like Thyself, my guide and stay can be?
Through cloud and sunshine, oh, abide with me!

Hold Thou Thy cross before my closing eyes;
Shine through the gloom and point me to the skies;
Heaven's morning breaks and earth's vain shadows flee!
In life, in death, O Lord, abide with me!

338 Pass Me Not

Key—A flat.

Pass me not, O gentle Saviour,
Hear my humble cry;
While on others Thou art calling,
Do not pass me by.

Cho.—Saviour, Saviour, hear my humble cry,
While on others Thou are calling,
Do not pass me by.

Let me at a throne of mercy
Find a sweet relief;
Kneeling there in deep contrition,
Help my unbelief:

Trusting only in Thy merit,
Would I seek Thy face;
Heal my wounded, broken spirit,
Save my by Thy grace.

Thou the Spring of all my comfort
More than life to me,
Whom have I on earth beside Thee?
Whom in heaven but Thee?

339 Alas! and Did My Saviour Bleed

Key—G.

Alas! and did my Saviour bleed,
And did my Sovereign die?
Would He devote that sacred head
For such a worm as I?

Was it for crimes that I have done
He groaned upon the tree?
Amazing pity, grace unknown,
And love beyond degree!

But drops of grief can ne'er repay
The debt of love I owe;
Here, Lord, I give myself away,
'Tis all that I can do!

340 Sowing in the Morning

Key—C.

Sowing in the morning, sowing seeds of kindness,
Sowing in the noontide and the dewy eve;
Waiting for the harvest, and the time of reaping,
We shall come rejoicing, bringing in the sheaves.

Cho.—||:Bringing in the sheaves,
Bringing in the sheaves,
We shall come rejoicing,
Bringing in the sheaves.:||

Sowing in the sunshine, sowing in the shadows,
Fearing neither clouds nor winter's chilling breeze;
By and by the harvest, and the labor ended,
We shall come rejoicing, bringing in the sheaves.

Going forth with weeping, sowing for the Master,
Tho' the loss sustain'd our spirit often grieves;
When our weeping's over, He will bid us welcome,
We shall come rejoicing, bringing in the sheaves.

341 Rescue the Perishing

Key—B flat.

Rescue the perishing,
Care for the dying,
Snatch them in pity from sin and the grave;
Weep o'er the erring one,
Lift up the fallen,
Tell them of Jesus, the mighty to save.

Cho.—Rescue the perishing,
Care for the dying;
Jesus is merciful,
Jesus will save.

Though they are slighting Him,
Still He is waiting,
Waiting the penitent child to receive.
Plead with them earnestly,
Plead with them gently:
He will forgive if they only believe.

Down in the human heart,
Crushed by the tempter,
Feelings lie buried that grace can restore:
Touched by a loving heart,
Wakened by kindness,
Chords that were broken will vibrate once more.

Rescue the perishing,
Duty demands it;
Strength for thy labor the Lord will provide:
Back to the narrow way
Patiently win them;
Tell the poor wanderer a Saviour has died.

342 Saviour Again

Key—A flat.

Saviour, again to Thy dear name we raise
With one accord our parting hymn of praise;
Once more we bless Thee ere our worship cease,
Then, lowly kneeling, wait Thy word of peace.

Grant us Thy peace upon our homeward way;
With Thee begun, with Thee shall end the day;
Guard Thou the lips from sin, the hearts from shame,
That in this house have called upon Thy name.

Grant us Thy peace, Lord, thro' the coming night,
Turn Thou for us its darkness into light;
From harm and danger keep Thy children free,
For dark and light are both alike to Thee.

Grant us Thy peace throughout our earthly life,
Our balm in sorrow, and our stay in strife;
Then, when Thy voice shall bid our conflict cease,
Call us, O Lord, to Thine eternal peace.

343 God Be With You

Key—D flat.

God be with you till we meet again!
By His counsels guide, uphold you,
With His sheep securely fold you;
God be with you till we meet again!

Cho.—Till we meet! Till we meet!
Till we meet at Jesus' feet;
Till we meet! Till we meet!
God be with you till we meet again!

God be with you till we meet again!
'Neath His wings securely hide you,
Daily manna still provide you;
God be with you till we meet again!

God be with you till we meet again!
When life's perils thick confound you,
Put His loving arms around you;
God be with you till we meet again!

God be with you till we meet again!
Keep love's banner floating o'er you,
Smite death's threatening wave before you;
God be with you till we meet again!

TOPICAL INDEX

ASPIRATION

Above the trembling elements ... 182
Earthly pleasures vainly call 189
Eternal source of joys ... 121
How beauteous were the marks ... 26
Jesus, my Savior ... 180
Jesus, the very thought of Thee ... 23
More holiness give me ... 187
My life, my love, I give to Thee ... 188
Nearer, still nearer ... 186
"Nearer the cross" ... 184
O Thou, in whose presence 32
Open now the gates of beauty ... 44
There is a story ever new .. 185

ASSURANCE

A wonderful Savior is Jesus 195
Amid the trials which I meet 202
Arise, my soul, arise ... 37
Be still, my soul ... 203
Blessed assurance ... 190
Conquering now, and still to 198
Dear to the heart of the Shepherd ... 201
Dying with Jesus by death reckoned ... 192
I know not why God's wondrous ... 194
I've reached the land of ... 196
In Thy cleft, O Rock of Ages ... 222
Jesus, I am resting ... 193
Joys are flowing like a river 197
My soul at last a rest hath found ... 204
Safe in the arms of Jesus .. 230
Shepherd of Israel, keeping 128
"Thou remainest" ... 205
Tho' the angry surges roll .. 199
Trembling soul, beset with fears ... 191
Under His wings, ... 206
Will your anchor hold ... 220

ATONEMENT

Christ has for sin atonement 119
"Man of sorrows" ... 82
On Calvary's brow ... 115
One there is above all others 161
Saved by the blood of the .. 110
There is a story ever new .. 185
When God of old the way of life ... 111

CHRIST, JESUS

His Advent, see Christmas

His Coming Again

Awake! Arise! ... 304
It may be at morn ... 312
Jesus came, the heavens- ... 318
Jesus is coming to earth ... 317
Lo! He comes with clouds .. 314
Pray, brethren, pray ... 136
Sons of God, beloved in Jesus ... 315
Till He come! ... 316
When Jesus comes to reward 313
When the trumpet of the Lord ... 212

His Faithfulness

Earthly friends may prove .. 80
InThy cleft, O Rock ... 222
Master, the tempest is raging 219
My faith is fixed on Jesus .. 96
O, thank the Lord ... 9
O why, O why, in dark Gethsemane ... 107
Oh, I love to talk with Jesus 57
Rejoice, ye pure in heart ... 11

His Fellowship and Indwelling

Come into my heart ... 142
Go with me, Master ... 267
Hold Thou my hand ... 209
I've found a Friend ... 88
Jesus, my Savior ... 180
Jesus, Rose of Sharon ... 22
Jesus, the very thought of Thee ... 23
Lord, I have shut the door. 60
O safe in the Rock ... 122
Oh, I love to talk with Jesus 57
Shine in my heart ... 178
Sitting at the feet of Jesus 91
There is a place of quiet ... 93
Thou, my everlasting portion 215
"Thou remainest," blest Redeemer ... 205
What a fellowship ... 213
When we walk with the Lord 211

His Kingship and Kingdom

All hail the power of ... 7
All hail the power of ... 8
All hail to Thee, Immanuel 15
For all Thy care ... 277
Forward thro' the ages ... 265
Jesus shall reign ... 40
King of the ages ... 280
Lo! He comes, with clouds. 314
True hearted, whole hearted 103
Who is He in yonder stall .. 10

His Love

A Friend I have, called Jesus 86
Behold, a Stranger at the door ... 158
Have you read the story of 84
How beauteous were the marks ... 26
I Love to tell the story ... 295
I stand amazed in the presence ... 77
I've found a Friend ... 88
Jesus comes with pow'r to .. 266
Jesus has loved me ... 75
Jesus, my Savior, to Bethlehem ... 168
Jesus, the sinner's Friend .. 166
Like a bird on the deep ... 130
"Man of sorrows" ... 82
More about Jesus ... 81
My Jesus, Thou art precious- 90
O Love that will not let me. 83
O the unsearchable riches .. 87
One there is above all others 161
Since Jesus, my Savior ... 74
The Shepherd's heart is saddened ... 144
We may not climb to heavenly ... 25
When the Lord of love ... 78

Love to Christ, and Loyalty

Fairest Lord Jesus ... 41
How beauteous were the marks ... 26
I love to steal awhile away 24
I've found a Friend, Oh, such ... 88
Jesus, the very thought of Thee ... 23
My faith is fixed on Jesus .. 96
My Jesus, I love Thee ... 95
My Jesus, Thou art Precious 90
O Savior, precious Savior .. 27
O Thou, in whose presence. 32
Saviour, teach me day by day 89
Sitting at the feet of Jesus. 91
There is a name I love ... 92
There is a story ever new .. 185
True-hearted, whole-hearted 103

The Mediator

Arise, my soul, arise ... 37
Shepherd of Israel ... 128
We may not climb ... 25

The Redeemer

Glory ever be to Jesus ... 114
I hear the Savior say ... 106
Not what these hands have done ... 127
O why, O why ... 107
On Calvary's brow ... 115
When God of old the way of life ... 111

The Resurrection, see Easter

The Savior

"For God so loved" ... 13
Galilee, bright Galilee ... 138
Jesus has loved me ... 75
Jesus shall reign ... 40
Life wears a different phase 125
My soul at last a rest ... 204
My soul is so happy ... 124
Not all the blood of beasts. 118
O Savior, precious Savior .. 27
Saved to the uttermost ... 123
Shepherd of Israel ... 128
The Lord is my Shepherd .. 129
There is a green hill ... 116
There is a story ever new .. 185
We have heard the joyful sound ... 305
What means this eager, anxious ... 143
When my life work ... 276
Wonderful grace of Jesus .. 112
Wounded for me ... 117

CHRISTMAS

As with gladness men of old 279
King of the Ages ... 280
In a lowly manger ... 278
The first Noel ... 281
There's a song in the air .. 282

CHURCH

Awake! Arise! O Church of God ... 304
"For Christ and the Church" 290
With joy we hail ... 43

COMFORT and ENCOURAGEMENT

A Friend I have, called ... 86
Be still, my soul ... 203
Christian walk carefully ... 243
Earthly friends may prove .. 80
Fierce and wild the storm. 224
God moves in a mysterious way ... 33
Hide me, O my Savior ... 221
I do not ask, O Lord ... 247
I heard the voice of Jesus .. 229
I sing the love of God ... 241
I've tried in vain ... 102
In heavenly love abiding ... 223
In Thy cleft, O Rock ... 222
Jesus, what a Friend ... 3
My soul, be on thy guard .. 246
Not now, but in the coming years ... 269
O Lord, to Thee I cry ... 257

TOPICAL INDEX

O the unsearchable riches.. 87
"Onward, upward, home-ward" 242
The Lord is my Shepherd.. 129
There is a place of quiet rest 93
There's not a bird......... 79
When the mists have rolled 150
When upon life's billows... 239

CONSECRATION

All for Jesus............ 250
All to Jesus I surrender... 248
Down in the valley........ 238
Faith of our fathers....... 261
"Follow me," the Master said 263
Follow the path of Jesus... 244
Forward through the ages.. 265
Go with me, Master....... 267
Hark, the voice of Jesus.. 262
Hushed was the evening hymn 253
I can hear the Savior calling 258
Jesus, I my cross have taken 252
Jesus, Thy name I bear.... 255
Just as I am............. 260
Lord, as I walk.......... 232
Must Jesus bear the cross alone 256
My life, my love I give.... 188
Not I, but Christ......... 307
O Love that wilt not let me go 83
Savior and Master......... 249
Shine in my heart......... 178
Simply trusting every day.. 251
Take my life and let it be.. 254
Take the world, but give me Jesus 264
Teach me Thy truth....... 301
To Thee, O Lord, I lift mine eyes 68
Where He may lead me I will go 259

EASTER

Christ, who left His home in glory 286
It was midnight in the garden 285
Jesus Christ is risen....... 289
Low in the grave He lay.. 284
Sing with all the sons..... 288
The strife is o'er.......... 287
Thou didst leave Thy...... 283

EVENING

Day is dying in the west.. 53
God that madest earth and heaven 55
Now, on land and sea...... 49
Now the day is over....... 51
Savior breathe an evening blessing 50
Savior breathe an evening blessing 52
The day is past and gone.. 54

EVANGELISTIC

Appeal

"Almost persuaded" 151
Behold a Stranger......... 158
Encamped along the hills.. 176
Galilee, bright Galilee...... 138
Hark, the voice of Jesus... 262
In Thy cleft, O Rock of.... 222
Jesus, my Savior, to Bethlehem 168
O happy day that......... 174
O lost one in the wilds.... 132
Sinners Jesus will receive.. 146
The Shepherd's heart is saddened 144
"There shall be showers of" 133
There were ninety and nine 154
Thou didst leave Thy throne 283
What means this eager..... 143
Who will open mercy's door 141
"Whosoever heareth" 140
Years I spent in vanity.... 145
Yield not to temptation.... 131

Confession

Come into my heart, blessed 142
Dear Lord, take up the tangled 113
God loved the world....... 167
I hear Thy welcome voice.. 172
I've wandered far away.... 171
Jesus, keep me near the cross 175
Jesus, my Lord, to Thee... 165
Jesus, the sinner's Friend.. 166
Just as I am............. 173
Lord Jesus, I long to be... 162
Naught have I gotten...... 149
O, hear my cry........... 160
Oh, what a Savior....... 139
Out of my bondage....... 169

Invitation

Behold a Stranger at the... 158
Free from the law......... 164
"Give me thy heart"...... 148
Have you any room for Jesus 170
I have a Savior........... 155
Jesus, gracious One....... 163
Open wide thy heart....... 157
Sinner, turn; why will...... 159
Today the Savior calls..... 153
Troubled heart, thy God is. 152

Warning

Jesus is standing in Pilate's hall 147
Pray, brethren, pray....... 136
Yield not to temptation.... 131

FAITH

Encamped along the hills of light 176
I know not why God's..... 194
My faith is fixed.......... 96
Not all the blood of beasts. 118
There is a green hill...... 116
We may not climb......... 25

FAITHFULNESS

Fight the good fight....... 302
Have you sought for the sheep 134
How beauteous were the marks 26
Jesus calls us o'er the..... 94
Jesus, Thy name I bear.... 255
Lord, as I walk with Thee. 232
My soul, be on thy guard.. 246
When Jesus comes to reward 313

FORGIVENESS

Arise, my soul, arise....... 37
Great God of wonders..... 35
Have you read the story of 84
Not all the blood of beasts 118
O my soul, bless thou...... 5

GOD

His Faithfulness

Fight the good fight....... 302
"Great is Try Faithfulness" 30
Guide me, O Thou great... 225
Jesus, Thy name.......... 255
There's not a bird......... 79

His Love

God loved the world of sinners 167
I sing the love of God..... 241
In heavenly love abiding... 223
Summer suns are glowing.. 34
There is a place of quiet... 93

His Mercy

Bless the Lord........... 29
Depth of mercy........... 126
God, the All powerful..... 231
Great God of wonders..... 35
Let us with a gladsome.... 76
O my bless, bless thou..... 5

His Power

God moves in a mysterious way 33
God of our strength....... 1
God of the earth, the sky.. 39
God, the All-powerful..... 231

His Providence

God of our fathers........ 66
I will extol Thee, O my.. 20
In some way or other..... 208
Praise to the Lord........ 31

GRACE

Depth of mercy........... 126
Glory ever be to Jesus..... 114
Great God of wonders..... 35
Hear us, O Savior........ 63
I hear the Savior say...... 106
In looking through my tears 104
Jesus, my Lord, to Thee... 165
Jesus, the sinner's Friend.. 166
Naught have I gotten...... 149
Not what these hands...... 127
O the unsearchable riches.. 87
Some day the silver chord. 268
Wonderful grace of Jesus.. 112

GUIDANCE (God's Presence)

Down in the valley with my 238
Goth hath not promised skies 237
God the All powerful...... 231
Guide me, O Thou great... 225
I heard the voice of Jesus.. 229
I must tell Jesus all of my 228
Jesus, Savior, pilot me.... 233
Jesus, still lead on......... 240
Like a shepherd, tender, true 227
Lord, as I walk with...... 232
Precious promise God hath. 234
When the early morning breaking 226
Yield not to temptation.... 131

HEAVEN

Be still, my soul.......... 203
In the land of fadeless.... 274
Jesus comes with power to. 266
Jesus, still lead on........ 240
Lead me gently home...... 236
Light after darkness....... 270
Not now, but in the coming 269
On Jordan's stormy banks. 275
On the Resurrection morning 271
"Onward, upward, home-ward" 242
Some day the silver cord.. 268
When I shall reach the more 272
When my life's work is... 276
When the mists have rolled 150
Will you meet me........ 273

HOLINESS

Fade, fade, each earthly... 181
Jesus, my Saviour........ 180
More holiness give me..... 187
Saviour, more than life... 183
Shine in my heart......... 178
Take time to be holy...... 177
Thou didst teach......... 179

HOLY SPIRIT

Joys are flowing 197

O worship the Lord....... 36
Open my eyes........... 69
Savior and Master....... 249
Spirit of God descend..... 73
Spirit so holy 72

HOPE (See also Heaven)
Be still, my soul.......... 203
I've reached the land of... 196
Jesus, still lead on........ 240
Not now, but in the coming 269
"Onward, upward, homeward" 242
Sing with all the sons..... 288

LORD'S DAY (see also Morning)
Open now Thy gates....... 44
The earth is hushed in.... 42
With joy we hail.......... 43

MISSIONARY
Anywhere with Jesus...... 310
Far and near the fields.... 308
Far in the desert......... 135
Fling out the banner...... 306
Give to the Lord.......... 299
Going forth at Christ's command 292
Have you sought for the sheep 134
Ho, reapers of life's....... 296
I can hear my Savior..... 258
Master, no offering costly.. 300
Speed away 311
Teach me Thy truth....... 301
There's a royal banner..... 97
Thy message, Lord, shall be 309
We have heard the joyful.. 305

MORNING
Glad welcome, happy morn. 46
God of the earth, the sky.. 39
Light of the world, we hail Thee 47
Savior, hear us, we pray.. 45

PEACE
Angel of peace.......... 217
God of our fathers........ 66
God, the all-powerful...... 231
O God of love............ 214

PRAISE AND WORSHIP
To Christ
All hail the power of...... 7
All hail the power of...... 8
All hail to Thee........... 15
Christ who left His home.. 286
Come, let us sing......... 18
Fairest Lord Jesus........ 41
Hosanna, loud Hosanna.... 14
Jesus came, the heavens... 318
Jesus, Rose of Sharon..... 22
Jesus, the very thought.... 23
Jesus, what a Friend...... 3
Light of the world, we hail 47
O Lord, who madest...... 28
O Savior, precious......... 27
O thank the Lord......... 9
O worship the Lord........ 36
Rejoice, ye pure in heart... 11
Round the Lord in glory.. 12
When His salvation bringing 294
Who is He in yonder..... 10
Wonderful grace of Jesus.. 112

To God
Bless the Lord, let all...... 29
For all Thy care.......... 277
"For God so loved"....... 13
God of the earth, the sky... 39
God of our strength....... 1
Great God of wonders..... 35
Great is Thy faithfulness.. 30
Honor and glory.......... 2
I will extol Thee, O my God 20
Let the whole creation.... 4
Let us with a gladsome.... 76
Lord, Thy glory fills...... 6
O Lord, who madest heav'n 28
O my soul, bless thou..... 5
O worship the Lord........ 36
On our way rejoicing...... 48
Praise to the Lord........ 31
The heavens declare Thy glory 17
This is my Father's world.. 38
To God be the glory....... 16
Ye watchers and ye........ 21

PRAYER
"Come ye apart".......... 59
Ere you left your room.... 70
God calls me to the hour... 67
I love to steal awhile away. 24
Lord, I have shut the door 60
O Lord, to Thee I cry.... 257
Oh, I love to talk with Jesus 57
My Father, this I ask..... 64
Open now thy gates....... 44
Prayer is the soul's sincere 71
There's a garden where Jesus 62
To Thee, O Lord, I lift mine 68
When on quiet seas........ 58
When storms of life are round me 61
When the weary, seeking rest 56

PROMISES
"Follow me," the Master said 263
Hear us, O Savior......... 63
Precious promise 234
"There shall be showers of" 133
Will you meet me in...... 273

REDEMPTION
(See also Atonement, Salvation)
Arise, my soul, arise...... 37
Come, let us sing the song. 18
Free from the law......... 164
God loved the world of sinners 167
I hear the Savior say...... 106
In looking through my tears 104
Lord Jesus, I long to be... 162
Not all the blood of beasts 118
Nor silver nor gold........ 108
Saved by the blood........ 110

REGENERATION
Arise, my soul, arise...... 37
Dear Lord, take up the tangled 113
Jesus, I am resting....... 193
Lord Jesus, I long to be... 162
O happy day............. 174
Once far from God and.... 109
Saved to the uttermost.... 123

REPENTANCE
Depth of mercy, can there be 126
Just as I am............ 173
Naught have I gotten...... 149
O, hear my cry, be gracious 160
Out of my bondage....... 169
Years I spent in vanity.... 145
Yield not to temptation.... 131

SALVATION
(See also Redemption and Christ-Savior)
Eternal source of joys..... 121
Glory ever be to Jesus..... 114
In Thy cleft, O Rock...... 222
Jesus, my Savior, to Bethlehem 168
Like a bird on the deep... 130
O safe to the Rock........ 122
Saved to the uttermost.... 123
Since Christ my soul....... 120
Since Jesus my Savior..... 74
There is a green hill...... 116
There is a name........... 92
'Tis the promise of God.... 105
Wounded for me.......... 117
Years I spent in vanity.... 145

SELF-DENIAL
All to Jesus I surrender.. 248
Have Thine own way, Lord 200
Lord Jesus, I long to be... 162
Not I, but Christ.......... 307
Spirit so holy 72

THANKSGIVING
For all Thy care we bless.. 277
Master, no offering costly. 300
Summer suns are......... 34
This is my Father's world. 38
On our way rejoicing...... 48

TRUST
Be still, my soul.......... 203
Fear not, for God the Father 210
God of our strength....... 1
Hold Thou my hand...... 209
I do not ask, O Lord...... 247
I sing the love of......... 241
If, on a quiet sea.......... 207
In some way of other..... 208
Master, the tempest is..... 219
Savior, hear us, we pray.. 45
Simply trusting every...... 251
The Lord is my.......... 218
Thou, my everlasting...... 215
'Tis so sweet to trust..... 216
What a fellowship 213
When on quiet seas....... 58
When the trumpet of the Lord 212

WORD
Break Thou the Bread of Life 100
How firm a foundation..... 101
I've tried in vain......... 102
Lamp of our feet......... 99
Oh, wonderful Word....... 98
When God of old the way. 111

SEPARATION
Jesus, I my cross have taken 252
Must Jesus bear the cross.. 256
Take the World, but give me Jesus 264
When the Lord of love.... 78

SERVICE
Awake! Arise! O Church.. 304
Brightly beams our Father's 303
Dear to the heart of the... 201
Far in the desert wild..... 135
Fight the good fight....... 302
Follow the path of........ 244
"For Christ and the Church" 290
Forward through the...... 265
Give as the Lord hath..... 299
Have you sought for the... 134
Ho! reapers of life's...... 296
I can hear my Saviour calling 258
I love to tell the......... 295
Lord of life.............. 298
Master no offering costly... 300
More like the Master...... 291
Not I, but Christ.......... 307
O scatter seed of.......... 297
On our way rejoicing...... 48
Savior and Master........ 249
Teach me Thy truth....... 301
Throw out the Life-Line.. 137
Ye fair green hills........ 293

General Index of Titles and First Lines

Titles are in SMALL CAPS; first lines in lower case type.
(*) indicates that only the words (no music) are printed.

*A CHARGE TO KEEP.................... 333
A friend I have, called Jesus.......... 86
A wonderful Savior is Jesus my Lord.. 195
*ABIDE WITH ME.................... 337
ABOVE THE TREMBLING ELEMENTS....... 182
*ALAS, AND DID MY SAVIOR BLEED......... 339
ALL FOR JESUS........................ 250
ALL HAIL, IMMANUEL.................. 15
ALL HAIL THE POWER (Coronation)..... 8
ALL HAIL THE POWER (Miles Lane)..... 8
All hail the power of Jesus' name...... 7
All hail to Thee, Immanuel............ 15
All to Jesus I surrender............... 248
ALMOST PERSUADED 151
ALONE WITH GOD...................... 61
*AM I A SOLDIER OF THE CROSS.......... 336
Amid the trials which I meet.......... 202
ANGEL OF PEACE..................... 217
ANGRY WORDS! O LET THEM NEVER...... 245
ANYWHERE WITH JESUS............... 310
ARISE, MY SOUL, ARISE................ 37
AS WITH GLADNESS MEN OF OLD........ 279
AT CALVARY 145
AWAKE! ARISE! 304
BE STILL 65
BE STILL, MY SOUL.................... 203
BEAUTY FOR ASHES.................... 241
BEHOLD A STRANGER AT THE DOOR...... 158
BELOVED NOW ARE WE................. 315
BEULAH LAND 196
BIBLE SCHOOL HYMN.................. 249
BLESS HIS NAME...................... 29
Bless the Lord, let all within me....... 29
BLESS THE LORD, O MY SOUL........... 19
BLESSED ASSURANCE 190
BLESSED QUIETNESS 197
BREAK THOU THE BREAD OF LIFE........ 100
Brightly beams our Father's mercy..... 303
CHRIST AROSE 284
Christ has for sin atonement made...... 119
CHRIST IS RISEN...................... 286
CHRIST LIVETH IN ME.................. 109
CHRIST RECEIVETH SINFUL MEN......... 146
CHRIST RETURNETH 312
Christ who left His home in glory...... 286
CHRISTIAN, WALK CAREFULLY........... 243
CLOSE TO THEE 215
COME, GREAT DELIVERER, COME......... 160
Come into my heart, blessed Jesus...... 142
COME LET US SING THE SONG OF SONGS... 18
*Come, we that love the Lord........... 324
"COME YE APART" 59
Conquering now and still to conquer.... 198
COUNT YOUR BLESSINGS.............. 239
DAY IS DYING IN THE WEST............ 53
Dear Lord, take up the tangled.......... 113
DEAR TO THE HEART OF THE SHEPHERD... 201
DEPTH OF MERCY..................... 126
DON'T FORGET TO PRAY................ 70
Down in the valley with my Savior..... 238
Dying with Jesus by death............ 192
Earthly friends may prove untrue...... 80
Earthly pleasures vainly call me........ 189
Encamped along the hills of light...... 176
Ere you left your room this morning.... 70
ETERNAL SOURCE OF JOYS DIVINE......... 121
EVENING PRAYER (Stebbins)............ 52
EVERY DAY WILL I BLESS THEE......... 20
FADE, FADE, EACH EARTHLY JOY.......... 181
FAIREST LORD JESUS.................. 41
FAITH IS THE VICTORY................. 176
FAITH OF OUR FATHERS............... 261
Far and near the fields are teeming.... 308
Far in the desert wild................. 135
FAST TO THINE ARM.................. 180
Fear not, for God the Father.......... 210
Fierce and wild the storm is raging..... 224
FIGHT THE GOOD FIGHT............... 302
FLING OUT THE BANNER, LET IT FLOAT... 306
FOLLOW ALL THE WAY.................. 258
FOLLOW ME 262
"FOLLOW ME," THE MASTER SAID......... 263
FOLLOW ON 238
FOLLOW THE PATH OF JESUS........... 244
FOR ALL THY CARE WE BLESS THEE....... 277
FOR CHRIST AND THE CHURCH.......... 290
"For God so loved!" O wondrous theme.. 13
FOR ME 107
FORWARD THROUGH THE AGES........... 265
Free from the law, O happy condition.. 164
GALILEE, BRIGHT GALILEE.............. 138
Give as the Lord hath prospered........ 299
GIVE ME JESUS 264
GIVE ME THY HEART.................. 148
GIVE TO THE LORD................... 299
GLAD WELCOME, HAPPY MORN.......... 46
GLORIA PATRI 320
Glory be to the Father................. 320
GLORY EVER BE TO JESUS.............. 114
GLORY TO GOD THE FATHER............ 13
GO WITH ME, MASTER................. 267
*GOD BE WITH YOU.................... 343
God calls me to the hour of prayer...... 67
God hath not promised skies.......... 237
God lov'd the world of sinners......... 167
GOD MOVES IN A MYSTERIOUS WAY....... 33
GOD OF OUR STRENGTH................. 1
GOD OF THE EARTH, THE SKY, THE SEA.... 39
GOD OF OUR FATHERS, WHOSE ALMIGHTY HAND 66
GOD THAT MADEST EARTH AND HEAVEN.... 55
GOD, THE ALL-MERCIFUL 231
God, the all-powerful................. 231
Going forth at Christ's command........ 292
GRACE ENOUGH FOR ME............... 104
GREAT GOD OF WONDERS.............. 35
GREAT IS THY FAITHFULNESS........... 30
GUIDE ME, O THOU GREAT JEHOVAH...... 225
HALLELUJAH, 'TIS DONE................ 105
HALLELUJAH, WHAT A SAVIOR.......... 82
Hark, the voice of Jesus calling........ 262
HAVE THINE OWN WAY, LORD........... 200
HAVE YOU ANY ROOM FOR JESUS......... 170
Have you read the story............... 84
HAVE YOU SOUGHT 134
HE DIED FOR THEE.................... 152
HE HIDETH MY SOUL.................. 195
*HE LEADETH ME...................... 331
HE SEEKS HIS WANDERING SHEEP TODAY.. 144
HEAR US, O SAVIOR.................. 63
HIDE ME 221
HIDE THOU ME....................... 222
HIDING IN THEE...................... 122
HIS LOVE CANNOT FAIL................ 74
HIS MERCY FLOWS.................... 9
HIS YOKE IS EASY.................... 218
HO! REAPERS OF LIFE'S HARVEST......... 296
HOLD THOU MY HAND................. 209
HONOR AND GLORY................... 2
HOSANNA, LOUD HOSANNA............. 14
HOW BEAUTEOUS WERE THE MARKS DIVINE 26
HOW FIRM A FOUNDATION............. 101
HUSHED WAS THE EVENING HYMN........ 253
I AM COMING HOME.................. 172
I AM HAPPY IN HIM................... 124
I AM PRAYING FOR YOU................ 155
I am so glad that our Father........... 85
I can hear my Savior calling........... 258
I DO NOT ASK, O LORD................ 247
I have a Savior, He's pleading.......... 155
I hear the Savior say.................. 106
I hear Thy welcome voice.............. 172
I HEARD THE VOICE OF JESUS SAY........ 229
I know not why God's wondrous........ 194
I KNOW WHOM I HAVE BELIEVED........ 194

GENERAL INDEX OF TITLES AND FIRST LINES

I love to steal awhile away.......... 24
I love to tell the story............ 295
I must tell Jesus.................. 228
*I need thee........................ 334
I remember Calvary 259
I shall be like him................ 272
I sing the love of God............. 241
I stand amazed in the presence......... 77
I surrender all 248
I want to love him more............ 185
I will extol Thee, O my God.......... 20
I will pass over you................ 111
I would be like Jesus.............. 189
I'll live for him.................... 188
I'll stand by until the morning...... 224
I've found a friend 88
I've reached the land of corn and wine.. 196
I've tried in vain a thousand ways...... 102
I've wandered far away from God....... 171
If, on a quiet sea.................. 207
If thou shalt confess................ 132
In a lowly manger sleeping........... 278
In heavenly love abiding............. 223
In his keeping....................... 226
In Jesus 102
In looking through my tears.......... 104
In some way or other................. 208
*In the cross of christ.............. 326
In the garden........................ 285
In the land of fadeless day........... 274
In thy cleft, O Rock of ages.......... 222
Into my heart 142
It may be at morn when the day........ 312
It was midnight in the garden......... 285
It's just like his great love......... 86

Jesus calls thee 163
Jesus calls us; o'er the tumult....... 94
Jesus came, the heavens adoring...... 318
Jesus christ is risen today.......... 289
Jesus comes with power to gladden..... 266
Jesus, gracious One, calleth now........ 163
Jesus has loved me 75
Jesus, I am resting.................. 193
Jesus, I come........................ 169
Jesus, I my cross have taken.......... 252
Jesus is coming to earth again......... 317
Jesus is standing in Pilate's hall........ 147
Jesus, keep me near the cross.......... 175
Jesus leads 227
Jesus loves even me.................. 85
Jesus, my Lord, to Thee I cry.......... 165
Jesus, my Savior, look Thou on me..... 180
Jesus, my Savior, to Bethlehem came.... 168
Jesus never fails 80
Jesus of Nazareth passeth by......... 143
Jesus paid it all..................... 106
Jesus, rose of Sharon................. 22
Jesus, Savior, pilot me.............. 233
Jesus saves 305
Jesus shall reign.................... 40
Jesus, still lead on................. 240
Jesus, the sinner's friend............ 166
Jesus, the very thought of thee...... 23
Jesus, thy name I bear............... 255
Jesus, what a Friend for sinners........ 3
Jesus will 141
Joys are flowing like a river........... 197
Just as I am, thine own to be........ 260
Just as I am without one plea........ 173
Just for today....................... 64

King of the ages..................... 280

Lamp of our feet whereby we trace.. 99
Lead me gently home, father......... 236
Lead me, Savior...................... 235
Leaning on the everlasting arms...... 213
Let the lower lights be burning...... 303
Let the whole creation cry........... 4
Let us crown him..................... 7
Let us with a gladsome mind......... 76
Life wears a different phase............ 125
Light after darkness................. 270
Light of the world, we hail thee.... 47
Like a bird on the deep............... 130
Like a Shepherd, tender, true........... 227
Lo, he comes......................... 314
Lord, as I walk with thee............ 232
Lord, I have shut the door............. 60
Lord, I'm coming home............... 171
Lord Jesus, I love to be perfectly whole. 162
Lord of life.......................... 298
Lord, thy glory fills the heaven..... 6
*Love divine 323
Low in the grave He lay................ 284

"Man of sorrows," what a name.......... 82
Master, no offering costly............ 300
Master, the tempest is raging........... 219
Meet me in the homeland.......... 273
Moment by moment................... 192
More about Jesus.................... 81
More holiness give me.................. 187
More like the master............... 291
Must Jesus bear the cross alone...... 256
My anchor holds..................... 199
My faith is fixed on Jesus............. 96
*My faith looks up to thee........... 330
My Father, this I ask of Thee.......... 64
My friend of Calvary................ 96
My Jesus, I love thee............... 95
My Jesus, thou art precious......... 90
My life, my love, I give to Thee......... 188
My prayer 187
My Savior first of all.............. 276
My Savior's love 77
My soul at last a rest hath found....... 204
My soul, be on thy guard............ 246
My soul is so happy in Jesus.......... 124

Naught have I gotten but what.......... 149
Near the cross 175
Near to the heart of God............ 93
*Nearer, my God, to thee............ 329
Nearer, still nearer................ 186
Nearer the cross..................... 184
No night there 274
Nor silver, nor gold................. 108
Not all the blood of beasts.......... 118
Not I, but Christ.................... 307
Not now, but in the coming years...... 269
Not what these hands have done..... 127
Now, on land and sea descend......... 49
Now the day is over.................. 51

O God of love, O King of peace........ 214
O happy day 174
O hear my cry, be gracious now to me.. 160
O Lord, to thee I cry................. 257
O Lord, who madest heaven and earth 28
O lost one in the wilds of sin......... 132
O love that wilt not let me go....... 83
O my soul, bless thou Jehovah........ 5
O rock of ages...................... 204
O safe to the Rock that is higher....... 122
O Savior, precious Savior........... 27
O scatter seeds of loving deeds...... 297
O thank the Lord, the Lord of love.... 9
O the unsearchable riches............. 87
O thou in whose presence............ 32
O why, O why, in dark Gethsemane.... 107
O worship the Lord.................. 36
Oh, I love to talk with Jesus........ 57
Oh, what a Savior that He died......... 139
Oh, wonderful, wonderful word......... 98
Oh, wonderful word 98
On Calvary's brow 115
On Jordan's stormy banks............ 275
On our way rejoicing................ 48
On the resurrection morn.......... 271
Once far from God, and dead in sin.... 109
Once for all......................... 164
One there is above all others....... 161
Only a sinner........................ 149
Onward, upward, homeward.......... 242
Open my eyes that I may see......... 69
Open now thy gates of beauty........ 44
Open wide thy heart................ 157
Our father, who art in heaven...... 321

GENERAL INDEX OF TITLES AND FIRST LINES

Our great savior.......................... 3
Out of my bondage, sorrow and......... 169
*Pass me not......................... 338
Peace! be still....................... 219
Praise god from whom all blessings flow 319
Praise to the lord, the almighty..... 31
Pray, brethren, pray................ 136
Pray for the wanderer................ 135
Prayer is the soul's sincere desire.... 71
Precious promise 234
Rejoice, ye pure in heart............. 11
*Rescue the perishing................ 341
*Rock of ages........................ 325
Round the lord in glory seated....... 12
Safe in the arms of jesus........... 230
Sanctuary 60
Saved by grace 268
Saved by the blood................... 110
Saved to serve 292
Saved to the uttermost............... 123
*Savior, again 342
Savior and Master, Thee we own........ 249
Savior, breathe an evening blessing (Hall) 50
Savior, breathe an evening blessing (Stebbins) 52
Savior, hear us, we pray............. 45
Savior, lead me lest I stray.......... 235
*Savior, like a shepherd............. 327
Savior, more than life............... 183
Savior, teach me, day by day......... 89
Seeking for me....................... 168
Shepherd of israel................... 128
Shine in my heart, lord jesus........ 178
Simply trusting every day............ 251
Since Christ my soul from sin set free.. 120
Since i found my saviour............. 125
Since Jesus my Savior from sin........ 74
Sing with all the sons of glory...... 288
Sinners Jesus will receive............ 146
Sinners, turn, why will ye die....... 159
Sitting at the feet of jesus......... 91
Softly and tenderly 156
Some day the silver cord will break.... 268
Some time we'll understand........... 269
Sons of God, beloved in Jesus.......... 315
*Sowing in the morning............... 340
Speed away 311
Spirit of god, descend upon my heart.. 73
Spirit so holy 72
Summer suns are glowing.............. 34
*Sweet hour of prayer................ 332
Take me as i am...................... 165
Take my life and let it be........... 254
Take the world, but give me Jesus...... 264
Take time to be holy................. 177
Teach me thy truth................... 301
The banner of the cross.............. 97
The beautiful garden of prayer....... 62
The broken heart 84
The call for reapers................. 308
The day is past and gone............. 54
The earth is hushed in silence...... 42
The first noel 281
*The gate ajar for me................ 335
The heavens declare thy glory........ 17
The hour of prayer................... 67
The isles await the king............. 309
The lord is my shepherd.............. 129
The Lord is my shepherd................ 218
The lord will provide................ 208
The ninety and nine.................. 154
The Shepherd's heart is saddened....... 144
The strife is o'er, the battle done.... 287
*There is a gate...................... 335
There is a green hill far away...... 116
There is a name i love............... 92
There is a place of quiet rest........ 93
There is a story ever new.............. 185
There shall be showers of blessing... 133
There were ninety and nine........... 154
There's a garden where Jesus is waiting.. 62
There's a royal banner given.......... 97
There's a song in the air............ 282
There's not a bird with lonely nest.. 79
This is my father's world............ 38
Thou didst leave thy throne.......... 283
Thou didst teach the thronging people 179
Thou, my everlasting portion.......... 215
"Thou remainest" 205
Thou thinkest, lord, of me........... 202
Though the angry surges roll.......... 199
Throw out the life-line.............. 137
Thy god reigneth 191
Thy message, Lord, shall be proclaimed.. 309
Till he come......................... 316
'Tis so sweet to trust in jesus...... 216
'Tis the promise of God full salvation... 105
To god be the glory.................. 16
To thee, o lord, i lift mine eyes..... 68
Today the savior calls............... 153
Tonight, my soul, be still.............. 65
Transformed 113
Trembling soul, beset by fears......... 191
Troubled heart thy God is calling....... 152
True-hearted, whole-hearted 103
Trust and obey....................... 211
Trust him 210
Trusting jesus 251
Under his wings...................... 206
Unsearchable riches 87
Verily, verily 139
Victory through grace................ 198
We have an anchor.................... 220
We have heard the joyful sound........ 305
We may not climb the heavenly steeps 25
*We praise thee, o god............... 322
*We're marching to zion.............. 324
Welcome for me....................... 130
*What a fellowship, what a joy...... 213
What a wonderful savior.............. 119
What god hath promised............... 237
What if it were today................ 317
What means this eager, anxious throng.. 143
What will you do with jesus.......... 147
When his salvation bringing.......... 294
When God of old the way of life........ 111
When I shall reach the more excellent glory 272
*When i survey the wondrous cross.... 328
When Jesus comes to reward His servants 313
When love shines in.................. 266
When my life work is ended............ 276
When on quiet seas i sail............ 58
When storms of life are round me beating 61
When the early morning breaking....... 226
When the lord of love was here...... 78
When the mists have rolled away.... 150
When the roll is called up yonder... 212
When the trumpet of the Lord.......... 212
When the weary, seeking rest........ 56
When we walk with the Lord............ 211
When upon life's billows............. 239
Where He may lead me I will go....... 259
Where jesus is, 'tis heaven.......... 120
Whiter than snow..................... 162
Who is he in yonder stall............ 10
Who will open mercy's door............ 141
"Whosoever heareth" shout.............. 140
Whosoever will 140
Will jesus find us watching......... 313
Will you meet me in the homeland...... 273
Will your anchor hold.................. 220
With joy we hail the sacred day...... 43
Wonderful grace of jesus............. 112
Wondrous love 167
Wounded for me....................... 117
Ye fair green hills of galilee....... 293
Ye watchers and ye holy ones......... 21
Years I spent in vanity and pride...... 145
Yield not to temptation.............. 131